Mill Level 1 Training Tutorial

To order more books:

Call 1-800-529-5517 or

Visit www.emastercam.com or

Contact your Mastercam dealer

Mastercam X⁸ Mill Level 1 Training Tutorial

Software: Mastercam X⁸

Author: Mariana Lendel

ISBN: 978-1-77146-045-3

Date: September 16, 2014

Notice

In-House Solutions Inc. reserves the right to make improvements to this manual at any time and without notice.

Disclaimer Of All Warranties And Liability

Copyrights

Trademarks

MASTERCAM SHORTCUTS

Icon	Function	Keyboard Shortcut	Icon	Function	Keyboard Shortcut
	Analyze entities	F4		Mastercam version, SIM serial number	Alt+V
	AutoSave	Alt+A		Motion controller rotation point	Alt+F12
	C-Hook or user app	Alt+C		Pan	Arrow keys
	Configure Mastercam	Alt+F8		Paste from clipboard	Ctrl+V
	Copy to clipboard	Ctrl+C		Redo an event that has been undone	Ctrl+Y
	Cut to clipboard	Ctrl+X		Repaint	F3
	Delete entities	F5		Rotate	Alt+Arrow keys
	Drafting global options	Alt+D		Select all	Ctrl+A
	Exit Mastercam	Alt+F4		Selection grid parameters	Alt+G
	Fit geometry to screen	Alt+F1		Shading on/off	Alt+S
	Gview—Back	Alt+3		Show/hide all axes (WCS, Cplane, Tplane)	Alt+F9
	Gview—Bottom	Alt+4		Show/hide coordinate axes	F9
	Gview—Front	Alt+2		Show/hide displayed toolpaths	Alt+T
	Gview—Isometric	Alt+7		Show/hide Operations Manager pane	Alt+O
	Gview—Left	Alt+6		Undo the last creation or event	Ctrl+U, Ctrl+Z
	Previous Plane	Alt+P		Unzoom to 80% of original	Alt+F2
	Gview—Right	Alt+5		Unzoom to previous or 50% of original	F2
	Gview—Top	Alt+1		Zoom around target point	Ctrl+F1
	Help	Alt+H		Zoom with window selection	F1
	Hide entities	Alt+E		Zoom/unzoom by 5%	Page Up/Page Down
	Level Manager	Alt+Z			
	Main attributes, set from entity	Alt+X			

CUSTOMIZE MASTERCAM

Create Your Own Keyboard Shortcuts

- **Choose Settings >Customize>Key Mapping.**

- Select the **Category.**

- Select a **Mastercam** function and under **Press new shortcut key** enter the key combinations you want to assign to it.

Change Toolbar Layouts

- **Choose Settings > Customize.**

- Set the **Workspace** and then choose the **Category.**
- Select a Mastercam function and add it to the **Toolbar.**

- Choose **Load Workspace** to hide or display toolbars.

Customize the right-click menu

- **Choose Settings > Customize > Context Menu tab**
- Select the **Category** and then the function that you want to add.
- Once you click on the **Add** button the function will be added to the **Right mouse button menu.**

WAYS TO GET THE MOST FROM MASTERCAM

Mastercam Training

In-House Solutions offers unsurpassed industrial training for Mastercam and Robotmaster. We have training facilities in a number of cities across Canada and some of our courses can also be offered onsite, depending on trainer availability. Learn more at **eMastercam.com/store**.

Our library of **Mastercam Training Solutions** consists of several product lines that cater to any learning style. Learn Mastercam at your own pace with our **Training Tutorials**, teach your students with the help of our **Instructor Kits,** learn the theory behind Mastercam with our **Handbooks**, get projects à-la-carte with our **Single Projects,** let our instructors show you best practices with our **Video Training** or go digital with our **eBooks.**

Mastercam Community

eMastercam is the one-stop web resource for Mastercam users. People from all over the world visit the site whether they are teaching, learning or working with Mastercam daily. Members can post questions, comments or share projects and success stories. Visit eMastercam.com and sign up for your free account today!

For downloaded pdf please visit

www.emastercam.com/qrc

Tutorial	Geometry Functions	Toolpath Creation
#1	Create Rectangle. Create Chamfer. Create Circle Center Point. Create Polar Arc. Xform Mirror. Join Entities.	Facing Toolpath. Circle Mill Toolpath. Contour Toolpath. Spot Drill Toolpath. Drill Toolpath. 2D Contour (Chamfer Toolpath).
#2	Create Rectangle. Create two Polygon. Create Fillets. Create Circle Center Point. Create Line Endpoint- Vertical Edit Trim Divide. Create Rectangular Shapes.	Setup 1 Slot Mill Toolpath. 2D HS Dynamic Mill Toolpath. Contour Toolpath. 2D HS Dynamic Contour Toolpath. Setup 2 Facing Toolpaths.
#3	Create Polar Arcs. Create Circle Center Point. Create Line Tangent. Create Fillet. Xform Mirror. Create Arc Tangent to Two Entities. Edit Trim 3 Entities. Create Ellipse. Xform Offset. Create Letters. Create Boundig Box. Xform Translate.	2D High Speed Area Mill Toolpath. 2D High Speed Dynamic Mill. Pocket with Island Toolpath. Pocket Remachine Toolpath.
#4	Create Circle Center Points. Create Line Tangent. Xform Mirror. Create Arc Tangent. Create Arc Polar. Edit Trim. Create Fillets. Xform Rotate. Xform Translate.	Setup 1 2D High Speed Area Mill Toolpath. 2D High Speed Dynamic Mill Toolpath. Transform Toolpath. Drill Toolpath. Circle Mill Toolpath. Contour (Chamfer Toolpath). Setup 2 2D High Speed Dynamic Mill Toolpath.

Tutorial	Geometry Functions	Toolpath Creation
#5	Import a SolidWorks file. Xform Translate 3D.	Setup 1- Top Tool Planes. 2D HS Area Mill toolpath. 2D HS Area Mill Rest toolpath. Setup 2 - Front Tool Plane. Drill Toolpath. Setup 3 - Left Tool Plane. Slot Mill Toolpath.
#6	Create Rectangle. Create Circle Center Point. Create arc Tangent to 1 Entity. Create Line Parallel. Create Chamfer. Create Line Polar. Edit Trim.	2D HS Dynamic Mill Toolpath. 2D HS Core Mill Toolpath. 2D HS Blend Mill Toolpath. 2D HS Peel Mill Toolpath.
#7	Import a SolidWorks file. Xform Translate 3D.	2D HS Area Mill Toolpath. Feature Based Drilling Toolpath. 2D HS Area Mill Toolpath. 2D Contour Toolpath.

Table of Contents

GETTING STARTED

Objectives:

✓ Starting Mastercam.
✓ The Student will learn about the Graphical User Interface.
✓ The Student will learn how to navigate through Mastercam.
✓ How to use the Status Bar to set the attributes.
✓ Set the Toolbar States.
✓ Setting the Grid.

STEP 1: STARTING MASTERCAM

1.1 Enable the Unified Backplot/Verify System

> **NOTE:** To be able to follow this tutorial you will need to enable the Unified Backplot /Verify System. The change has to be done in Mastercam Advanced Configuration as shown in this step.

- Select the **Start** button.
- Select **All Programs** and click on **Mastercam X8** as shown.
- Select **Utilities** as shown.

- Select **Advanced Configuration** as shown.

> **NOTE:** If you are running **Windows 8**, from the **Start** page, right mouse click and in the lower right corner click on the **All Aps** icon. Under **Mastercam X8** select **Advanced Configuration**.

• Select **Backplot** from the list and set the **Classic Backplot** to **Disable**.

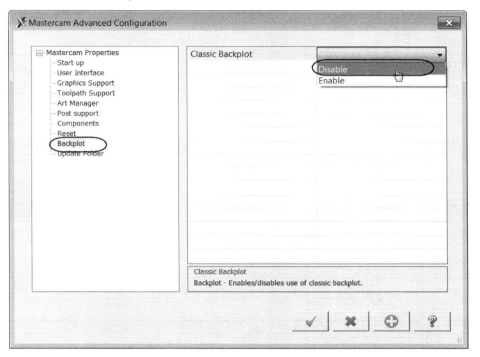

• Select the **Apply** button to apply the changes.

• Select the **OK** button to exit.

1.2 Start Mastercam X8

• To start the software, from Desktop, click on the shortcut icon as shown.

STEP 2: GUI - GRAPHICAL USER INTERFACE

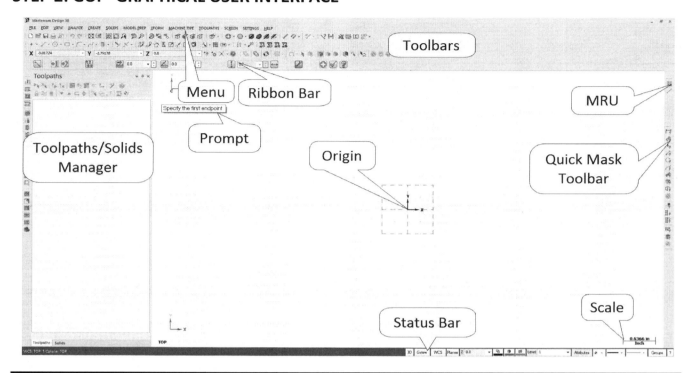

Menu	Allows you to select all the functions in Mastercam to create geometry and toolpaths.
Toolbars	Can be used instead of the menu to create geometry and toolpaths.
Ribbon Bar	Allows you to enter the values and settings that define the entities that you are currently creating or modifying.
Function prompt	Prompts the user for info.
Status Bar	Allows you to set the attributes (color, level, style, and width) and the View/Plane and Z depth currently used.
Toolpaths/Solid Manager	Lists the history of the toolpath operations and solids.
Origin	Geometry origin from which the system measures the point coordinates in X,Y and Z axes in the current plane.
Graphic Area	Workspace area in Mastercam where the geometry displays.
MRU Toolbar	Lists the most recently used functions.
Quick Mask Toolbar	Lets you select all entities of a specific type.
Scale	Shows you a scale of the object on the screen.
View Port XYZ Axes	Inform you which Graphics view, WCS and Toolplane/Construction plane you are working in.

Mill Level 1 Training Tutorial

Mastercam. X

STEP 3: NAVIGATE THROUGH MASTERCAM

In this step you will learn how to use the menu functions in Mastercam to create geometry.

3.1 Using the Menu to select the command Create Line Endpoint

- Left click on **CREATE.**
- Move the cursor on the drop-down menu to the **Line** function. This will open a flyout menu with all the commands related to create lines.
- Left-click on the desired command Endpoint as shown in Figure: 3.1.1.

Figure: 3.1.1

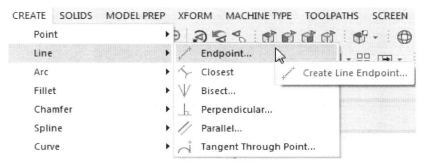

3.2 Using the Toolbars to select the command Create Line Endpoint

- Left Click on the **Create Line Endpoint** command icon as shown in Figure: 3.2.1.

Figure: 3.2.1

- To see the commands which are found under Create Line, in the menu bar choose the drop down arrow to the right of the icon as shown.

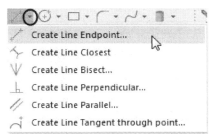

3.3 Reorganizing the Toolbars

> **NOTE:** Mastercam is fully customizable meaning you can move the toolbars anywhere you desire allowing you to work more efficiently.

* To move a toolbar select the left vertical line in front of the toolbar and drag it to the desired location on the screen as shown in <u>Figure: 3.3.1</u>.

Figure: 3.3.1

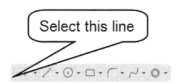
Select this line

> **NOTE:** To customize the toolbars please see the General Notes.

3.4 Create Line Endpoint Ribbon Bar example

Multi-Line   Distance   Angle   Vertical   Horizontal   Tangent

* To create a line left click on the screen. Then enter the distance and angle if necessary.

* To continue making lines choose the **Apply** ⊕ button from the ribbon bar or press enter. To exit the current command select the **OK** ✓ button or press the **Esc** button.

* To undo the last command use the **Undo** button. ↺ The Undo button can be used to go back to the beginning of geometry creation or to the last point of the saved file. Mastercam also has a **Redo** button ↻ for your convenience.

3.5 Function Prompt

Prompts the user to execute a command.

* For example this prompt is used in the **Create Line Endpoint** command as shown in <u>Figure: 3.5.1</u>.

Figure: 3.5.1

Specify the first endpoint

3.6 Status Bar

The Status bar is used to set the drawing attributes, view, plane, Z depth and construction mode.

| 3D | Gview | Plan... | Z 0.0 | ▼ | ▣ ▣ ▣ Level 1 | ▼ | Attributes | o ▼ | ——— ▼ | ——— ▼ | WCS | Groups | Plane Info: Abs | ? |

2D / 3D Construction	Toggles between 2D and 3D construction modes. In 2D mode all geometry is created parallel to the current Cplane at the current system Z depth. In 3D mode you can work freely in various Z depths, unconstrained by the current system Z depth and Cplane setting.
Gview	Sets the graphics view which you will view your geometry from. You can choose a different standard Gview, an existing named view, create a new named view or set the Gview to the current Cplane.
Planes	Sets the construction plane in which you create and manipulate your geometry. You can change the current plane by selecting a different standard plane, selecting an existing named view, creating a new named view and by setting the plane to equal the current Gview.
Z Depth	Sets the current construction depth. To set this click the drop down arrow and pick one from the most recently used list or click the **Z:** label and pick a point in the graphics window to use the Z depth values based on the selected entity.
Color	Assigns the current color to wireframe, solid and surface entities. To change the current color click in the specific color field and select a color from the color pallet. To change an existing geometry color, select the geometry first and then right mouse click in the color field and select a color from the color pallet.
Level	Sets the main level you want to work with in the graphics window. To change the current working level, type the level number in the box.
Attributes	Lets you set or change one or more drawing attributes.
Point Style	Displays and sets the systems point style.
Line Style	Shows and sets the system line style.
Line Width	Displays and sets the current system line width.
Work Coordinate System (WCS)	Allows you to redefine the WCS. You can choose from a list of stand views, specify origin coordinates, access the view manager or use the named function to access the view selection dialog box.
Groups	Defines a collection of entities or operations that can be manipulated as a single entity.
Plane info	Can be set to WCS or Absolute and shows the active plane info relative to WCS or Absolute.

3.7 Change the Current Wireframe Color

* Left click on the **Wireframe Color** field as shown.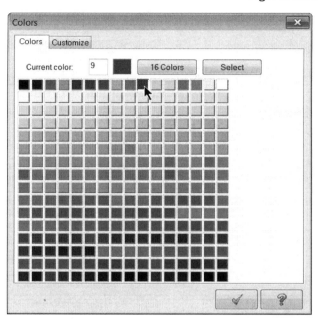
* Select the desired color from the dialog box as shown in <u>Figure: 3.7.1</u>.

Figure: 3.7.1

* Select the **OK** button to exit the command and begin creating geometry in the color of your choice.

> **NOTE:** Any geometry on your screen will remain in the previous system colour. This change will only affect the geometry you create going forward.
> To change the colour of existing geometry, for example the wireframe color, select all entities first and then right mouse on the Wireframe color.

3.8 The Toolpath Manager

The **Toolpath Manger** displays all the operations for the current part. You can sort, edit, regenerate, verify and post

any operations as shown in <u>Figure: 3.8.1</u>. For more information on the **Toolpath Manager**, please refer to

General Notes or click on the **Help** icon.

Figure: 3.8.1

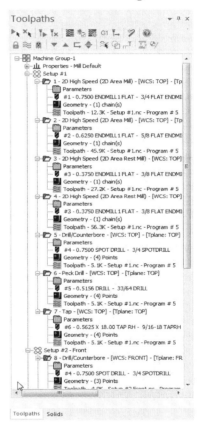

* The **Toolpaths Manger** or **Solids Manager** can be hidden to gain more space in the graphics area for creating geometry. Use the x in the upper right corner to close both Toolpaths and Solids managers. To reopen the managers, from the **Menu** select **VIEW** and **Toggle Toolpaths** or **Solids Manager.**

*

STEP 4: SET THE WORKSPACE

Before starting the geometry creation we should load the workspace to see the toolbars required to create the geometry and machine a part.

♦ Right mouse click in the Toolbars area and select **Load Workspace** and select the **2D Toolpaths** as shown.

♦ The 2D Toolpaths icons will be displayed to the left of the **Toolpaths Manager** as shown in Figure: 4.0.1.

Figure: 4.0.1

STEP 5: SETTING THE GRID

◆ Before beginning to create geometry you will enable the **Grid**. This will show you where the origin is.

SETTINGS

◆ ⚙ **Configuration.**
◆ Select **Screen** from the configuration **Topics.**
◆ Select the plus sign (+) beside screen as shown in Figure: 5.0.1.

Figure: 5.0.1

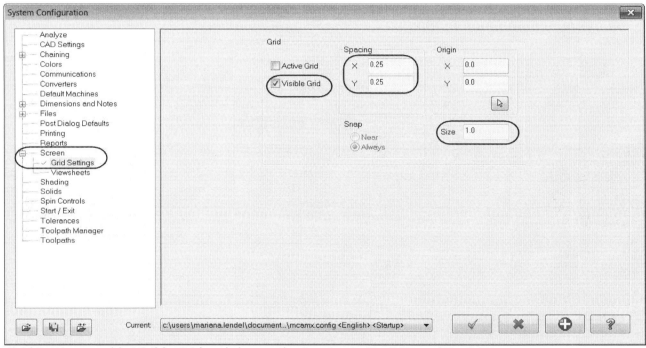

◆ In **Grid Settings** enable **Visible Grid** and change the **Spacing** to **X = 0.25 and Y = 0.25.**
◆ Set the **Size** to **1.0.**

◆ Choose the **OK** button to exit.
◆ Select **Yes** to save the setting as shown.

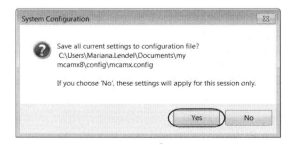

◆ The grid will appear on your screen as shown in <u>Figure: 5.0.2</u>.

Figure: 5.0.2

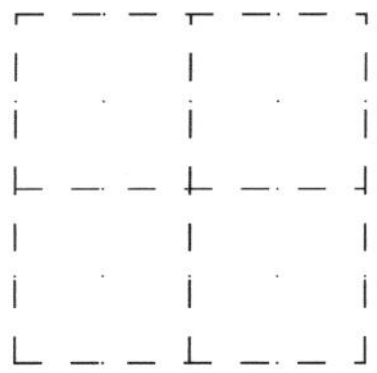

Mastercam. X⁸

TUTORIAL #1

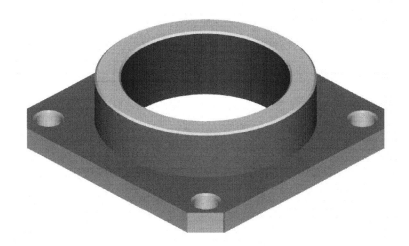

OVERVIEW OF STEPS TAKEN TO CREATE THE FINAL PART:

From Drawing to CAD Model:
- The student should examine the drawing on the following page to understand what part is being created in the tutorial.
- From the drawing we can decide how to go about creating the geometry in Mastercam.

Create the 2D CAD Model used to generate Toolpaths from:
- The student will create the Top 2D geometry needed to create the toolpaths.
- Geometry creation commands such as create rectangle, chamfer, arc polar, circle center point, mirror and join will be used.

Create the necessary Toolpaths to machine the part:
- The student will set up the stock size to be used and the clamping method used.
- A Facing toolpath will be created to machine the top of the part.
- A Circle mill toolpath will remove the material inside of the large hole.
- A Contour toolpath will be created to remove the material ouside the boss shape.
- A Drilling toolpath will be created to spot drill the four holes.
- A Drilling toolpath will be created to machine the through holes.
- A Contour toolpath with 2D chamfer option will be created to chamfer the top of the boss.

Backplot and Verify the file:
- The Backplot will be used to simulate a step by step process of the tool's movements.
- The Verify will be used to watch a tool machine the part out of a solid model.

Post Process the file to generate the G-code:
- The Student will then post process the file to obtain an NC file containing the necessary code for the machine.

 This tutorial takes approximately an hour and a half to complete.

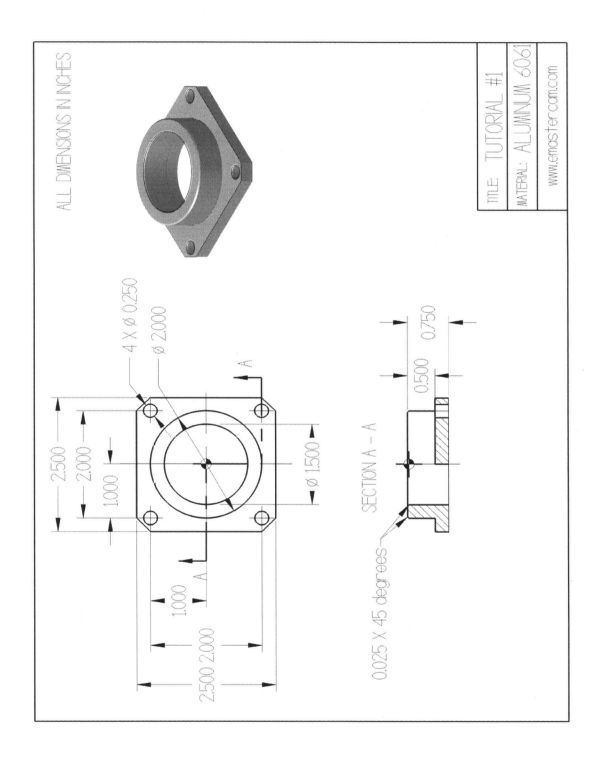

GEOMETRY CREATION

STEP 1: SETTING UP THE GRAPHIC USER INTERFACE

Please refer to the **Getting Started** section to set up the graphics user interface.

STEP 2: CREATE RECTANGLE

NOTE: The drawing is symmetric about both X and Y axis. You will create only a quarter of the geometry and then use **Mirror** command to complete it.

In this step you will learn how to create a rectangle knowing the width, the height and the anchor position.

Step Preview:

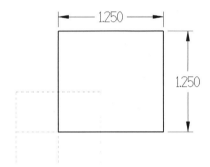

2.1 Create a 1.25" by 1.25" Rectangle

CREATE

◆ ▢ **Rectangle.**

◆ Enter the **Width** ⬚ and **Height** ⬚ as shown.
◆ Press **Enter** after typing the values to see a preview of the rectangle as shown.

NOTE: Make sure that neither the **Anchor to center** or the **Create Surface** icons are selected.
Anchor to center sets the base point of the rectangle to its center and draws the rectangle outward from the center.
Create Surface creates a surface inside of the rectangle. Surface creation and Surface toolpath are covered in Mill Level 3.

◆ [Select position for first corner]: Select the **Origin** as shown in <u>Figure: 2.1.1</u>.

Figure: 2.1.1

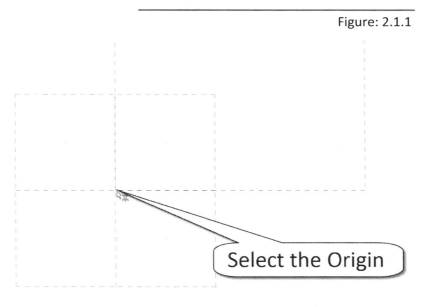

Select the Origin

◆ Make sure that when selecting the origin, the visual cue of the cursor changes as shown.

◆ Select the **OK** button to exit the **Rectangle** command.

◆ Use the **Fit** icon to fit the drawing to the screen.

> **NOTE:** During the geometry creation of this tutorial, if you make a mistake you can undo the last step using the **Undo** icon. You can undo as many steps as needed. If you delete or undo a step by mistake, just use the **Redo** icon. To delete unwanted geometry, select it first and then press **Delete** from the keyboard.

STEP 3: CREATE A CHAMFER

In this step you will create the 0.25 X 45 degrees chamfer.

Step Preview:

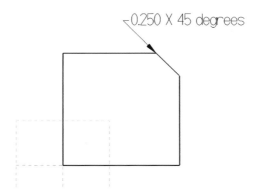

CREATE
- **Chamfer.**

- **Entities.**
- Enter the distance **0.25** in the ribbon bar and ensure the chamfer style is set to **1 Distance** and **Trim** is enabled.

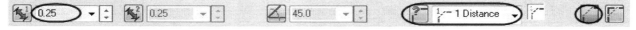

- Select the two lines to create the chamfer as shown in Figure: 3.0.1.

Figure: 3.0.1

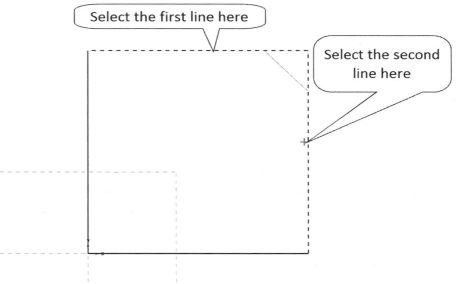

NOTE: A preview of the chamfer will appear when you select the second line as shown.

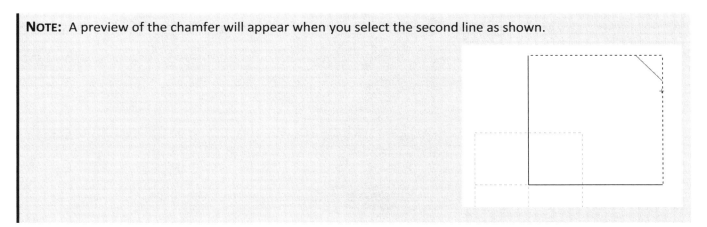

♦ Select the **OK** button to exit the command.

STEP 4: CREATE THE CIRCLE

In this step you will create a circle knowing the diameter and location. To use **Create Circle Center Point** you need to know the center point and the radius or the diameter of the circle. For the center point you need to know the **Cartesian Coordinate System.** A **Cartesian Coordinate System** is a coordinate system that specifies each point uniquely in a plane by a pair of numerical coordinates, which are the signed distances from the point to two fixed perpendicular directed lines, measured in the same unit of length as shown in Figure: 4.0.1.

Figure: 4.0.1

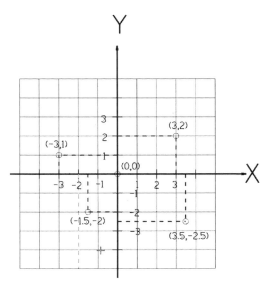

Step Preview:

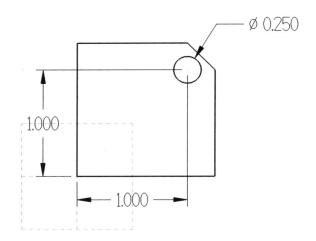

CREATE
- **Arc.**

-  **Circle Center Point.**

- Enter the **Diameter** 0.25 in the ribbon bar.
- [Enter the center point}: Enter the coordinates as shown.

| X | 1 | Y | 1 | Z | 0.0 |

- Press **Enter** for the circle to be positioned.

- Once complete choose the **OK** button to exit the command.

STEP 5: CREATE POLAR ARCS

In this step you will create two polar arcs knowing the radius, the center point, the start angle and the end angle.

Step Preview:

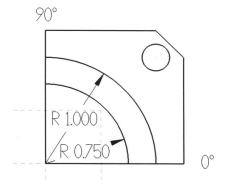

CREATE
* **Arc.**

*  **Arc Polar.**
* Enter the values in the **Ribbon Bar** as shown and press **Enter** after all values are entered.

* [Enter the center point]: Select the **Origin**.

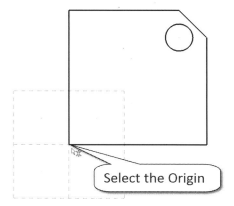

Select the Origin

* Select the **Apply** button to continue in the same command. ⊕

- The part will appear as shown once complete.

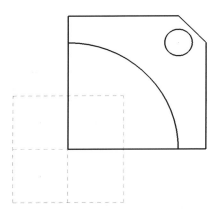

NOTE: If the arc is not generated as shown, from the **Ribbon bar**, select the **Flip** button.

- Enter the values in the **Ribbon Bar** as shown and press **Enter** after all values are entered.

NOTE: To enter the values in the Ribbon Bar, type the radius and then to move to the next field press tab. The diameter will be automatically updated. To move to the next field press again tab.

• [Enter the center point]: Select the **Origin**.

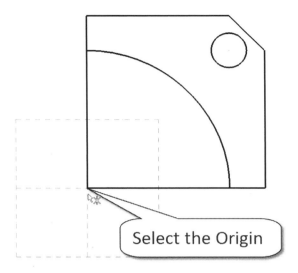

Select the Origin

• Once complete choose the **OK** button to exit the command.
• The geometry should look as shown.

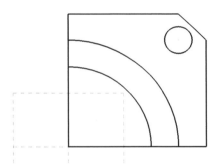

STEP 6: DELETE THE CONSTRUCTION LINES

In this step you will delete the center lines that are going throug the origin.

Step Preview:

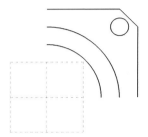

♦ Select the two lines as shown in Figure: 6.0.1.

Figure: 6.0.1

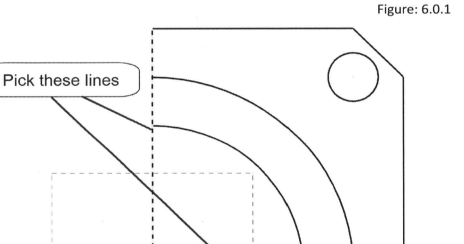

♦ Click on the **Delete** key from the keyboard.

STEP 7: MIRROR THE GEOMETRY

The **Mirror** command allows you to complete the geometry. You will mirror the geometry about both X and Y axis.

Step Preview:

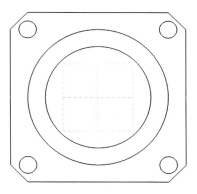

XFORM

-  **Mirror.**
- [Mirror: select entities to mirror]: From the **General Selection** toolbar, select the **All** button.

- Make sure that **All Entities** is enabled to select all entities as shown.

- The selected geometry should look as shown.

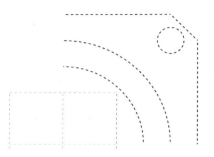

NOTE: Selected geometry will be shown with hidden lines in black and yellow.

- Press **Enter** on your keyboard.

- In the **Mirror** dialog box, make sure that **Copy** is enabled, the radio button in front of the **X axis** is enabled and **Fit** is enabled as shown in Figure: 7.0.1.

Figure: 7.0.1

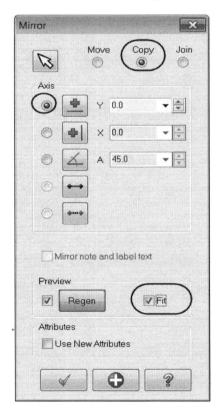

• The preview of the mirror will look as shown.

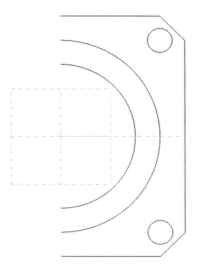

• Select the **Apply** button to continue in the same command.
• [Mirror: select entities to mirror]: From the **General Selection** toolbar, select the **All** button.

• Make sure that **All Entities** is enabled to select all entities as shown.

• Select the **OK** button.
• Press **Enter** to finish the selection.

• In the **Mirror** dialog box, make sure that **Copy** is enabled, the radio button in front of the **Y axis** is enabled and **Fit** is enabled as shown in <u>Figure: 7.0.2</u>.

Figure: 7.0.2

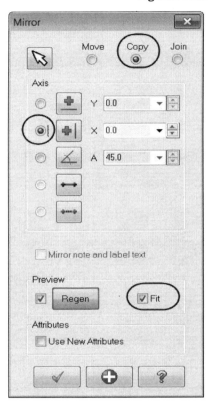

• The preview of the resulting geometry should look as shown.

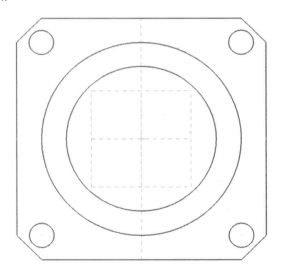

• Select the **OK** button to exit the command.

NOTE: When performing a transform function (**Xform**), Mastercam creates a temporary group from the originals (red) and a result (purple) from the transformed entities. However, they stay in effect only until you use the **Screen**, **Clear Colors** function or perform another transform function.

SCREEN

♦      **Clear Colors.**

♦ The geometry should look as shown.

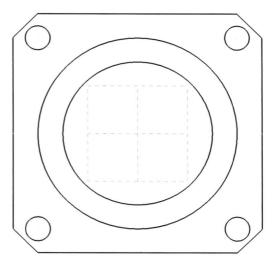

NOTE: The lines and the two big circles are broken in 2 and 4 segments due to the mirror command. To be able to select the circle for the circle mill toolpath you will have to join the arcs.

STEP 8: JOIN THE ENTITIES

Join function allows you to join collinear lines, arcs that have the same center and radius, or splines that were originally created as the same entity.

EDIT

* 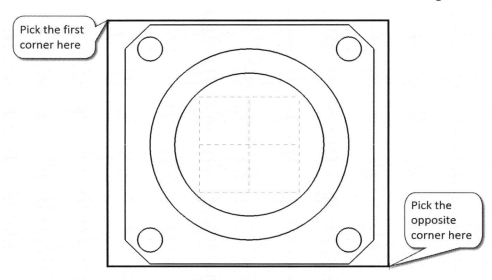 **Join entities.**
* [Select entities to join]: Make a window around all entities as shown in Figure: 8.0.1.

Figure: 8.0.1

Pick the first corner here

Pick the opposite corner here

> **NOTE:** To make a window, pick a point to the upper left corner and drag the cursor to the opposite corner and click. All the entities inside of the window should be selected (color yellow).

* Press **Enter** to finish the selection.

> **NOTE:** The entities are automatically joined.

STEP 9: SAVE THE FILE

FILE

*  **Save As.**
* File name: "Your Name_1".

TOOLPATH CREATION

SUGGESTED FIXTURE:

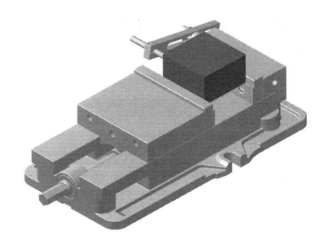

SETUP SHEET:

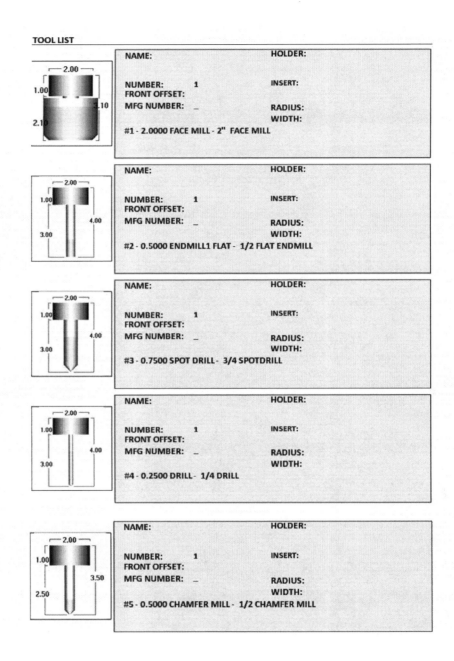

STEP 10: SELECT THE MACHINE AND SET UP THE STOCK

In Mastercam, you select a **Machine Definition** before creating any toolpaths. The **Machine Definition** is a model of your machine's capabilities and features. It acts like a template for setting up your machine. The machine definition ties together three main components. The schematic model of your machines components. The control definition that models your control capabilities and the post processor that will generate the required machine code (G-code). For a Mill Level 1 exercise (2D toolpaths) we need just a basic machine definition.

> **NOTE:** For the purpose of this tutorial, we will be using the **Default mill** machine.

◆ To display the **Toolpaths Manager** press **Alt + O**.

◆ Use the **Fit** icon to fit the drawing to the screen.

MACHINE TYPE
◆ **Mill.**
◆ **Default**

◆ Select the plus sign in front of **Properties** in the **Toolpaths Manager** to expand the **Toolpaths Group Properties.**

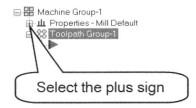

◆ Select **Tool settings** to set the tool parameters.

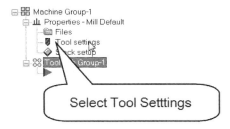

• Change the parameters to match the screen shot as shown in <u>Figure: 10.0.1</u>.

Figure: 10.0.1

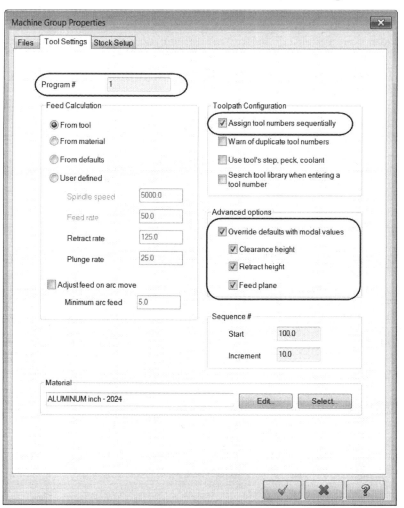

Program # is used to enter a number if your machine tool requires a number for a program name.

Assign tool numbers sequentially allows you to overwrite the tool number from the library with the next available tool number. (First operation tool number 1; Second operation tool number 2, etc.)

Warn of duplicate tool numbers allows you to get a warning if you enter two tools with the same number.

Override defaults with modal values enables the system to keep the values that you enter.

Feed Calculation set **From tool** uses feed rate, plunge rate, retract rate and spindle speed from the tool definition.

• Select the **Stock Setup** tab to define the stock.
• Select the **All Entities** button near the bottom of the **Stock setup** page as shown.

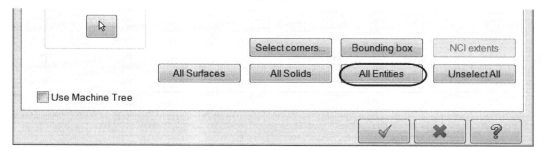

◆ In the **Stock Setup**, enter in the **Z** field **0.85** and the **Z Stock Origin 0.1** make sure that the rest of the parameters are as shown in <u>Figure: 10.0.2</u>.

Figure: 10.0.2

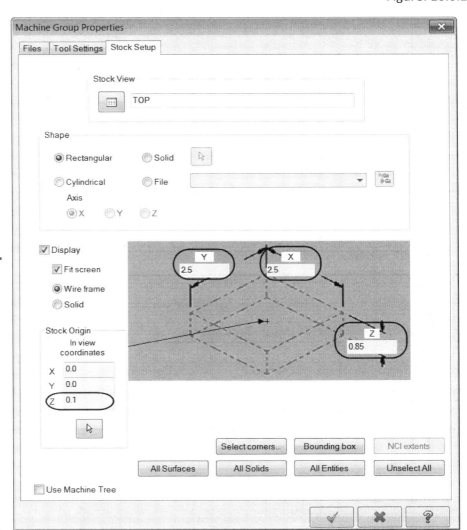

The **X**, **Y**, **Z** values in the graphic area are the dimensions of the stock model. They are always positive values.

The **Stock Origin** values adjust the positioning of the stock, ensuring that you have equal amount of extra stock around the finished part.
In the graphics, the plus shows you where the stock origin is. The default position is the middle of the stock.

Display options allow you to set the stock as **Wireframe** and to fit the stock to the screen. (Fit Screen)

NOTE: The **stock** model that you create can be displayed with the part geometry when viewing the file or the toolpaths, during backplot, or while verifying toolpaths.

◆ Select the **OK** button to exit **Machine Group Properties**.

◆ Select the **Isometric** view from the graphics view toolbar to see the stock.

◆ Use the **Fit** icon to fit the drawing to the screen.

● The stock model will appear as shown.

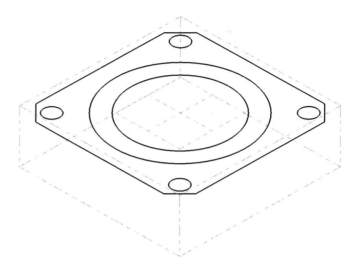

> **NOTE:** The stock is not geometry and can not be selected.

● Select the **Top** view from the view toolbar to see the part from the top.

Mastercam. X⁸

STEP 11: FACE THE PART

A **Facing** toolpath quickly removes material from the top of the part to create an even surface for future operations.

Toolpath Preview:

TOOLPATHS

♦ ▤ **Face.**

♦ If a prompt appears, **Enter new NC name**, select the **OK** button to accept the default.

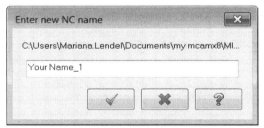

* When the chaining dialog box appears choose the **OK** button to use the defined stock and exit the **Chaining** dialog box.

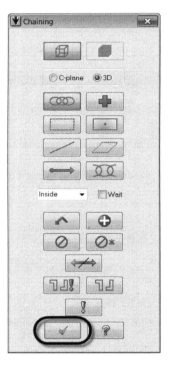

> **NOTE:** Mastercam will create the **Facing** toolpath defined from the stock setup.
>
> For more information on the **Chaining** button and **Options** click on the **Help** button.

* In the **Toolpath Type** page, the **Facing** icon will be automatically selected.

 Contour   Pocket   Facing   Slot Mill

> **NOTE:** Mastercam updates the pages as you modify them and then marks them, in the **Tree view list,** with a green check mark. Pages that are not enabled are marked with a red circle and slash.

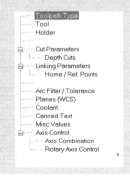

11.1 Select a 2.0" Face Mill from the library and set the Tool parameters

◆ Select **Tool** from the **Tree view list.**

◆ Click on the **Select library tool** button. Select library tool...

◆ To be able to see all the tools from the library disable **Filter Active**.

◆ Pick the **2" Face Mill** as shown.

316	--	1-1/2 BA...	--	1.5	0.75	2.75	4	En...	Full
317	--	2 INCH ...	--	2.0	1.0	2.75	4	En...	Full
318	--	1/4 CHA...	--	0....	0.0	0.5	4	Ch...	None
319	--	1/2 CHA...	--	0....	0.0	0.75	4	Ch...	None
320	--	3/4 CHA...	--	0....	0.0	1.0	4	Ch...	None
321	--	1 INCH ...	--	1....	0.0	1.0	4	Ch...	None
322	--	2" FAC...	--	2.0	0.0	1.575	2	Fa...	None
323	--	2-1/2" F...	--	2.5	0.0	1.575	4	Fa...	None
324	--	3" FACE...	--	3.0	0.0	1.969	4	Fa...	None
325	--	4" FAC...	--	4.0	0.0	1.969	2	Fa...	None
326	--	5" FACE...	--	5.0	0.0	2.48	4	Fa...	None
327	--	6" FACE...	--	6.0	0.0	2.48	2	Fa...	None
328	--	8" FACE...	--	8.0	0.0	2.5	2	Fa...	None
329	--	10" FAC...	--	1....	0.0	2.48	2	Fa...	None

Filter...

☐ Filter Active

427 of 427 tools

Display mode
○ Tools
○ Assemblies
◉ Both

◆ Select the tool in the **Tool Selection** page and then select the **OK** button to exit.

♦ Make all the necessary changes as shown in Figure: 11.1.1.

Figure: 11.1.1

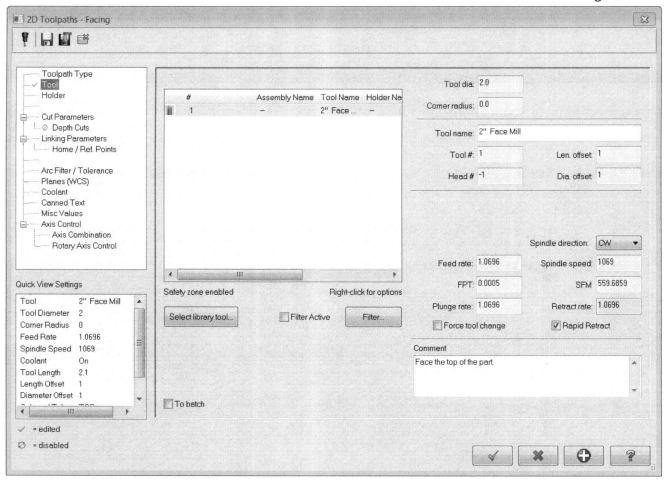

The **Feed rate**, **Plunge rate**, **Retract rate** and **Spindle speed** are based on the tool definition as set in the **Tool Settings**. You may change these values as per your part material and tools.

In the **Comment** field enter a comment to help identify the toolpath in the **Toolpaths Manager** such as the one shown above.

NOTE: If by mistake you click the **OK** button the toolpath will be generated without all the parameters set properly. To go back in the parameters area, in the Toolpaths Manager, click on the **Parameters** as shown.

◆ Select **Cut Parameters** and make the necessary changes as shown in <u>Figure: 11.1.2</u>.

Figure: 11.1.2

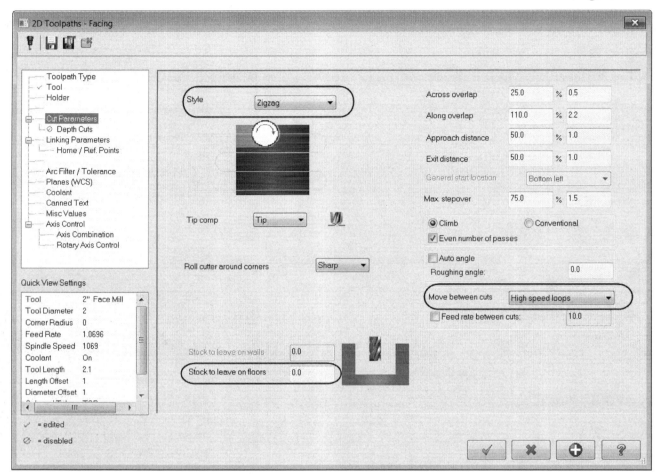

The **Style** (facing cutting method) **Zigzag** creates a back and forth cutting motion.

Move between cuts determines how the tool moves between each cut. This is only available if you select the zigzag cutting method.

High speed loops to create 180 degrees arcs between each cut.

◆ Select the **Linking Parameters** page and make the necessary changes as shown in Figure: 11.1.3.

Figure: 11.1.3

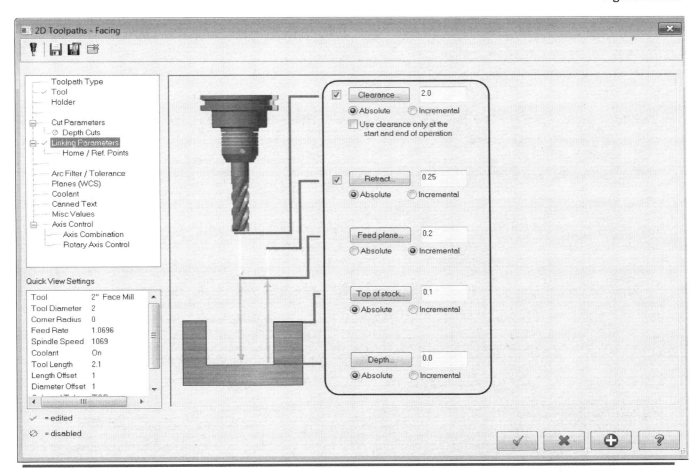

Clearance sets the height at which the tool moves to and from the part.

Retract sets the height that the tool moves up to before the next tool pass.

Feed Plane sets the height that the tool rapids to before changing to the plunge rate to enter the part.

Top of stock sets the height of the material in the Z axis.

Depth determines the final machining depth that the tool descends into the stock.

NOTE: The **Top of stock** is set to **0.1"** because the **Stock Origin** was set to **0.1"** above the origin. The depth is set to **0.0"** because this is the finish depth. The majority of the values are set to absolute (measured from Z zero which is set at the top of the finished part). Feed plane set to incremental is measured from the Top of the stock.

◆ Select the **OK** button to exit the **Facing Parameters**.

NOTE: If you exit the toolpath in the middle of setting the parameters, in the Toolpaths Manger you will have a red X on the Face Toolpath as shown in Figure: 11.1.4 . This shows that you modified the toolpath and you need to update it. You will have to select regenerate all dirty operation icon each time you change something in the toolpath parameters.

Figure: 11.1.4

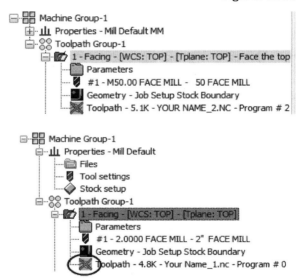

STEP 12: CIRCLE MILL THE INSIDE HOLE

Circle Mill Toolpaths remove circular pockets based on a single point. You can select either point entities, center points of arcs. Mastercam will then pocket out a circular area of the diameter and to the depth that you specify.

Toolpath Preview:

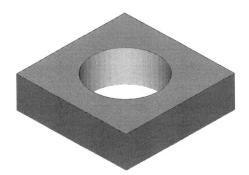

12.1 Drill Point Selection

◆ Press **Alt +T** to remove the toolpath display.

TOOLPATHS
Circle Paths.

◆ 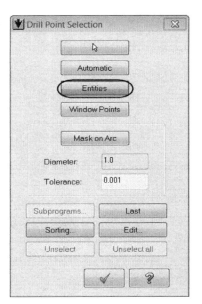 **Circmill.**
◆ From the **Drill Point Selection**, click on **Entities.**

◆ Select the **1.5"** diameter circle as shown.

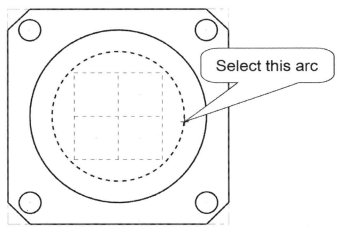

◆ Select the **OK** button to exit **Drill Point Selection.**

Mill Level 1 Training Tutorial

♦ In the **Toolpath Type** page, the **Circle Mill** icon will be selected.

Drill   Circle Mill   Point   Helix Bore   Thread Mill

12.2 Select a 1/2" Flat endmill from the library and set the Tool parameters

♦ Select **Tool** from the **Tree view list**.

♦ Click on **Select library tool** button. | Select library tool... |

♦ To be able to see all the tools from the library disable **Filter Active**.

♦ Scroll down and select the **1/2" Flat Endmill** as shown.

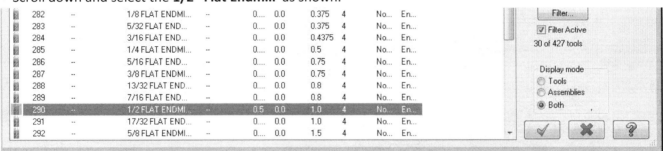

♦ Select the tool in the **Tool Selection** page and then select the **OK** button to exit.

◆ Make all the necessary changes as shown in Figure: 12.2.1.

Figure: 12.2.1

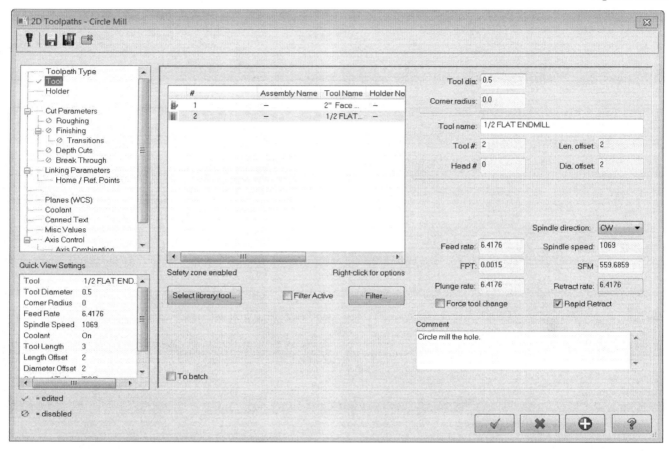

12.3 Cut Parameters

• From the **Tree view list**, select **Cut Parameters** and ensure the settings appear as shown in Figure: 12.3.1.

Figure: 12.3.1

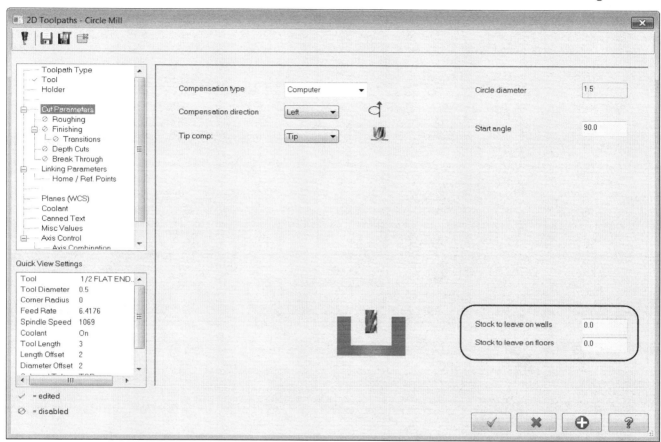

12.4 Roughing

- From the **Tree view list**, select **Roughing** and enabled. Set the Stepover to 50% and enable Helical Entry and set the parameters as shown in Figure: 12.4.1.

Figure: 12.4.1

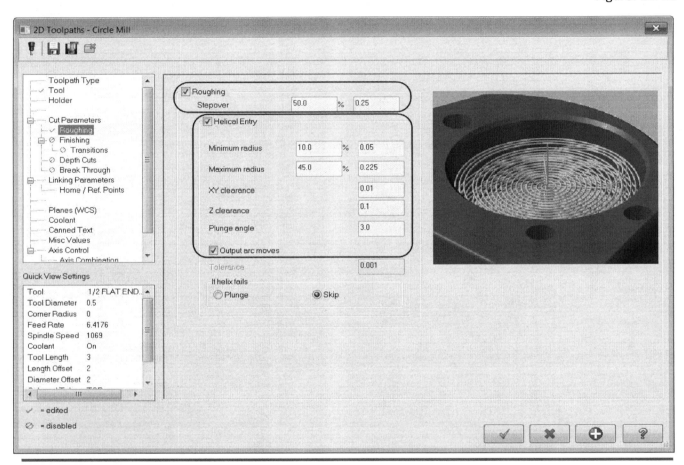

Stepover set the distance between cutting passes in the X and Y axes as a percentage of the tool diameter.

Helical entry creates a helix at the center of the circle to begin the roughing motion.If off, the tool plunges to start the toolpath.

Mill Level 1 Training Tutorial

Mastercam. X

12.5 Depth Cuts

♦ From the **Tree view** list, enable **Depth Cuts** and set the **Max rough step** to **0.5** and enable **Keep tool down**.
♦ Make any necessary changes as shown in Figure: 12.5.1.

Figure: 12.5.1

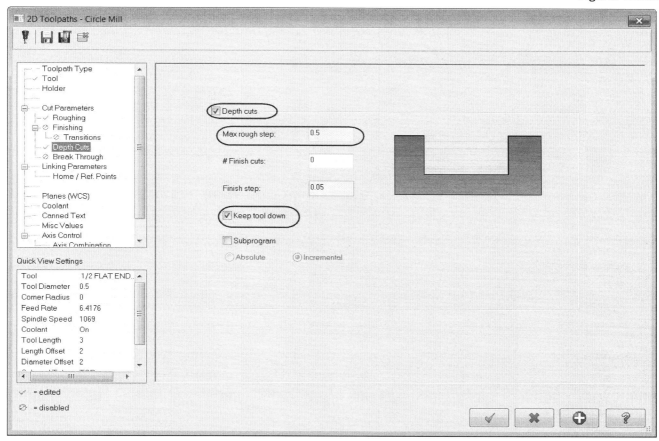

Depth Cuts, Mastercam will take the total depth and divide it into separate depth cuts. Mastercam never performs unequal depth cuts.

Max rough step sets the maximum amount of material removed in the Z axis with each rough cut. Mastercam will calculate equal rough cuts no larger than the maximum rough step until it reaches the final Z depth.

Keep tool down determines whether or not to retract the tool between depth cuts.

12.6 Set the Break Through

* From the **Tree view list**, select **Break Through** and set the parameters to completely cut through the material by an amount that you specify as shown in Figure: 12.6.1.

Figure: 12.6.1

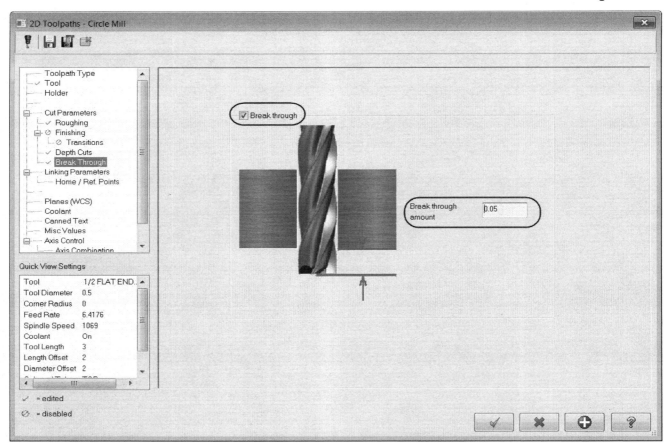

Mastercam. X⁸

12.7 Linking Parameters

♦ Select **Linking Parameters** from the **Tree view list.**
♦ Change the top of stock to **0.0** and set the depth to **-0.75.** Ensure all the values are set to **Absolute** as shown in Figure: 12.7.1.

Figure: 12.7.1

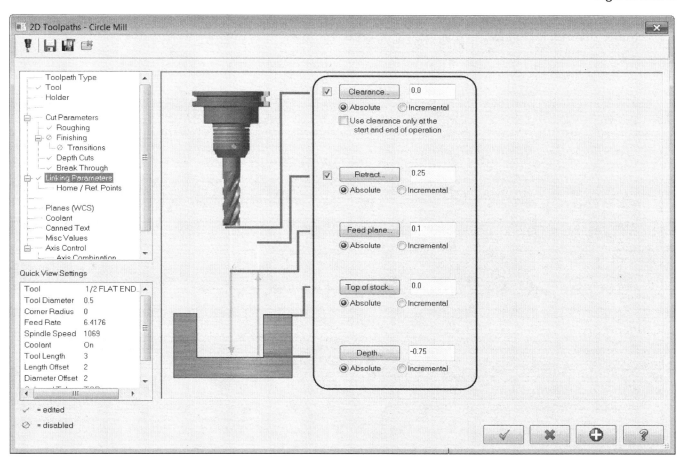

Absolute values are always measured from the origin 0,0,0.

Incremental values are relative to other parameters or chained geometry.

STEP 13: BACKPLOT THE TOOLPATHS

Backplotting shows the path the tools take to cut the part. This display lets you spot errors in the program before you machine the part. As you backplot toolpaths, Mastercam displays additional information such as the X, Y, and Z coordinates, the path length , the minimum and maximum coordinates and the cycle time. It also shows any collisions between the workpiece and the tool.

♦ Make sure that the toolpaths are selected (signified by the green check mark on the folder icon). If both operations are not selected choose the select all operations icon.

♦ Select the **Backplot** selected operations button.

♦ Select the **Backplot** tab and have the following settings enabled as shown.

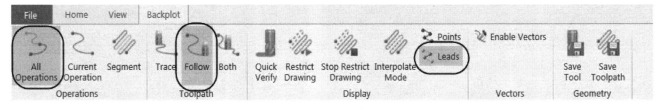

♦ Select the **Home** tab and make sure that you have the following settings on as shown.

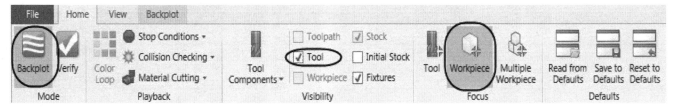

♦ To see the part from an **Isometric** right mouse click in the graphics window and select **Isometric** as shown.

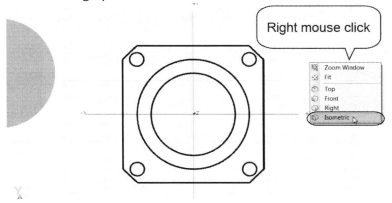

◆ To fit the workpiece to the screen, right mouse click in the graphics window again and select the **Fit**.

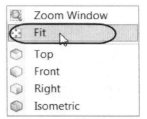

◆ You can step through the **Backplot** by using the **Step forward**  or **Step back** buttons.
◆ You can adjust the speed of the backplot.

◆ Select the **Play** button in the **VCR** bar to run **Backplot**.
◆ The toolpath should look as shown Figure: 13.0.1.

Figure: 13.0.1.

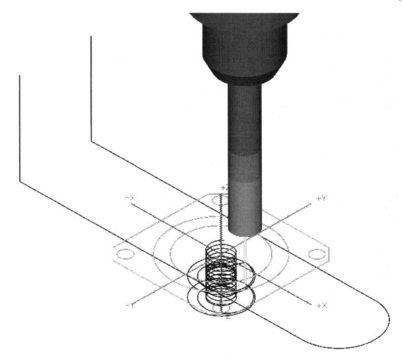

STEP 14:   SIMULATE THE TOOLPATH IN VERIFY

Verify Mode shows the path the tools take to cut the part with material removal. This display lets you spot errors in the program before you machine the part. As you verify toolpaths, Mastercam displays additional information such as the X, Y, and Z coordinates, the path length , the minimum and maximum coordinates and the cycle time. It also shows any collisions between the workpiece and the tool.

♦ In **Mastercam Simulator**, switch to **Verify** and change the settings as shown.

♦ Select the **Play** button in the **VCR** bar to run **Verify**.

♦ The part should appear as shown in Figure: 14.0.1.

Figure: 14.0.1

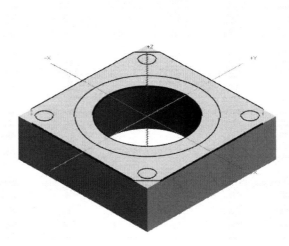

> **NOTE:** To rotate the part, move the cursor to the center of the part and click and hold the mouse wheel and slowly move it in one direction.
> To **Zoom In** or **Out** hold down the mouse wheel and scroll up or down as needed.

♦ Right mouse click in the graphics window and select **Isometric** and then right mouse click again and select **Fit** to see the part in the original position.

◆ To check the part step by step, click first on the **Reset simulation** icon.

◆ Click on the **Step Forward** to see the tool moving one step at a time.

◆ The part should look as shown after several steps.

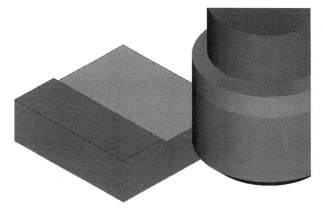

◆ Click on the **Step Forward** until the toolpath is completed.
◆ To go back to Mastercam window, minimize **Mastercam Simulator** window as shown.

STEP 15: CONTOUR TOOLPATH

A **Contour** toolpath removes material along a path defined by a chain of curves. A Contour toolpath only follows a chain, it does not clean out an enclosed area.

Toolpath Preview:

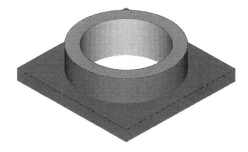

15.1 Chain selection

A chain of entities consists of one or more entities linked together in order and direction. The distance between the endpoints of two consecutive entities of the chain has to be equal or less than the chaining tolerance (0.0001"). In an open chain, the start point is placed at the end of the chain closest to the selection point and the chain direction points to the opposite end of the chain. See the **User Notes** chapter for more information on chaining.

TOOLPATHS

* 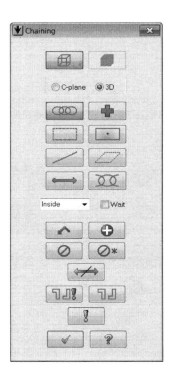 **Contour.**
* Leave the default settings in the **Chaining dialog** box as shown.

NOTE: The **Chain** button is enabled in the **Chaining** dialog box. This lets you chain the entire contour by clicking on one entity.

* Change the **Graphic view** to **Top**.

- Select the chain and ensure the chaining direction is the same as shown in <u>Figure: 15.1.1</u>.

Figure: 15.1.1

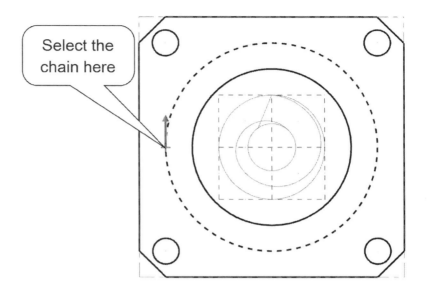

Select the chain here

- Select the **OK** button to exit the **Chaining** dialog box.
- In the **Toolpath Type** page, the **Contour** toolpath will be selected.

Contour   Pocket   Facing   Slot Mill

15.2 Select the 1/2" Flat endmill from the list and set the Tool Parameters

◆ Select **Tool** from the **Tree view list**.
◆ Make all the necessary changes as shown in <u>Figure: 15.2.1</u>.

Figure: 15.2.1

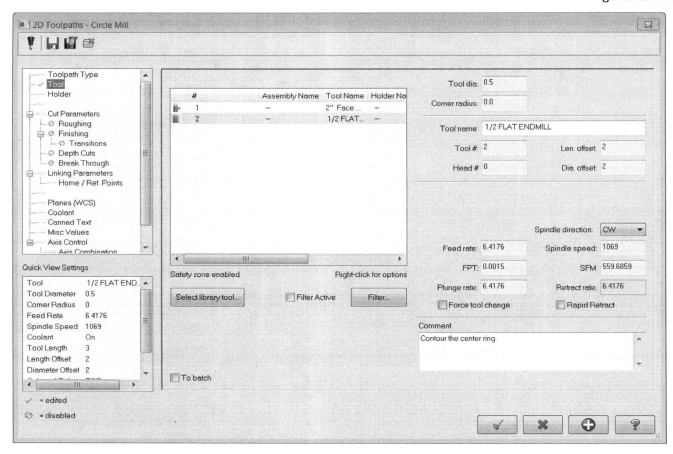

15.3 Cut Parameters

◆ Select the **Cut Parameters** and make the necessary changes as shown in Figure: 15.3.1.

Figure: 15.3.1

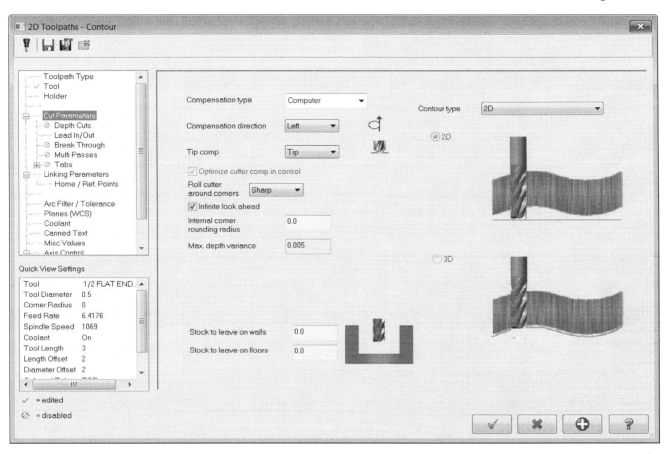

Roll cutter around corners inserts arc moves around corners in the toolpath.

None guarantees all sharp corners.

Sharp rolls the tool around sharp corners (135 degrees or less).

All rolls the tool around all corners and creates smooth tool movement.

15.4 Depth Cuts

• Select **Depth cuts** and enable it. Input a **Max rough step** of **0.25** and enable **Keep tool down** as shown in <u>Figure: 15.4.1</u>.

Figure: 15.4.1

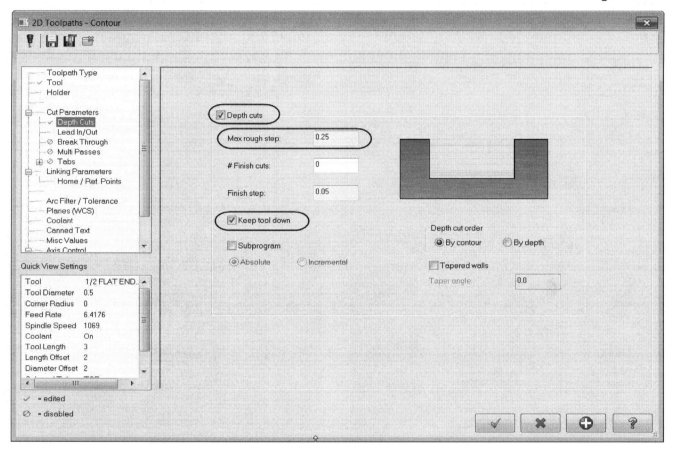

Mill Level 1 Training Tutorial *Mastercam. X*

15.5 Lead In/Out

◆ Choose the option **Lead In/Out** and input an **Overlap** value. Make any other necessary changes as shown in <u>Figure: 15.5.1</u>.

Figure: 15.5.1

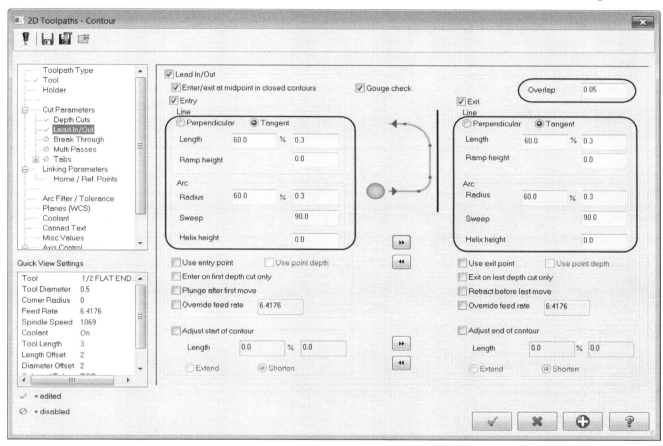

Lead In/Out allows you to select a combination of a Line and an Arc at the beginning and/or end of the contour toolpath for a smooth entry/exit while cutting the part.

Length set to 60% of the tool diameter to ensure that the linear movement is bigger than the tool radius in case **Cutter Compensation** in **Control** was used.

Radius set to 60% of the tool diameter ensures that the arc movement is bigger than the tool radius to generate an arc output.

Overlap sets how far the tool goes past the end of the toolpath before exiting for a cleaner finish.

15.6 Multi Passes

* Select **Multi Passes** from the **Tree view list** and enable the option.
* To clean the entire material set the Number of **Rough** passes to **2** with **spacing** of **0.25**.
* For a smooth finish surface set the **Finish** passes to **1** with **spacing** of **0.02.** This will have the system make two rough passes and then proceed with a **0.02** finish pass.
* Enable the option to **Machine finish passes** at the **Final depth** as shown in Figure: 15.6.1.

Figure: 15.6.1

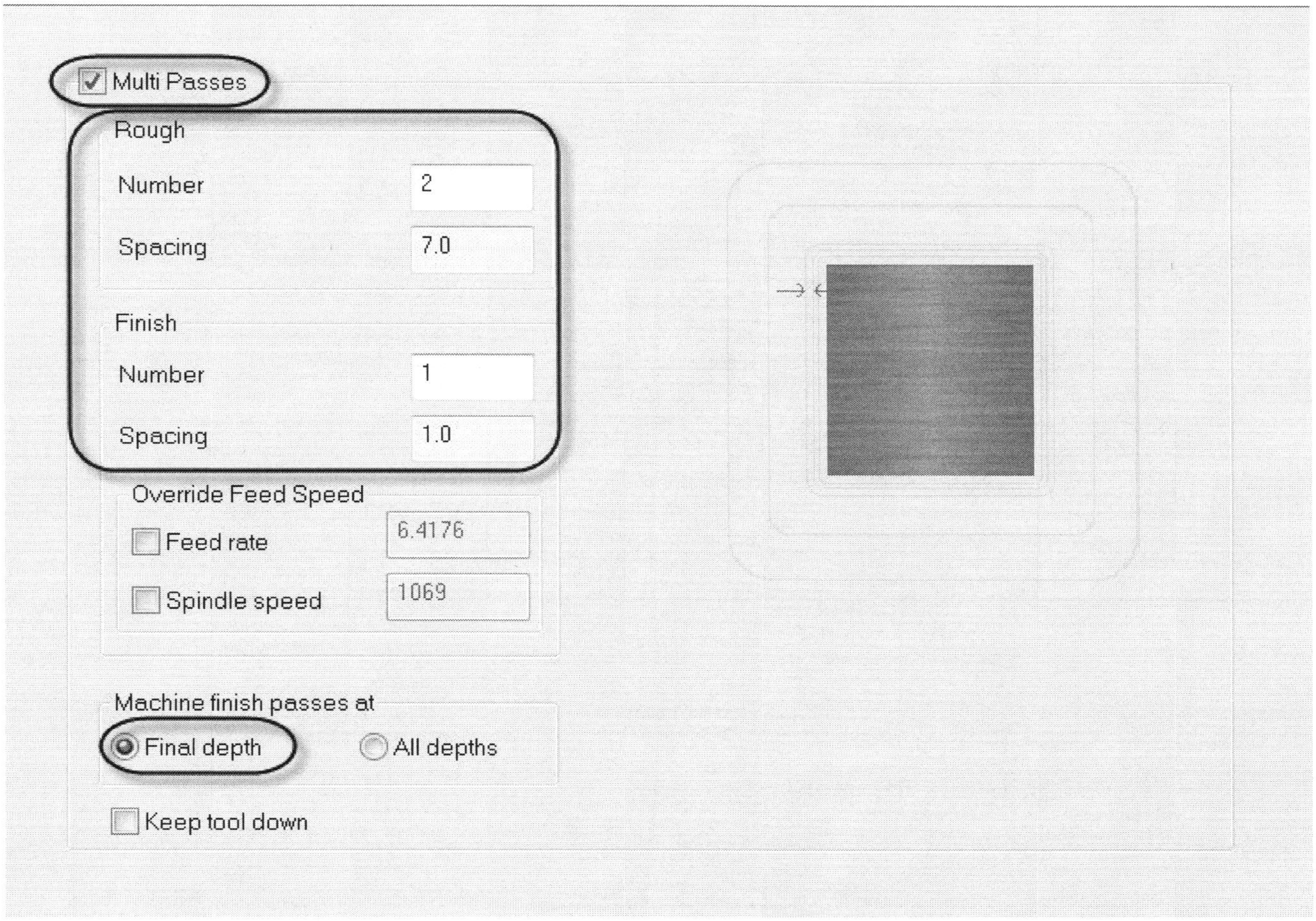

☑ Multi Passes

Rough

Number   2

Spacing   7.0

Finish

Number   1

Spacing   1.0

Override Feed Speed

☐ Feed rate   6.4176

☐ Spindle speed 1069

Machine finish passes at

◉ Final depth   ○ All depths

☐ Keep tool down

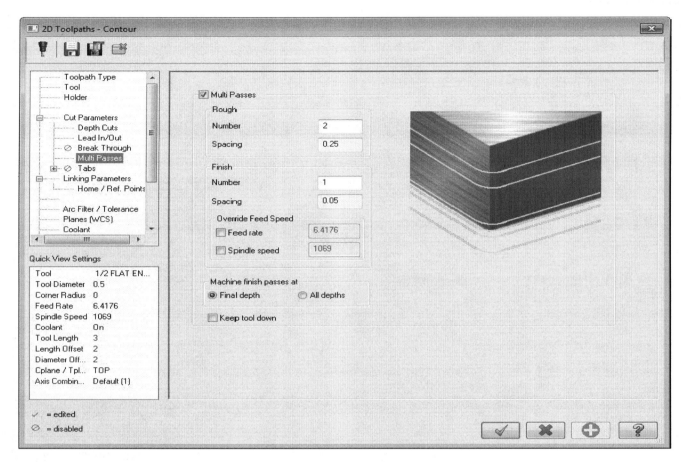

Multipasses allows the tool to approach the part geometry at the cutting depth in steps instead of cutting right to the part geometry.

Number sets the number of cutting passes you want to create for the roughing or finish.

Spacing sets the amount of stock to be removed with each cut.

Override Feed Speeed allows you set different Feed rate and Spindle speed for the finish passes.

Machine finish passes at the final depth performs the finish pass at the final depth only.

15.7 Linking Parameters

♦ Select **Linking Parameters** from the **Tree view list**. Set the **Top of stock** to **zero** and the **Depth** to **-0.5** as shown in Figure: 15.7.1.

Figure: 15.7.1

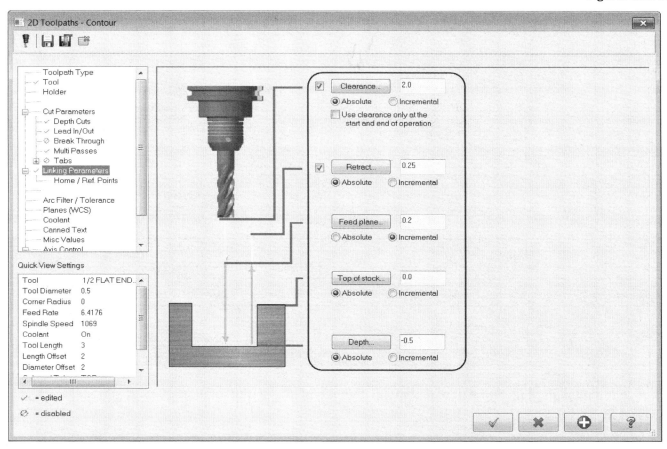

♦ Select the **OK** button to exit the 2D Toolpaths - Contour.

15.8 Verify the toolpaths

◆ From the **Toolpaths Manager**, click on the **Select all operations** icon.

◆ Click on the **Verify selected operation** icon.

◆ For information on how to set the verify parameters and to simulate the toolpath, please check page 56.

◆ The part will appear as shown in <u>Figure: 15.8.1</u>.

Figure: 15.8.1

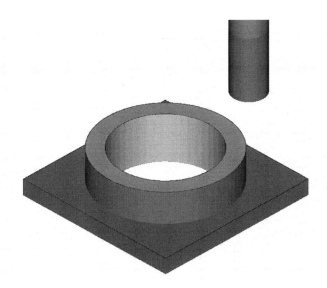

◆ To go back to Mastercam window, minimize Mastercam Simulator window as shown.

STEP 16: SPOT DRILL THE HOLES

Spot Drilling the holes allows you to start the hole. In this operation we will use the spot drill to chamfer the hole before drilling it.

Toolpath Preview:

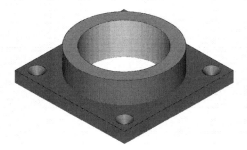

◆ Select all toolpaths and press **Alt +T** to remove the toolpath display if needed.

TOOLPATHS

♦   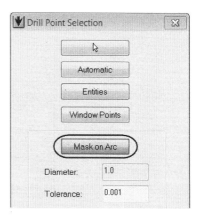 **Drill.**

♦ In the **Drill Point Selection** dialog box choose the option **Mask on Arc**.

NOTE: Mask on Arc is a tool for selecting arcs whose diameters match the one that you select within the specified tolerance.

♦ Select one of the four arcs as shown in <u>Figure: 16.0.1</u>.
♦ Left click in the upper left corner of the graphics window, holding the left button down drag a rectangle to the lower right corner of the part as shown in <u>Figure: 16.0.1</u>.

Figure: 16.0.1

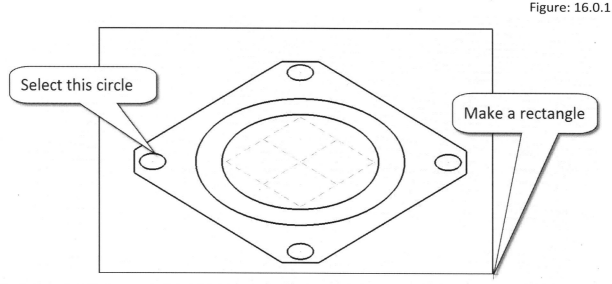

♦ Release the left mouse button and click it again once you have created a window encompassing the entire part.

NOTE: All the arcs inside of the window will be selected. Once you hit the Enter key only the circles with the same diameter as the original selected circle will be selected.

♦ Hit **Enter** once complete.

- Select the **OK** button in the **Drill Point Selection** dialog box to accept the 4 drill points.
- In the **Toolpath Type** page, the **Drill** toolpath will be selected.

Drill   Circle Mill   Point   Helix Bore   Thread Mill

16.1 Select a 3/4" Spot Drill from the library and set the Tool Parameters

- Select **Tool** from the **Tree view list**.

- Click on the **Select library tool** button. | Select library tool... |
- To be able to see just the spot drill, select the filter button.

| Filter... |
☐ Filter Active
367 of 367 tools

- Under **Tool Types** select the **None** button to unselect any unwanted tools.
- Hovering the cursor over each icon, the tool type will be displayed; choose the **Spot drill** icon as shown in <u>Figure: 16.1.1</u>.

Figure: 16.1.1

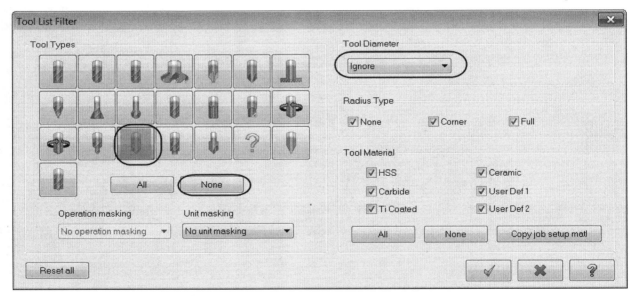

- Select the **OK** button to exit the **Tool List Filter** dialog box.
- At this point you should only see **Spot Drills**.

♦ From that list select the **3/4" Spot Drill** as shown.

21	--	1/8 SPOTDRILL	--	0....	0.0	2.0	2	No...	Sp...
22	--	1/4 SPOTDRILL	--	0....	0.0	2.0	2	No...	Sp...
23	--	3/8 SPOTDRILL	--	0....	0.0	2.0	4	No...	Sp...
24	--	1/2 SPOTDRILL	--	0.5	0.0	2.0	2	No...	Sp...
25	--	3/4 SPOTDRILL	--	0....	0.0	2.0	4	No...	Sp...
26	--	1. SPOTDRILL	--	1.0	0.0	2.0	4	No...	Sp...
27	--	1/64 DRILL	--	0....	0.0	1.0	2	No...	Drill

♦ Select the tool in the **Tool Selection** page and then select the **OK** button to exit.
♦ Make the necessary changes to the **Tool** page as shown in <u>Figure: 16.1.2</u>.

Figure: 16.1.2

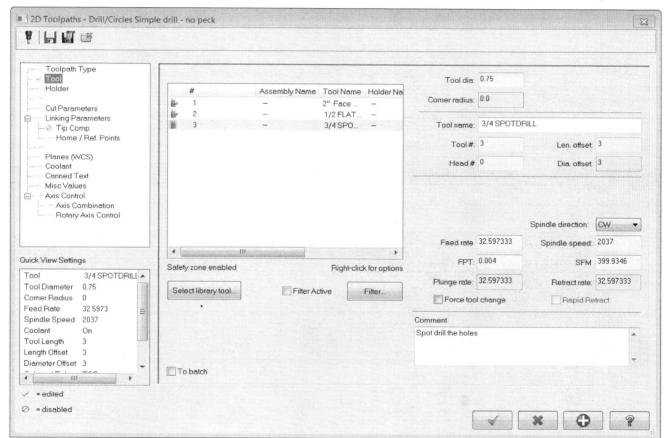

16.2 Set the Cut Parameters

♦ Select **Cut Parameters** and make the necessary changes as shown in Figure: 16.2.1.

Figure: 16.2.1

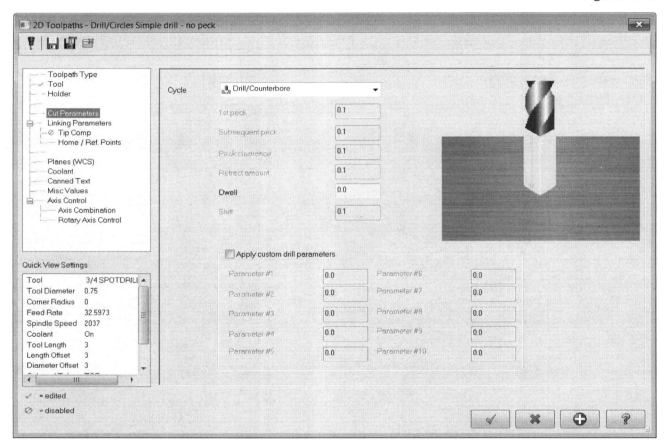

Drill/Counterbore recommended for drilling holes with depths of less than three times the tools diameter.

Dwell sets the amount of time in seconds that the tool remains at the bottom of a drilled hole.

16.3 Linking Parameters

- Choose **Linking Parameters**, ensure clearance is enabled and set the **Top of stock** and the **Depth** to **Absolute** and **-0.5** as shown.
- To input the depth select the **Calculator** icon as shown.

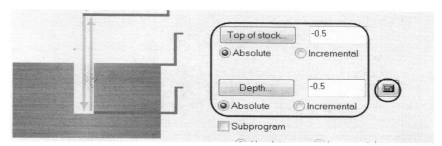

- To generate a 0.025 chamfer, input the following equation in the **Finish diameter** area: **0.25+0.05** and hit **Enter** to calculate the **Depth** as shown in Figure: 16.3.1.

Figure: 16.3.1

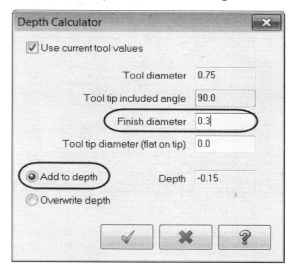

- Select the **OK** button to exit the **Depth Calculator**.

- You will now see the depth we calculated for the spot drilling operation set in the **Depth** field. Change the rest of the parameters as shown in Figure: 16.3.2.

Figure: 16.3.2

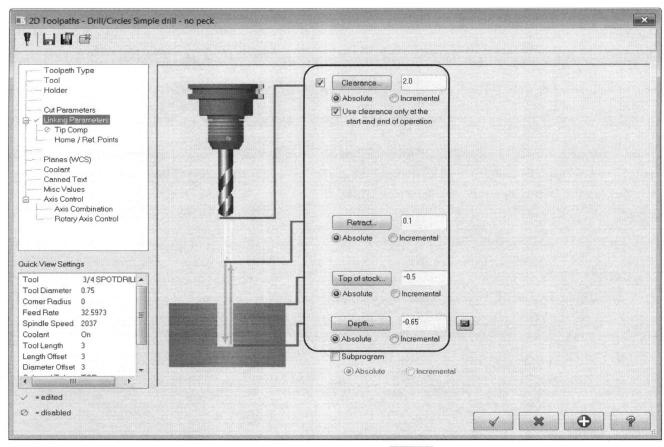

- Select the **OK** button to exit the **Drill/Counterbore** parameters.

16.4 Verify the toolpaths

- See page 56 to review the procedure.

STEP 17: DRILL THE HOLES

In this step we will drill the holes to a specified depth.

Toolpath Preview:

TOOLPATHS

- **Drill.**
- In the **Drill Point Selection** dialog box choose the option **Last**.

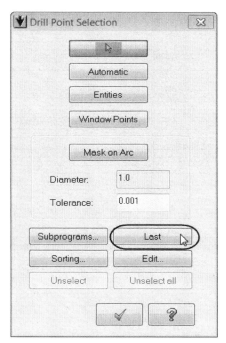

- This option will automatically select the 4 holes for you based off the selection from the previous drill operation.

- Select the **OK** button in the **Drill Point Selection** dialog box to accept the 4 drill points.

• In the **Toolpath Type** page, the **Drill** toolpath will be selected as shown in <u>Figure: 17.0.1</u>.

Figure: 17.0.1

Drill   Circle Mill   Point   Helix Bore   Thread Mill

17.1 Select a 1/4" Drill from the library and set the Tool Parameters

• Select **Tool** from the **Tree view list**.

• Click on the **Select library tool** button. Select library tool...
• To be able to see just the spot drill select the **Filter** button.

• Under **Tool Types** select the **None** button and then choose the drill Icon. Under **Tool Diameter** select **Equal** and input a value of **0.25.**

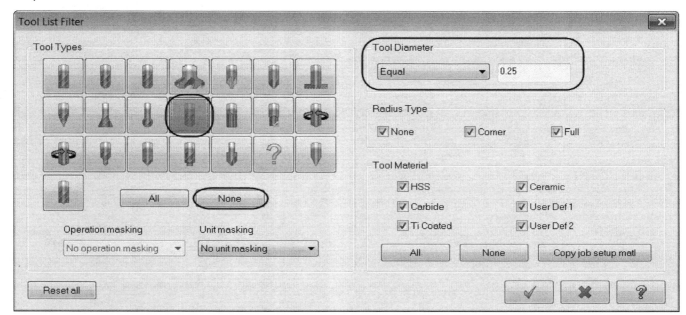

• Select **OK** button to exit the **Tool List Filter** dialog box.
• At this point you should only see a **1/4" Drill**. Select the drill as shown.

#	Assembly Name	Tool Name	Holder Name	Dia.	Cor. rad.	Length	# Flutes	Type	Rad. Type
104	--	1/4 DRILL	--	0.25	0.0	2.0	2	Drill	None

• Select the tool in the **Tool Selection** page and then choose the **OK** button to exit.

DRILL THE HOLES | **TUTORIAL #1**

◆ Make the necessary changes to the **Tool** page as shown in Figure: 17.1.1.

Figure: 17.1.1

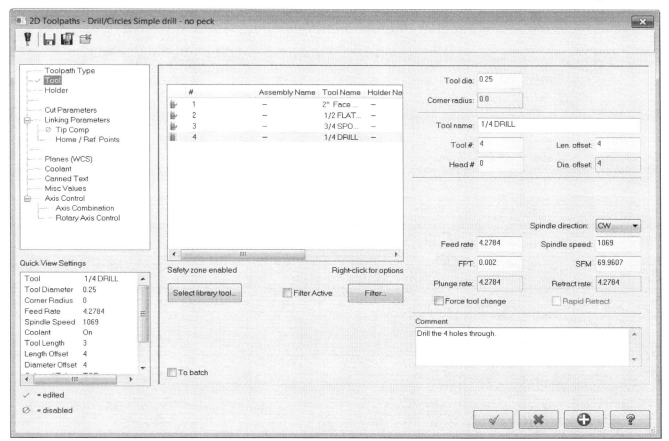

17.2 Cut Parameters

◆ Select **Cut Parameters**, change the drill **Cycle** to **Drill/Counterbore** as shown in Figure: 17.2.1.

Figure: 17.2.1

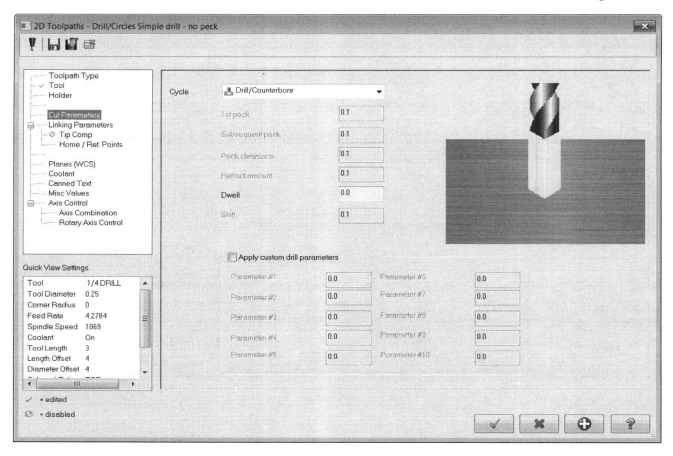

17.3 Linking Parameters

◆ Choose **Linking Parameters**, and set the **Top of stock** to **-0.5**. Input a depth value of **-0.75**as shown in
<u>Figure: 17.3.1</u>.

Figure: 17.3.1

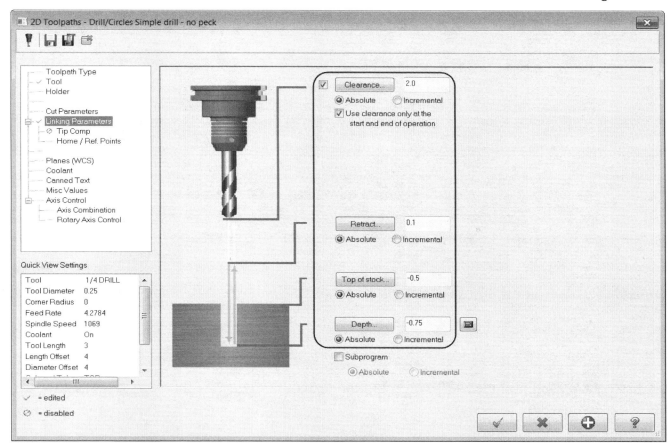

17.4 Set the Tip Compensation

- Select **Tip Comp** and enable it.
- Set the **Breakthrough amount** to **0.01** as shown in Figure: 17.4.1.

Figure: 17.4.1

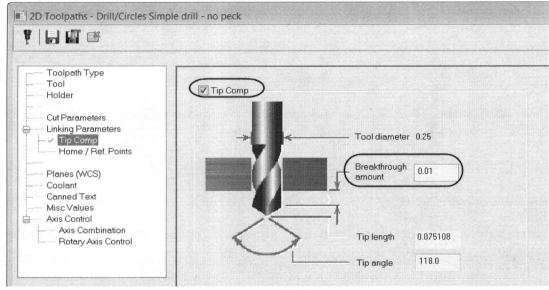

- Select the **OK** button to exit the **Drill/Counterbore** parameters.

17.5 Verify the toolpaths

- To **Verify** the toolpaths see page 56 to review the procedure.

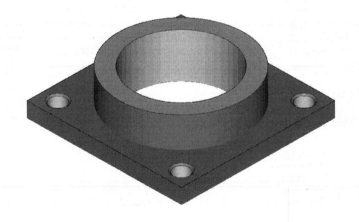

◆ To rotate the part, click in the center of the part with the mouse wheel. Hold down the mouse wheel and slightly drag the cursor to rotate.

STEP 18: CHAMFER THE TOP OF THE PART

Chamfer Toolpath automatically cuts a chamfer around a contour using a chamfer mill.

Toolpath Preview:

TOOLPATHS

◆ 　 **Contour.**

◆ Leave the default settings in the **Chaining** dialog box as shown.

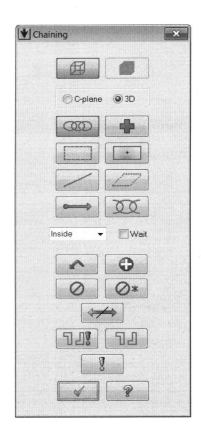

◆ Select the chains and ensure the chaining direction is the same as shown in Figure: 18.0.1.

Figure: 18.0.1

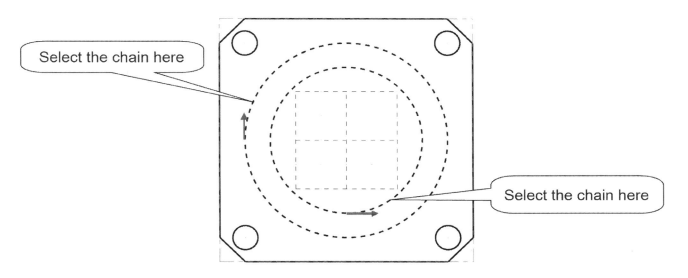

NOTE: It does not matter which contour you select first. However the first contour you select will be the first

contour cut. Select the contours as shown in Figure: 18.0.1 to ensure that the chaining directions for both

chains are correct. Use Reverse button to reverse the chains if needed.

When you select the second chain the arrow indicated the starting point and the machining direction will

disappear from the graphics.

◆ Select the **OK** button to exit the **Chaining** dialog box.
◆ In the **Toolpath Type** page, the **Contour** toolpath will be selected.

Contour   Pocket   Facing   Slot Mill

18.1 Select a 1/2" Chamfer Mill from the library and set the Tool parameters

* Select **Tool** from the **Tree view list**.

* Click on the **Select library tool** button. | Select library tool... |
* To be able to see just the spot drill select the **Filter** button.

* Under **Tool Types** select the **None** button and then choose the **Chamfer Mill** Icon.

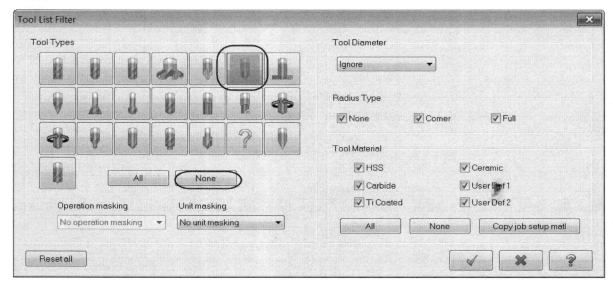

* Select the **OK** button to exit the **Tool List Filter** dialog box.
* At this point you should only see a list of chamfer mills.
* From the **Tool Selection** list select the **1/2" Chamfer Mill**.

#	Assembly Name	Tool Name	Holder Name	Dia.	Cor. rad.	Length	# Flutes	Type	Rad. Type
304	–	1/4 CHA...	–	0....	0.0	0.5	4	Ch...	None
305	–	1/2 CHA...	–	0....	0.0	0.75	4	Ch...	None
306	–	3/4 CHA...	–	0....	0.0	1.0	4	Ch...	None
307	–	1 INCH C...	–	1....	0.0	1.0	4	Ch...	None

* In the **Tool Selection** page choose the **OK** button to exit. A warning message that the tool selected is not defined as being capable of both roughing and finish will appear on the screen.

> **NOTE:** The chamfer mill is defined for finish operation only. For chamfer toolpath we only need a finish operation.

* Select the OK button to continue.

◆ Make all the necessary changes as shown in Figure: 18.1.1.

Figure: 18.1.1

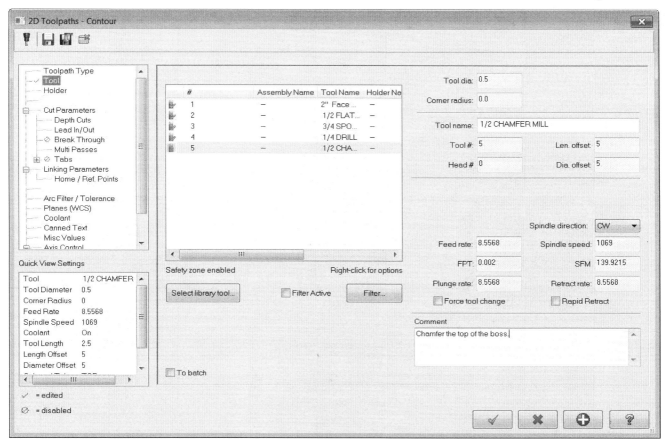

18.2 Cut Parameters

- Select the **Cut Parameters** page and change the **Contour type** to **2D chamfer**.
- Input a **Width** of **0.025** and a **Tip offset** of **0.05** as shown in <u>Figure: 18.2.1</u>.

Figure: 18.2.1

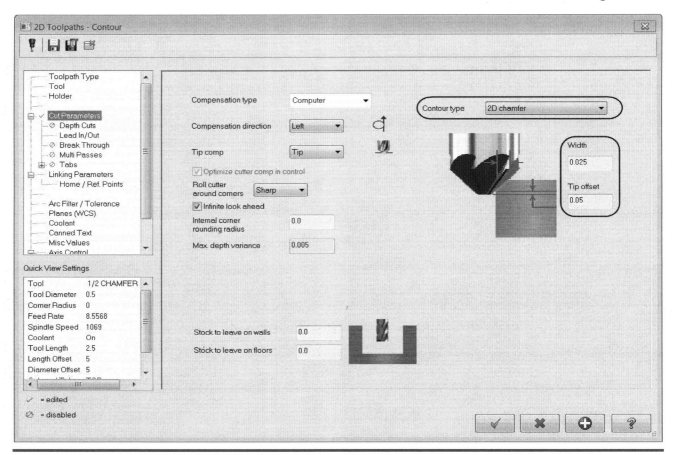

2D chamfer cuts chamfers around a contour.

Width sets the chamfer width. Mastercam measures the width from the chained geometry adjusted by the cut depths defined on the linking parameters page.

Tip offset is an amount to ensure that the tip of the tool clears the bottom of the chamfer.

18.3 Depth Cuts

◆ Select **Depth Cuts** and **disable** it as shown in Figure: 18.3.1.

Figure: 18.3.1

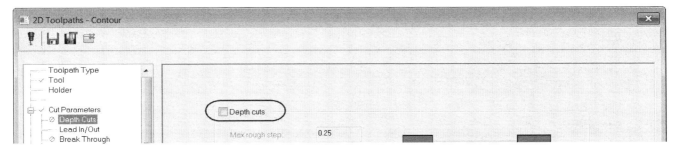

18.4 Lead In/Out

◆ Choose the option **Lead In/Out** and input an **Overlap value** of **0.02**.
◆ Make any other necessary changes as shown in Figure: 18.4.1.

Figure: 18.4.1

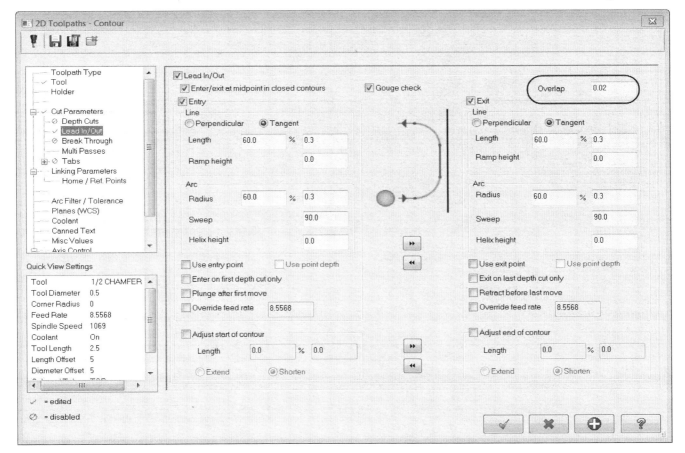

18.5 Multi Passes

◆ Select **Multi Passes,** disable this option as shown in Figure: 18.5.1.

Figure: 18.5.1

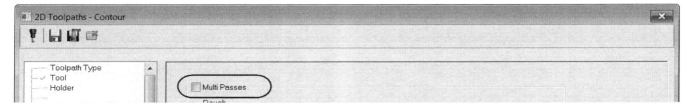

18.6 Linking Parameters

◆ Select the **Linking Parameters** from the **Tree view list**. Set the **Top of stock** to **zero** and the **Depth** to **zero** as shown in Figure: 18.6.1.

Figure: 18.6.1

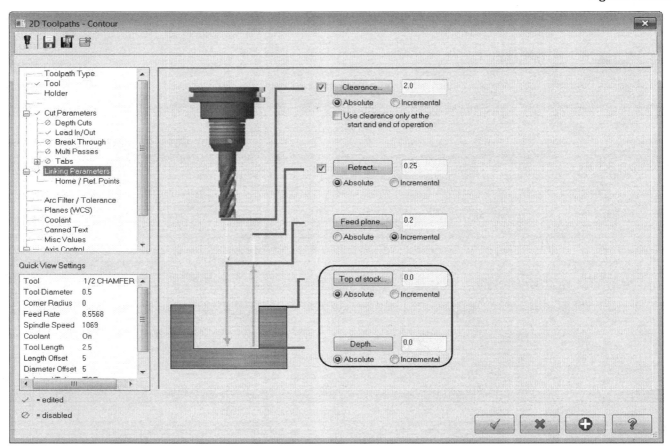

NOTE: The depth of the chamfer is based on the width and tip offset set in the Cut Parameters page. This is why we set the depth here to zero.

18.7 Verify the toolpaths

◆ To **Verify** the toolpaths see page 56 to review the procedure.
◆ Ensure all operations are selected, if they are not use the button **Select all operations** in the **Toolpaths**

Manager.
◆ Your part will appear as shown.

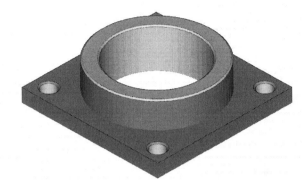

◆ To exit Mastercam Simulator click on the **Close** icon.

STEP 19: MACHINE THE CHAMFERS AT THE CORNERS USING CONTOUR TOOLPATH

In this step you will machine the corners of the part using **ContourToolpath**.

Toolpath Preview:

TOOLPATHS

◆ Contour.

- In the **Chaining** dialog box, to be able to select only one entity at a time, select **Single** button as shown.

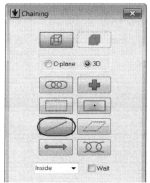

- Select the chains and ensure the chaining direction is the same as shown in Figure: 19.0.1.

Figure: 19.0.1

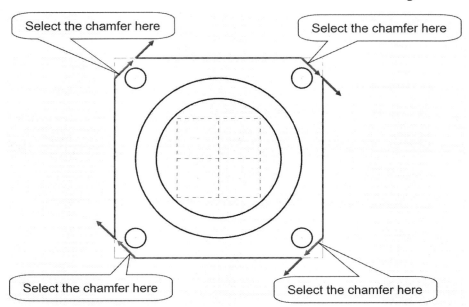

NOTE: Select the contour as shown in Figure: 19.0.1 to ensure that the chaining directions for all four chains are correct. Use Reverse button to reverse the chains if needed.

The green color arrow shows the chain start location and the red color arrow shows the end of the chain. The chain selection arrows disappear as you select the next chamfer.

- Select the **OK** button to exit the **Chaining** dialog box.

• In the **Toolpath Type** page, the **Contour** toolpath will be selected.

19.1 Select a 1/2" Flat Endmill and set the Tool parameters

• Make all the necessary changes as shown in Figure: 19.1.1.

Figure: 19.1.1

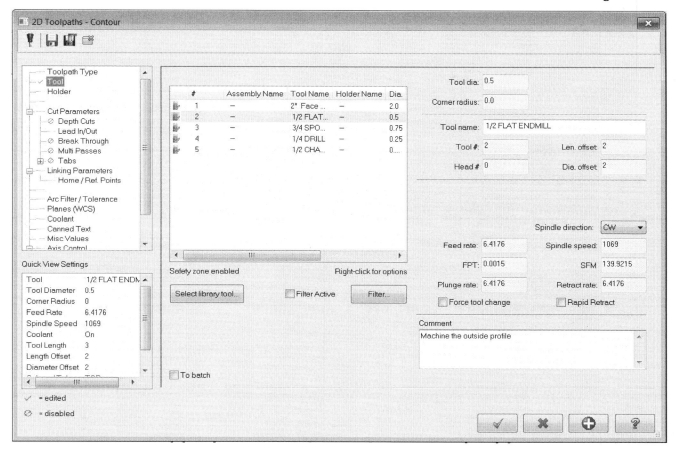

19.2 Cut Parameters

• Select the **Cut Parameters** page and change the **Contour type** to **2D** as shown in <u>Figure: 19.2.1</u>.

Figure: 19.2.1

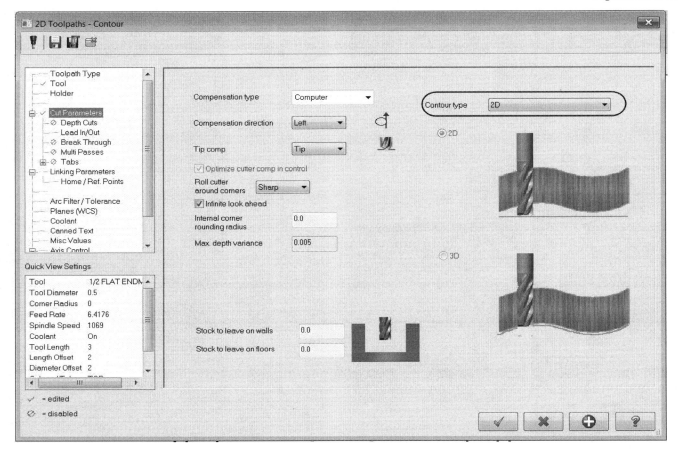

Mastercam X

19.3 Depth Cuts

* Select **Depth Cuts** and enable it as shown in Figure: 19.3.1.
* Make sure that the parameters are set as shown in Figure: 19.3.1.

Figure: 19.3.1

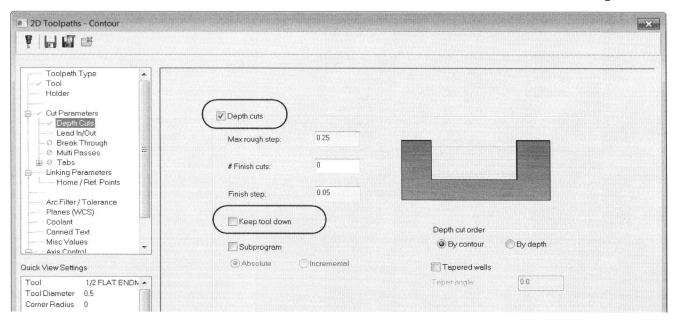

19.4 Lead In/Out

◆ Choose the option **Lead In/Out** and make sure the parameters are set as shown in Figure: 19.4.1.

Figure: 19.4.1

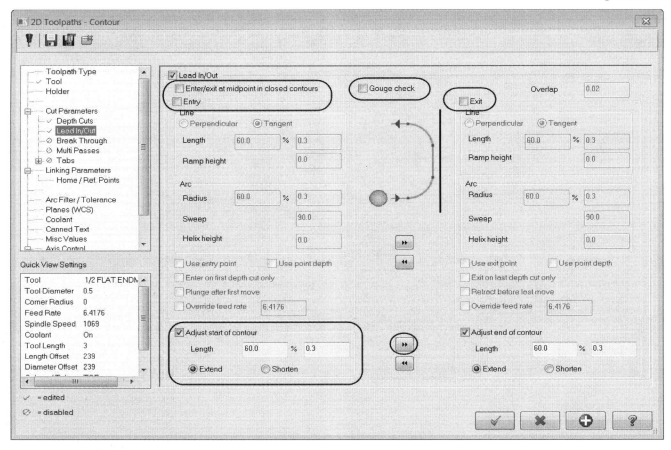

Adjust start/end of contour moves the starting/ending position in open contours by adding (Extend) or removing (Shorten) the specified length.

19.5 Linking Parameters

♦ Select the **Linking Parameters** from the **Tree view list**. Set the **Top of stock** and the **Depth** as shown in Figure: 19.5.1.

Figure: 19.5.1

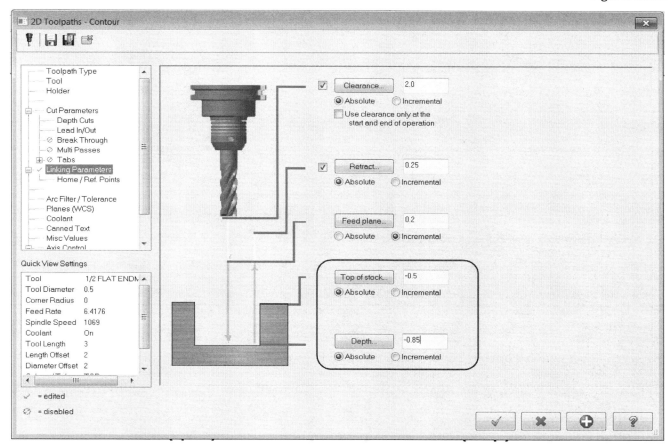

> **NOTE:** The Top of stock is set to -0.5 as the previous contour machine the part up to this depth.

19.6 Verify the toolpaths

- To **Verify** the toolpaths see page 56 to review the procedure.
- Ensure all operations are selected, if they are not use the button **Select all operations** in the **Toolpaths Manager.**
- Your part will appear as shown.

- To exit Mastercam Simulator click on the **Close** icon.

STEP 20: POST THE FILE

- Ensure all operations are selected, if they are not use the button **Select all operations** in the **Toolpaths Manager.**
- Select the **Post selected operations** icon from the **Toolpaths Manager** as shown.

* In the **Post processing** window make the necessary changes as shown in <u>Figure: 20.0.1</u>.

Figure: 20.0.1

Post processing

Active post: _____ [Select Post]

MPFAN.PST

☐ Output MCX file descriptor   [Properties...]

☑ NC file
   ○ Overwrite   ☑ Edit
   ◉ Ask   NC extension:
                  .NC

   ☐ Send to machine   [Communications]

☐ NCI file
   ○ Overwrite   ☐ Edit
   ◉ Ask   ☑ Output Tplanes
                  relative to WCS

[✓]   [✗]   [?]

NC File enabled allows you to keep the NC file and to assign the same name as the MCX file.

Edit enabled allows you to automatically launch the default.

* Select the **OK** button to continue.
* Save the NC file.

• A window with **Mastercam Code Expert** will be launched and the NC program will appear as shown in <u>Figure: 20.0.2</u>.

<u>Figure: 20.0.2</u>

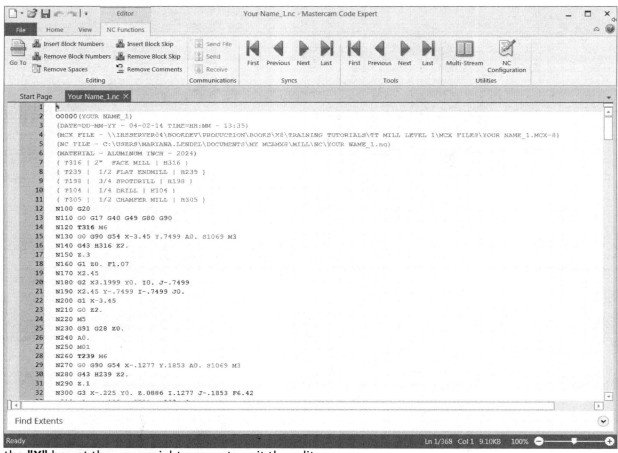

• Select the **"X"** box at the upper right corner to exit the editor.

STEP 21: SAVE THE UPDATED MCX FILE

REVIEW EXERCISE -STUDENT PRACTICE

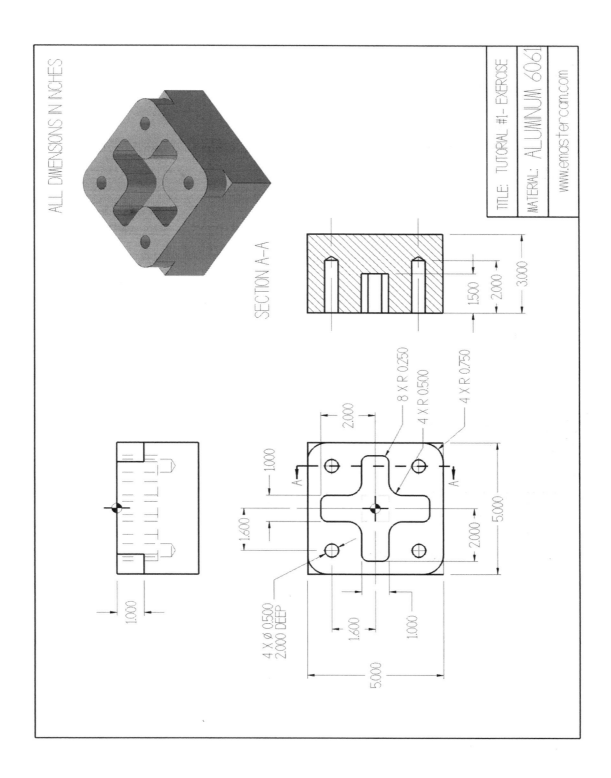

CREATE THE GEOMETRY FOR TUTORIAL #1 EXERCISE

Use these commands to create the geometry.
- Create Rectangle.
- Create Fillets.
- Create Lines.
- Create Line Parallel.
- Create Circle Center Points.
- Fast Point to position the Circles.
- Trim.

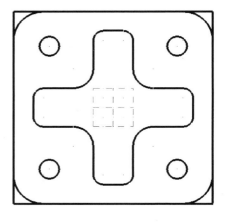

CREATE THE TOOLPATHS FOR TUTORIAL #1 EXERCISE

Create the Toolpaths for Tutorial #1 Exercise as per the instructions below.

Set the machine properties including the stock.

Remove the material on the outside of the part Contour (2D).
- Use a **1/2" Flat Endmill**.
- Based on your chaining direction ensure the **Compensation direction** is set correctly.
- Enable **Depth Cuts** and set the **Max rough step** to **0.25"**.
- **Lead In/Out** set **Length** and **Radius** to **60%** with a **90** degree sweep.
- No **Break Through**, **Multi Passes**.
- Set the depth according to the drawing.

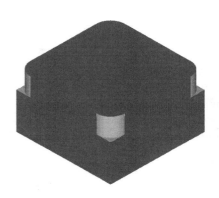

Mastercam. X^8

Spot drill the holes.
- Use a **3/4" Spot Drill**.
- Set the **Cycle** to **Drill/Counterbore** and set a **Dwell** to **1.0** second.
- Use the depth calculator to set a **0.05"** chamfer on the hole.

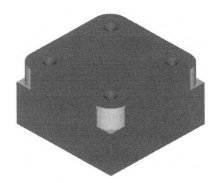

Drill the holes.
- Use a **1/2" Drill**.
- Set the Cycle to Peck Drill and set your peck values.
- Set the depth according to the drawing.

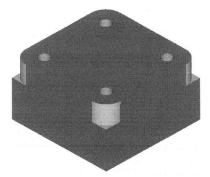

Remove the Material in the center of the part (Pocket Standard).
- Use a **1/2" Flat Endmill**.
- Choose to leave no stock on the walls.
- Set the **Cutting method** to **Constant Overlap Spiral**.
- The **Entry Motion** will be **Helix**.
- Enable **Finish** and set the parameters.
- **Lead In/Out** set **Length** and **Radius** to **60%** with a **90** degree sweep.
- Enable **Depth Cuts** and set the **Max rough step** to **0.25"**.
- Disable **Break Through**.
- Set the depth according to the drawing.

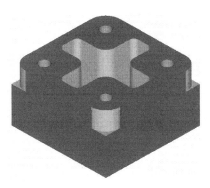

NOTES:

TUTORIAL #1 QUIZ

◆ What is a Contour Toolpath used for?

◆ What is a Facing Toolpath used for?

◆ What does a Pocket Toolpath allow you to do?

◆ What does Backplot do?

◆ What does Verify allow you to do?

TUTORIAL #2

OVERVIEW OF STEPS TAKEN TO CREATE THE FINAL PART:

From Drawing to CAD Model:
- The student should examine the drawing on the following page to understand what part is being created in the tutorial.
- From the drawing we can decide how to go about creating the geometry in Mastercam.

Create the 2D CAD Model used to generate Toolpaths from:
- The student will create the Top 2D geometry needed to create the toolpaths.
- Geometry creation commands such as rectangle, polygon, fillet entities, fillet chain, arc circle center point, line endpoints, rectangular shapes and trim will be used.

Create the necessary Toolpaths to machine the part:
- The student will set up the stock size to be used and the clamping method used.

Setup 1
- A Slot Mill toolpath will be created to machine the slot.
- 2D High Speed Dynamic Mill toolpath will be created to rough out the outside profile.
- A Contour toolpath will be created to finish the outside profile.
- 2D High Speed Dynamic Contour mill toolpath will be created to machine the small radii.

Setup 2
- A Facing toolpath will be used to face the bottom of the part.

Backplot and Verify the file:
- The Backplot will be used to simulate a step by step process of the tool's movements.
- The Verify will be used to watch a tool machine the part out of a solid model.

Post Process the file to generate the G-code:
- The Student will then post process the file to obtain an NC file containing the necessary code for the machine.

 This tutorial takes approximately two hours to complete.

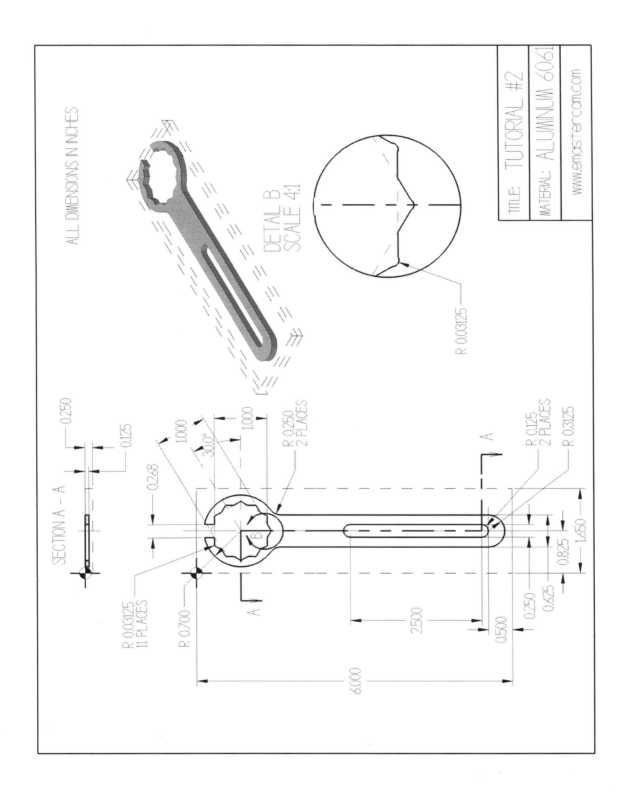

GEOMETRY CREATION

STEP 1: SETTING UP THE GRAPHIC USER INTERFACE

Please refer to the **Getting Started** section to set up the graphics user interface.

STEP 2: CREATE A RECTANGLE

In this step you will learn how to create a rectangle knowing the width, the height and the anchor position.

Step Preview:

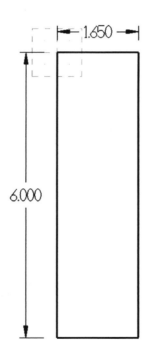

CREATE

• ☐ **Rectangle.**

• Enter the **Width** 📏 **1.65** and **Height** 📏 **-6.0** as shown. [graphic toolbar showing: 1.65 and -6.0]

> **NOTE:** The **Anchor to center** and the **Create Surface** icons should not be selected as explained in Tutorial 1.

• Press **Enter** after typing the values to see a preview of the rectangle.

◆ [Select position of first corner]: Select the **Origin** as shown in Figure: 2.0.1.

Figure: 2.0.1

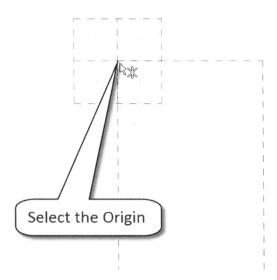

Select the Origin

◆ Make sure that when selecting the origin, the visual cue of the cursor changes as shown.

◆ Select the **OK** button to exit the **Rectangle** command.

◆ Use the **Fit** icon to fit the drawing to the screen. 🄷

> **NOTE:** During the geometry creation of this tutorial, if you make a mistake you can undo the last step using the
>
> **Undo** icon. ↺ You can undo as many steps as needed. If you delete or undo a step by mistake, just use the
>
> **Redo** icon. ↻ To delete unwanted geometry, select it first and then press **Delete** from the keyboard.

STEP 3: CREATE TWO POLYGONS

In this step you will learn how to create two six side polygons. To Create A Polygon you need to define the number of sides, the radius of the arc based on which the polygon is created and how it is measured (Corner or Flat) and the center point.

Step Preview:

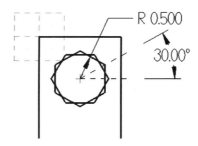

3.1 Create the straight polygon

CREATE

* ⬠ **Polygon.**
* Change the settings in the dialog box to create a six side polygon with the arc radius **0.5"** measured to the flats as shown in <u>Figure: 3.1.1</u>.

Figure: 3.1.1

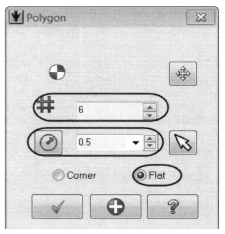

* [Select position of base point]: Select the **Fast point** icon ⚡ and enter the coordinates as shown.

> 0.825,-0.875

NOTE: When entering coordinates for the center point using **Fast Point** option, first value is the **X** coordinate value, then **Y** value follow by the **Z** value only if it is different than zero. The coordinate values are separated with comma. You do not need to use the coordinate labels if you enter the values in this order.

- Press **Enter** to see the polygon created in the windows graphics as shown.

- Select the **Apply** button to continue in the same command.

3.2 Create the 30 degrees rotated polygon

- Expand the dialog box by selecting the upper left arrow as shown.

◆ Re-enter the arc radius **0.5** (although the value is still showing in the dialog box) and enter the rotation angle **30** degrees as shown in Figure: 3.2.1.

Figure: 3.2.1

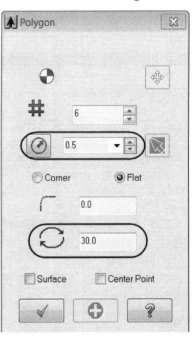

◆ [Select position of base point]: Select the **Fast point** icon and enter the coordinates as shown.

    0.825,-0.875

• Press **Enter** to see the polygon created in the windows graphics as shown.

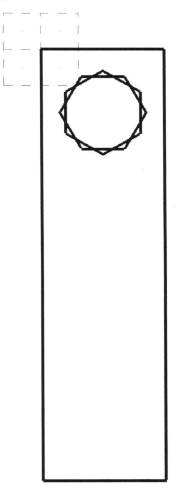

• Select the **OK** button to exit the command.

STEP 4: USE TRIM DIVIDE TO CLEAN THE POLYGONS

In this step you will learn how to trim the geometry using **Divide** option. **Divide** allows you to trim an entity into two disjointed segments by removing the segment that lies between two dividing intersections. It can also allow you to delete entities based on the nearest intersection. Pick always the segment in the area that has to be removed.

Step Preview:

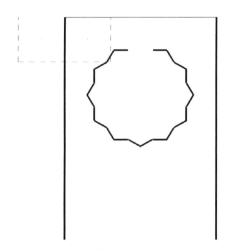

- To better see the area that we are working on, **Zoom in** by moving the cursor as shown and then scroll up the mouse wheel.
- The geometry should look as shown.

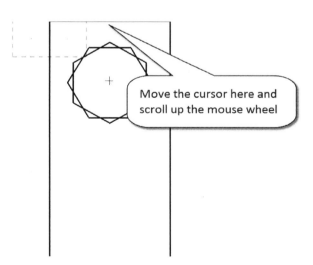

Move the cursor here and scroll up the mouse wheel

EDIT
- **Trim/Break.**

-  **Trim/Break/Extend.**
- Select the **Divide** command and ensure the option to **Trim** is enabled (blue color) as shown.

* Select the lines as shown in Figure: 4.0.1.

Figure: 4.0.1

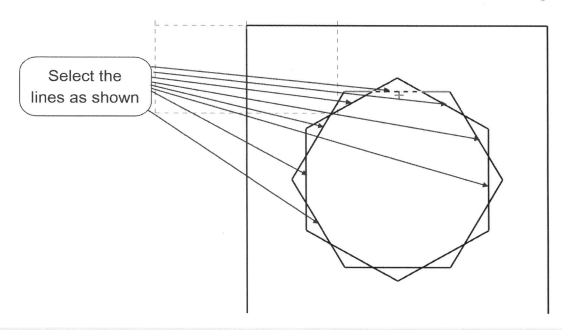

Select the
lines as shown

NOTE: When haver above the line you will notice that the line changes to a hidden line style. This is a preview of what is going to be deleted and lets you select another segment of the line if necessary.

* Repeat the step selecting the lines as shown in Figure: 4.0.2.

Figure: 4.0.2

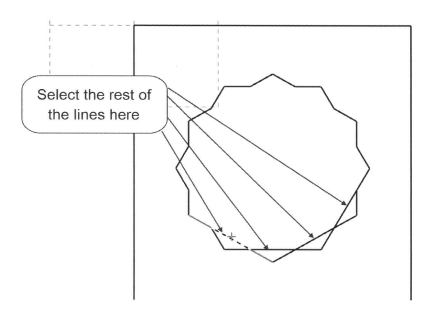

Select the rest of
the lines here

◆ Your drawing will appear as shown.

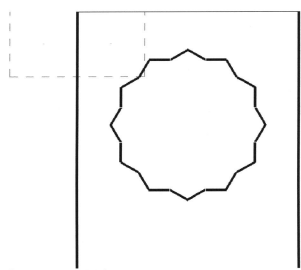

◆ Select the lines shown in <u>Figure: 4.0.3</u> to delete them using **Divide**.

Figure: 4.0.3

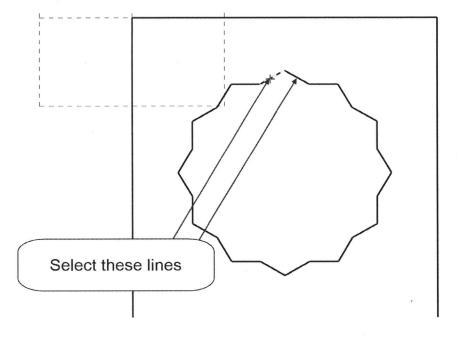

Select these lines

Mastercam. X

• The geometry should look as shown.

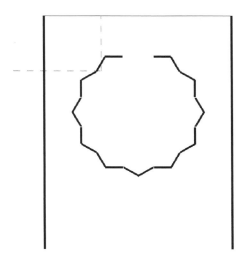

• Select the **OK** icon to exit the command.

STEP 5: CREATE THE CLEARANCE STYLE ARCS

In this step you will learn how to use **Fillet chains** command to create the clearance style arcs with the 0.035 radius.

Step Preview:

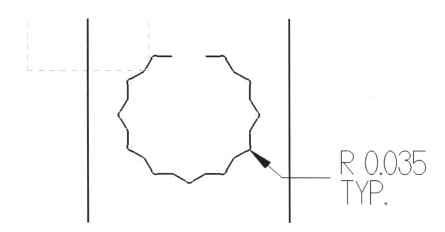

CREATE
• **Fillet.**

•  **Chains.**

• The Chaining dialog box appears on the screen as shown.

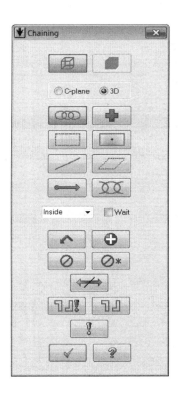

• [Select chain1]: Select the chain as shown in Figure: 5.0.1.

Figure: 5.0.1

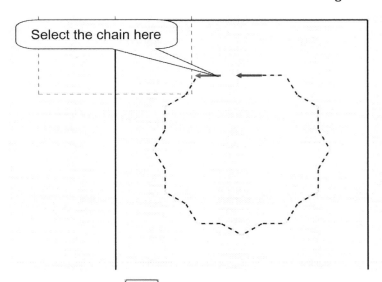

Select the chain here

• From the **Chaining** dialog box, select the **OK** button to continue.

- In the **Ribbon bar**, enter the **Radius 0.035** and click on the down arrow to change the fillet **Style** to **Clearance** as shown.

> **NOTE: Clearance** style creates fillets inside the contour corners so that the tool can reach completely into the corners to remove the material.

- The **Trim** icon should be selected too as shown.

- Select the **OK** icon to exit the command.
- The drawing will appear as shown.

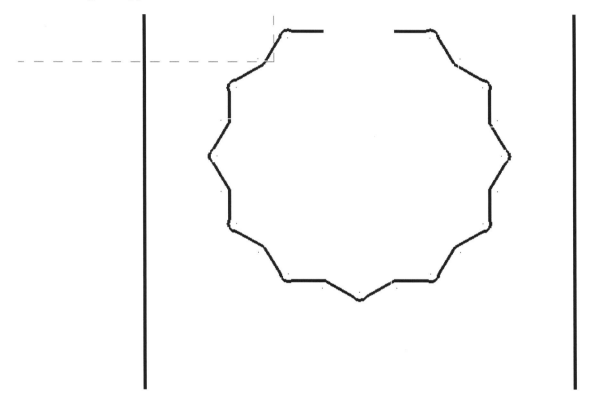

- Select the **Fit** icon to fit the geometry to the screen.

STEP 6: CREATE CIRCLES

In this step you will create two circles knowing the radii and the center locations.

Step Preview:

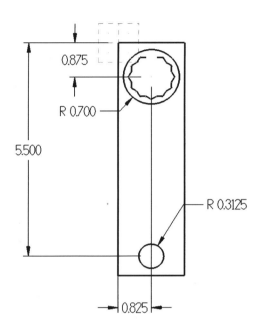

CREATE
* **Arc.**

*  **Circle Center Point.**

* Input the **0.7 Radius** in the **Ribbon bar** as shown.

* Select the **Fast Point** icon from the **AutoCursor Ribbon Bar.**

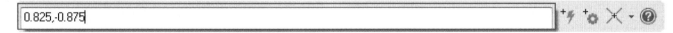

0.825,-0.875

* Enter the dimensions as shown, then hit **Enter** on your keyboard to place the circle.

* From the **Ribbon bar**, select the **Apply** icon to finish the circle and to continue in the same command.

* Input the **0.3125 Radius** in the **Ribbon bar** as shown.

* Select the **Fast Point** again.
* Enter the dimensions **0.825, -5.5** and hit **Enter** on the keyboard once again.

* Once complete choose the **OK** button to exit the command.

- To see the entire geometry in the graphics window, select the **Fit** icon.
- The geometry should look as shown.

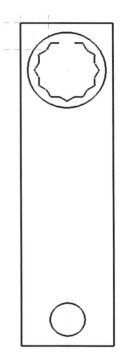

STEP 7: CREATE THE VERTICAL LINES

In this step you will learn how to create vertical lines.

Step Preview:

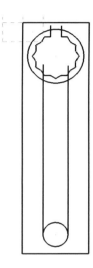

CREATE
* Line.

*  Endpoint.

* Select the **Vertical** icon as shown.

NOTE: Once this icon has been selected you will only be able to create vertical lines.

◆ [Specify the first endpoint]: Select the **Endpoint** as shown in Figure: 7.0.1.

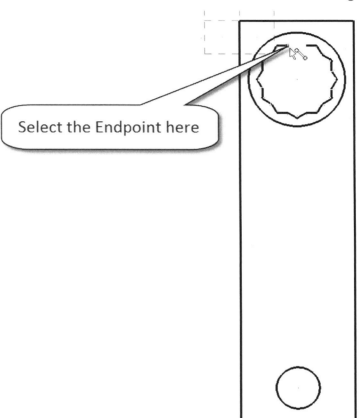

Figure: 7.0.1

Select the Endpoint here

◆ [Specify the second endpoint]: Pick a point above the circle to create a vertical line as shown in <u>Figure: 7.0.2</u>.

Figure: 7.0.2

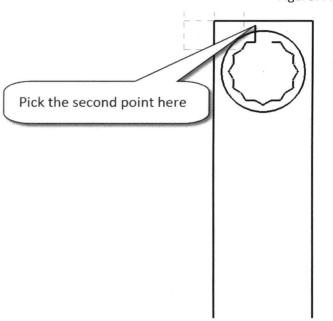

Pick the second point here

◆ Repeat this same step creating the second line as shown in <u>Figure: 7.0.3</u>.

Figure: 7.0.3

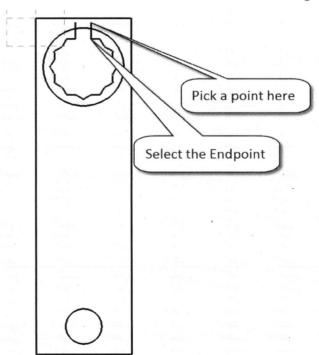

Pick a point here

Select the Endpoint

◆ Choose the **Apply** button to continue.

◆ [Specify the first endpoint]: Select the **Midpoint** as shown in <u>Figure: 7.0.4</u>.

Figure: 7.0.4

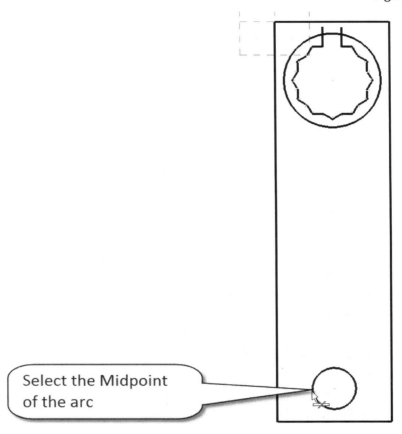

Select the Midpoint
of the arc

◆ [Specify the second endpoint]: Pick a point inside the polygon shape to create a vertical line as shown in
  Figure: 7.0.5.

Figure: 7.0.5

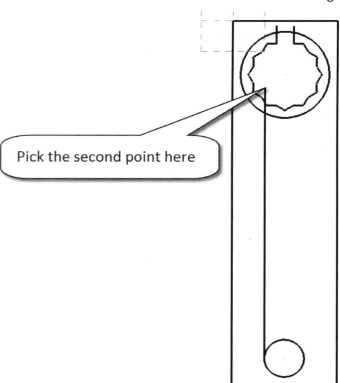

◆ Repeat this same step creating the second line as shown in <u>Figure: 7.0.6</u>.

Figure: 7.0.6

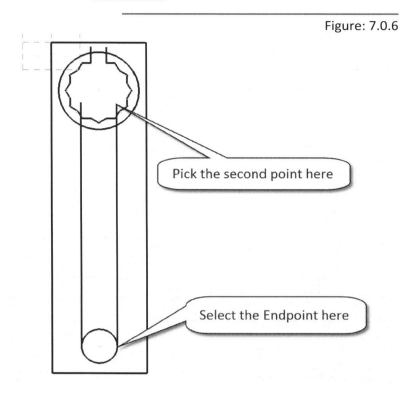

Pick the second point here

Select the Endpoint here

◆ Select the **OK** button once complete.

STEP 8: USE TRIM DIVIDE TO CLEAN THE GEOMETRY

Step Preview:

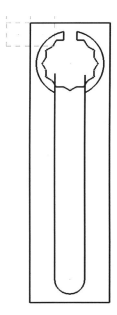

♦ To better see the area that we are working on, **Zoom in** by placing the cursor as shown and then scroll up the mouse wheel.

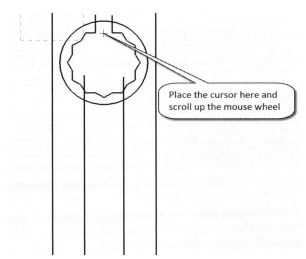

Place the cursor here and scroll up the mouse wheel

EDIT
♦ **Trim/Break.**

♦ ✎ **Trim/Break/Extend.**

♦ Select the **Divide** command and ensure the option to **Trim** is enabled as shown.

◆ Select the lines and the arcs as shown in Figure: 8.0.1.

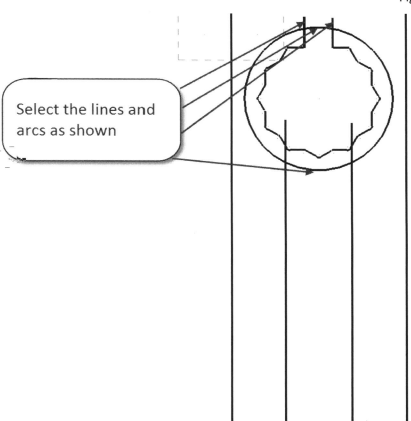

Figure: 8.0.1

Select the lines and arcs as shown

◆ Select the **Fit** icon.

• Repeat the step selecting the lines as shown in Figure: 8.0.2.

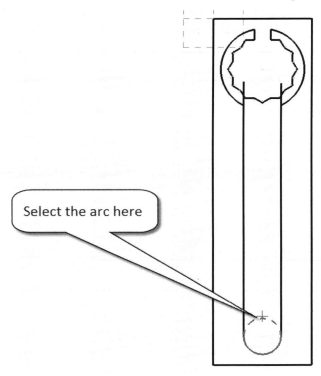

Select the arc here

• Select the **OK** icon to exit the command.
• The geometry should look as shown.

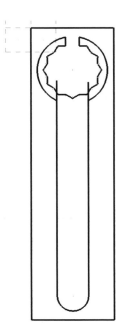

STEP 9: CREATE FILLETS

Fillets are used to round sharp corners.

Step Preview:

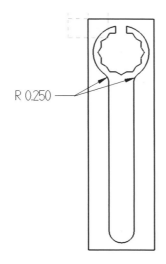

R 0.250

CREATE
* **Fillet.**

* **Entities.**
* Enter a fillet radius of **0.25**. Ensure the fillet style is set to **Normal** and **Trim** is enabled as shown.

- [Select an entity]: Select Entity A as shown in Figure: 9.0.1.
- [Select another entity]: Select Entity B as shown.

Figure: 9.0.1

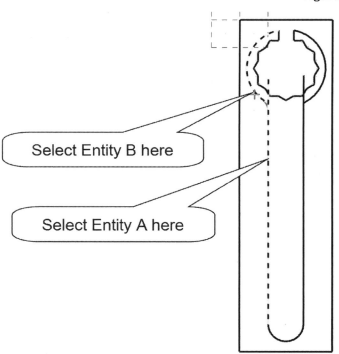

Select Entity B here

Select Entity A here

Mastercam. X

◆ [Select an entity]: Select Entity C as shown in Figure: 9.0.2.

◆ [Select another entity]: Select Entity D as shown.

Figure: 9.0.2

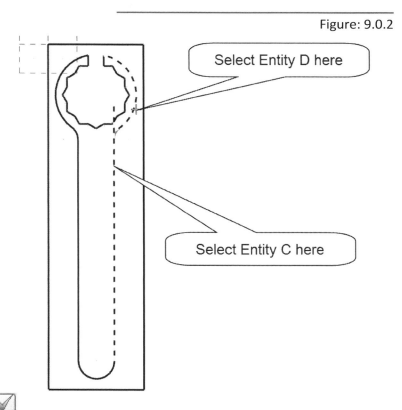

Select Entity D here

Select Entity C here

◆ Select the **OK** button to exit the command.

◆ The geometry should look as shown.

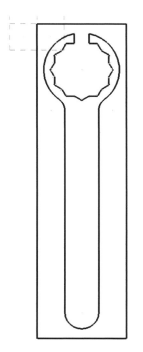

STEP 10: CREATE THE RECTANGULAR SHAPE

Create the **Obround Shape** which consists of 2 straight lines and two 180 degrees arcs at the ends using **Rectangular shapes** command.

Step Preview:

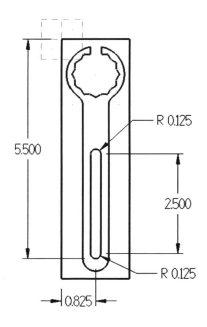

CREATE

◆ ▢ **Rectangular Shapes.**

◆ Enter the **Width** and the **Height** in the **Rectangular Shapes Options** dialog box as shown in Figure: 10.0.1.

> **NOTE:** Mastercam can perform basic math functions as shown in Figure: 10.0.1.

Figure: 10.0.1

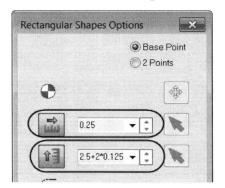

◆ Set the rest of the parameters as shown in <u>Figure: 10.0.2</u>.

Figure: 10.0.2

◆ [Select position of base point]: Select the **Fast point** icon and enter the values **0.825,-5.5** as shown.

◆ Press **Enter** to place the obround shape.

• The geometry should look as shown.

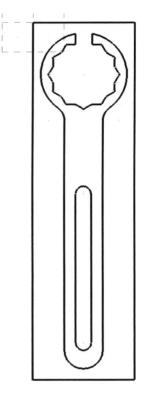

• Select the **OK** button to exit the **Rectangular Shape Options**. ✓

STEP 11: SAVE THE FILE

FILE

• 🖫 **Save As.**
• File name: "Your Name_3".

TOOLPATH CREATION - SETUP 1

SUGGESTED FIXTURE:

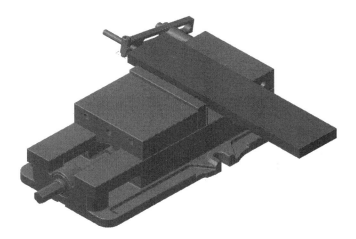

NOTE: In order to machine this part we will have 2 setups and output 2 NC files. To view the second setup, see page 185.

SETUP SHEET:

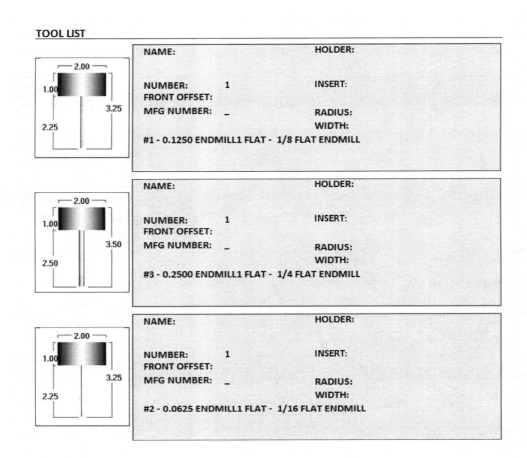

TOOL LIST

NAME:	HOLDER:
NUMBER: 1	INSERT:
FRONT OFFSET:	
MFG NUMBER: _	RADIUS:
	WIDTH:
#1 - 0.1250 ENDMILL1 FLAT - 1/8 FLAT ENDMILL	

NAME:	HOLDER:
NUMBER: 1	INSERT:
FRONT OFFSET:	
MFG NUMBER: _	RADIUS:
	WIDTH:
#3 - 0.2500 ENDMILL1 FLAT - 1/4 FLAT ENDMILL	

NAME:	HOLDER:
NUMBER: 1	INSERT:
FRONT OFFSET:	
MFG NUMBER: _	RADIUS:
	WIDTH:
#2 - 0.0625 ENDMILL1 FLAT - 1/16 FLAT ENDMILL	

Mastercam. X⁸

STEP 12: SELECT THE MACHINE AND SET UP THE STOCK

In Mastercam, you select a **Machine Definition** before creating any toolpaths. The **Machine Definition** is a model of your machines capabilities and features. It acts like a template for setting up your machine. The machine definition ties together three main components. The schematic model of your machines components. The control definition that models your control capabilities and the post processor that will generate the required machine code (G-code). For a Mill Level 1 exercise (2D toolpaths) we need just a basic machine definition.

> **NOTE:** For the purpose of this tutorial, we will be using the Default milling machine.

- To display the **Toolpaths Manager** press **Alt + O**.

- Use the **Fit** icon to fit the drawing to the screen.
MACHINE TYPE
- **Mill.**
- **Default.**

- Select the plus sign in front of **Properties** in the **Toolpaths Manager** to expand the **Toolpaths Group Properties.**

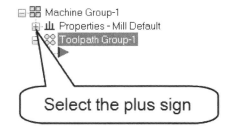

- Select **Tool Settings** to set the tool parameters.

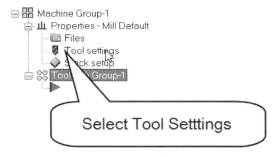

◆ Change the parameters to match the screen shot as shown in Figure: 12.0.1.

Figure: 12.0.1

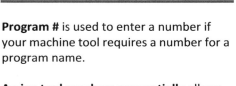

Program # is used to enter a number if your machine tool requires a number for a program name.

Assign tool numbers sequentially allows you to overwrite the tool number from the library with the next available tool number. (First operation tool number 1; Second operation tool number 2, etc.)

Warn of duplicate tool numbers allows you to get a warning if you enter two tools with the same number.

Override defaults with modal values enables the system to keep the values that you enter.

Feed Calculation set **From tool** uses feed rate, plunge rate, retract rate and spindle speed from the tool definition.

◆ Select the **Stock setup** tab to define the stock.
◆ Select the **All Entities** button near the bottom of the **Stock Setup** page as shown.

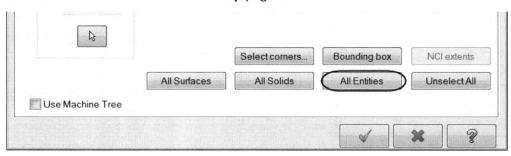

- In the **Stock thickness** enter **0.25** as shown in Figure: 12.0.2. This will add **0.125"** of stock on the bottom of the model.
- Click in the graphics area at the upper left corner to move the arrow where the origin is set and then change the **Stock origin** values to zero as shown in Figure: 12.0.2.

Figure: 12.0.2

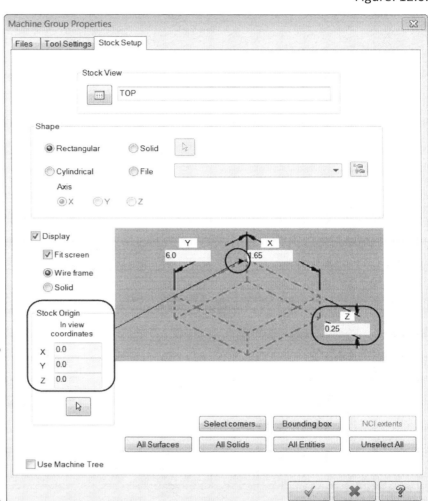

The **Stock Origin** values adjust the positioning of the stock, ensuring that you have equal amount of extra stock around the finished part.

Display options allow you to set the stock as **Wireframe** and to fit the stock to the screen. (Fit Screen)

- Select the **OK** button to exit **Machine Group Properties**.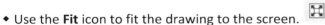

- Select the **Isometric** view from the graphics view toolbar to see the stock.

- Use the **Fit** icon to fit the drawing to the screen.

* The stock model will appear as shown.

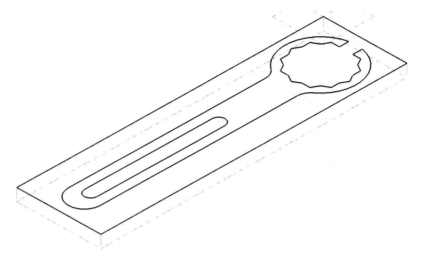

> **NOTE:** The stock is not geometry and can not be selected.

* Select the **Top** view from the view toolbar to see the part from the top.

> **NOTE:** There will not be facing toolpath because the stock is already to size.

STEP 13: SLOT MILLING

Slot Mill toolpath allows Mastercam to efficiently machine obround slots. These are slots that consist of 2 straight lines and two 180-degree arcs at the ends.

Toolpath Preview:

TOOLPATHS

- **Circle Paths.**
- **Slot Mill.**
- If a prompt appears, **Enter new NC name**, select the **OK** button to accept the default.

- When the chaining dialog box appears, choose **Chain** as the chaining method as shown.

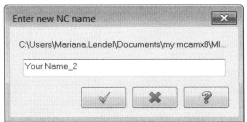

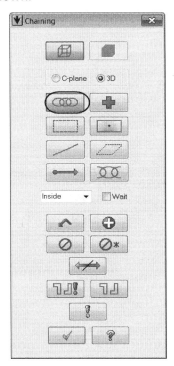

* Select the chain as shown in Figure: 13.0.1.

Figure: 13.0.1

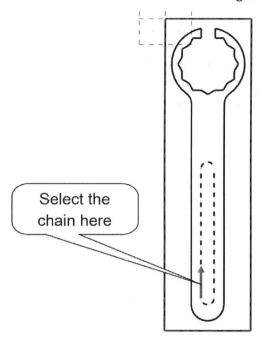

Select the chain here

* Choose the **OK** button to exit the **Chaining** dialog box.
* In the **Toolpath Type** page, the **Slot Mill** icon will be selected.

Contour   Pocket   Facing   Slot Mill

NOTE: Mastercam updates the pages as you modify them and then marks them, in the **Tree view list,** with a green check mark. Pages that are not changed are marked with a red circle and slash.

13.1 Select a 1/8" Flat Endmill and set the Tool Parameters

* Select **Tool** from the **Tree view list**.

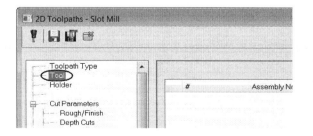

♦ Click on **Select library tool** button.
♦ Select the **Filter** button.

♦ Select the **None** button and then under **Tool Types** choose the **Flat Endmill** icon.
♦ Under tool diameter pick **Equal** and input a value **0.125** as shown in Figure: 13.1.1.

Figure: 13.1.1

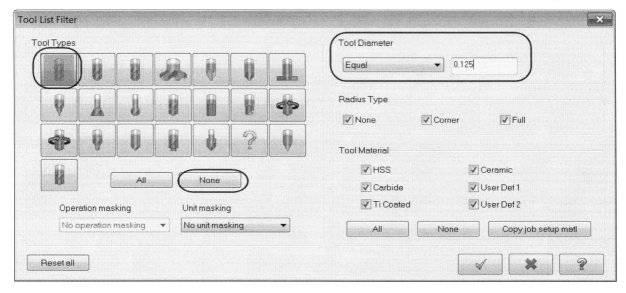

♦ Select the **OK** button to exit the **Tool List Filter.**
♦ In the **Tool Selection** dialog box you should only see a **1/8" Flat Endmill**.

#	Assembly Name	Tool Name	Holder Name	Dia.	Cor. rad.	Length	# Flutes	Type	Rad. Type
232	--	1/8 FLAT...	--	0...	0.0	0.375	4	En...	None

♦ Select the **1/8" Flat Endmill** in the **Tool Selection** page and then select the **OK** button to exit.

◆ Make all the necessary changes as shown in Figure: 13.1.2.

Figure: 13.1.2

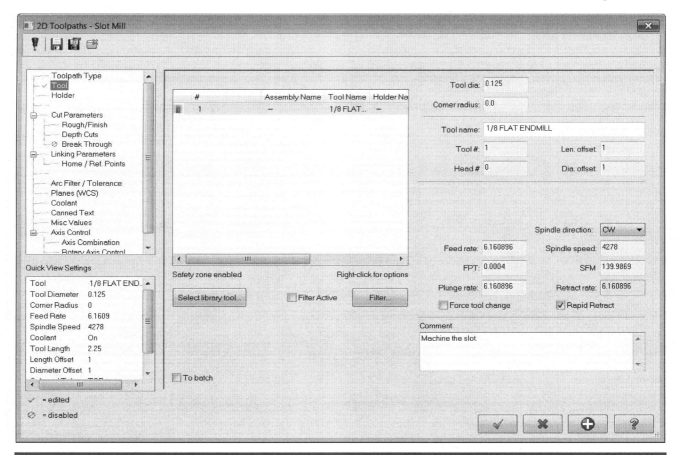

The **Feed rate, Plunge rate, Retract rate** and **Spindle speed** are based on the tool definition as set in the **Tool Settings**. You may change these values as per your part material and tools.

In the **Comment** field enter a comment to help identify the toolpath in the **Toolpaths/ Toolpaths Manager** such as the one shown above.

13.2 Cut Parameters

♦ Select **Cut Parameters** and make the necessary changes as shown in Figure: 13.2.1.

Figure: 13.2.1

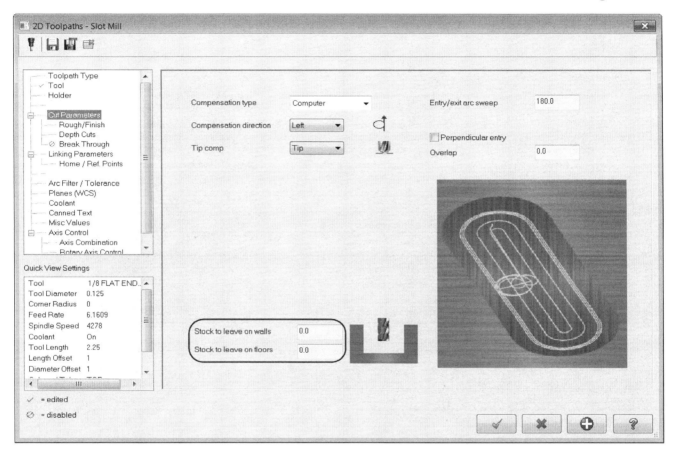

Compensation type allows you to choose how you want to handle cutter compensation. Computer sets Mastercam to compute the compensated toolpath and does not output control codes for compensation.

Entry/exit arc sweep sets the included angle of each entry and exit arc. If the entry/exit arc sweep is less than 180 degrees, the system applies an entry/exit line.

Perpendicular entry enters the toolpath perpendicular to the first tool move.

13.3 Rough/Finish

◆ Select **Rough/Finish** and make the necessary changes as shown in Figure: 13.3.1.

Figure: 13.3.1

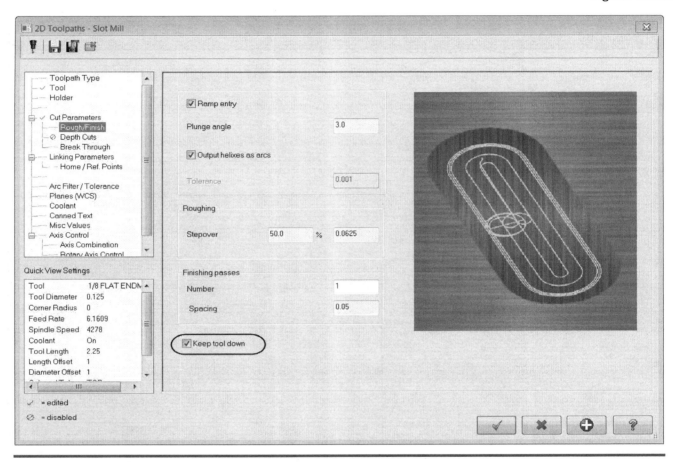

Ramp entry creates a smoother entry motion rather than plunging directly.

Plunge angle sets the angle of descent for the entry move, and determines the pitch. A smaller plunge angle means that the entry move takes longer to descend in the Z axis. A recommended angle is 3 to 5 degrees.

Output arc moves writes the entry helix to the NCI file as arcs. Using this option can create shorter NC files. If you turn off this option, the helix breaks into linear segments in the NCI file.

Roughing Stepover sets the distance between cutting passes in the X and Y Axes. Enter a percentage of the tool diameter or a distance.

Finish passes allows you to set the finish cuts for the toolpath. This **Number** multiplied by the finish **Spacing** value equals the total amount of stock cut by the finish passes. Setting the number of finish cuts to 0 creates no finish cuts.

Keep tool down enabled does not allow the tool to retract between multipasses.

Mastercam. X

13.4 Depth Cuts

◆ Choose **Depth Cuts** and enable this option. Input a **Max rough step** of **0.1** .
◆ Enable the option **Keep tool down** as shown in Figure: 13.4.1.

Figure: 13.4.1

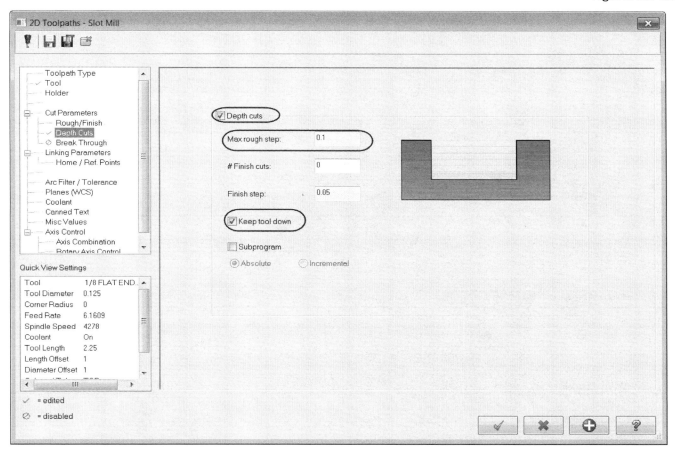

13.5 Break Through

♦ Pick **Break Through** from the **Tree view list**. Enable this option and input a break through amount of **0.1** as shown in Figure: 13.5.1.

Figure: 13.5.1

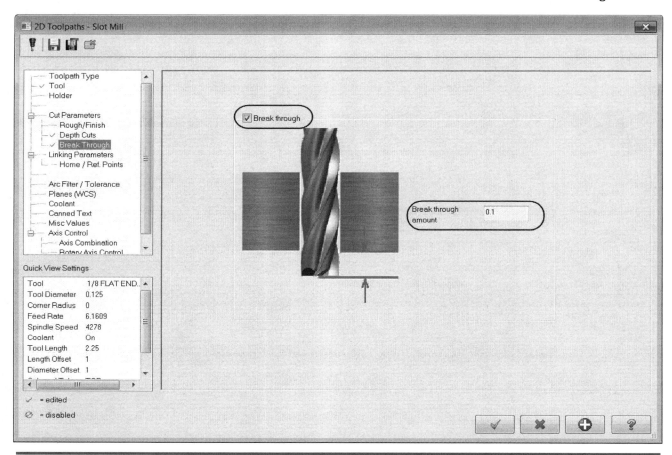

Break Through allows you to specify an amount that the tool will completely cut through the material by. This values is always a positive number.

13.6 Linking Parameters

◆ Pick **Linking Parameters** and make the necessary changes as shown in Figure: 13.6.1.

Figure: 13.6.1

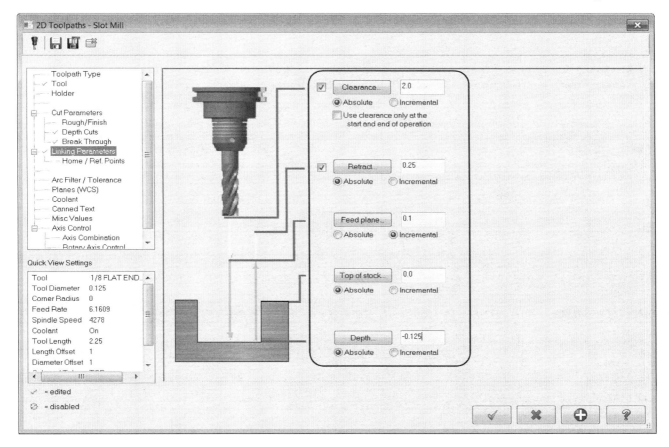

Clearance sets the height at which the tool moves to and from the part.

Retract sets the height that the tool moves up to before the next tool pass.

Feed Plane sets the height that the tool rapids to before changing to the plunge rate to enter the part.

Top of stock sets the height of the material in the Z axis.

Depth determines the final machining depth that the tool descends into the stock.

◆ Select the **OK** button to exit the **Slot Mill** parameters.

STEP 14: BACKPLOT THE TOOLPATHS

Backplotting shows the path the tools take to cut the part. This display lets you spot errors in the program before you machine the part. As you backplot toolpaths, Mastercam displays additional information such as the X, Y, and Z coordinates, the path length, the minimum and maximum coordinates and the cycle time. It also shows any collisions between the workpiece and the tool.

♦ Make sure that the toolpaths are selected (signified by the green check mark on the folder icon). If the operation is not selected choose the **Select all operations** icon.

♦ Select the **Backplot selected operations** button.

> **NOTE:** Mastercam launches a new window that allows you to check the part using **Backplot** or **Verify.**

♦ Select the **Backplot** tab and have the following settings enabled as shown.

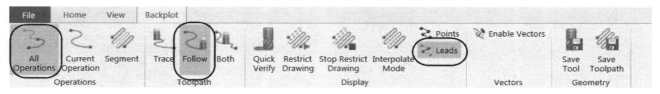

♦ Select the **Home** tab and make sure that you have the following settings on as shown.

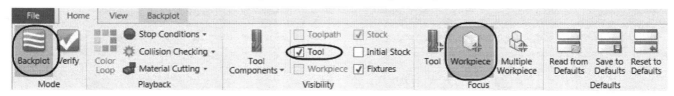

- To see the part from an **Isometric** right mouse click in the graphics window and select **Isometric** as shown.

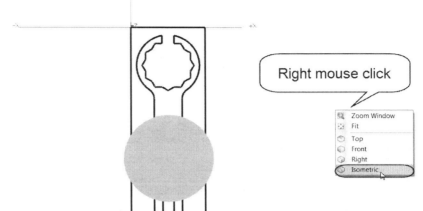

Right mouse click

- To fit the workpiece to the screen, right mouse click in the graphics window again and select the **Fit**.

- You can step through the **Backplot** by using the **Step forward** or **Step back** buttons.

- You can adjust the speed of the backplot.

- Select the **Play** button in the **VCR** bar to run **Backplot**.

◆ The toolpath should look as shown in <u>Figure: 14.0.1</u>.

Figure: 14.0.1.

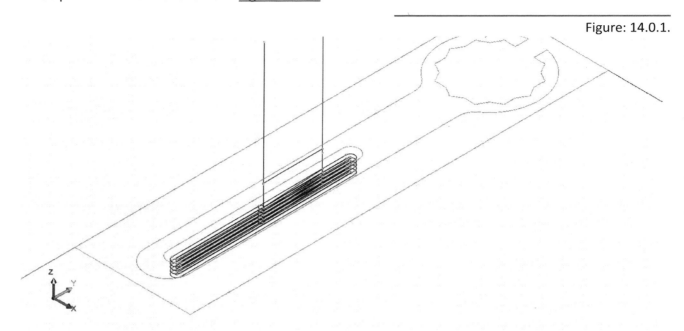

STEP 15: SIMULATE THE TOOLPATH IN VERIFY

Verify Mode shows the path the tools take to cut the part with material removal. This display lets you spot errors in the program before you machine the part. As you verify toolpaths, Mastercam displays additional information such as the X, Y, and Z coordinates, the path length , the minimum and maximum coordinates and the cycle time. It also shows any collisions between the workpiece and the tool.

♦ In **Mastercam Simulator**, switch to **Verify** and change the settings as shown.

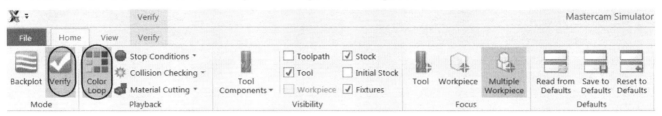

♦ Select the **Play** button in the **VCR** bar to run **Verify**.
♦ The part should appear as shown in Figure: 15.0.1.

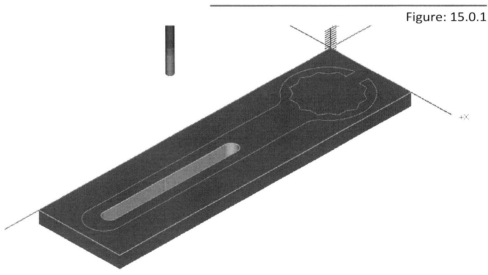

Figure: 15.0.1

♦ To go back to Mastercam window, minimize **Mastercam Simulator** window as shown.

STEP 16: ROUGH THE OUTSIDE USING HIGH SPEED DYNAMIC MILL

In this step you will machine the outside profile using **2D HS Dynamic Mill** toolpath.
Dynamic Mill Toolpath machines cores or pockets using the entire flute length. The Toolpath supports many powerful entry methods, including a custom entry method. Entry methods and micro lifts support custom feeds and speeds to optimize and generate safe tool motion.

The toolpath depends on the **Machining strategy** that you choose in the **Chain Options**. If the strategy choosed is **From outside**, the toolpaths starts at the outmost chain and works its way in taking on the final shape of the part as it approaches the final pass. You can also machine pockets in which case the strategy selected is **Start inside** which keeps the tool inside the machining regions.

Toolpath Preview:

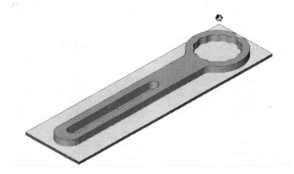

16.1 Chain selection

♦ Press **Alt + T** to remove the toolpath display.

TOOLPATHS
♦ **2D High Speed.**

♦ 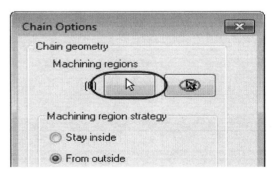 **Dynamic Mill.**

♦ In the **Chaining Options** dialog box, **Machining regions** click on the **Select** button as shown to definmed the area to be machined.

• The **Chaining** dialog box will open and leave the **Chain** button enable as shown.

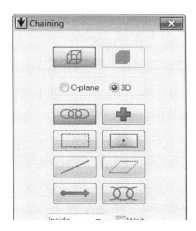

• [2D HST machining chain 1]: Select the rectangle as shown in Figure: 16.1.1.

Figure: 16.1.1

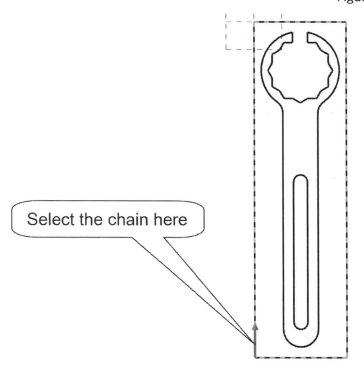

Select the chain here

• Select the **OK** button to exit the **Chaining** dialog box.

* To start the toolpath from the outside, in the **Machining region strategy**, make sure that **From outside** is enabled.
* In the **Avoidance regions**, click on the **Select** button as shown.

* [Select 2D HST avoidance chain 1]: Select the profile as shown in <u>Figure: 16.1.2</u>.

Figure: 16.1.2

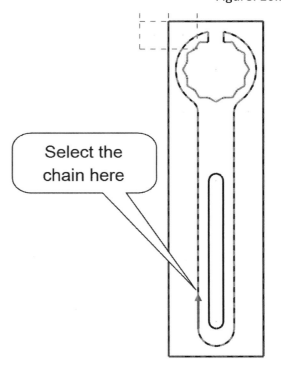

Select the chain here

* Select the **OK** button to exit the **Chaining** dialog box.
* Select the **OK** button to exit the **Chain Options** dialog box.

◆ In the **Toolpath Type** page, **Dynamic Mill** will be selected as shown in <u>Figure: 16.1.3</u>.

Figure: 16.1.3

16.2 Select a 1/4" Flat endmill from the library and set the Tool Parameters

◆ Select **Tool** from the **Tree view list**.

◆ Click on **Select library tool** button. Select library tool...

◆ Select the **Filter** button.

◆ Select the **None** button and then under **Tool Types** choose the **Flat Endmill** Icon.
◆ Under tool diameter pick **Equal** and input a value **0.25** as shown in <u>Figure: 16.2.1</u>.

Figure: 16.2.1

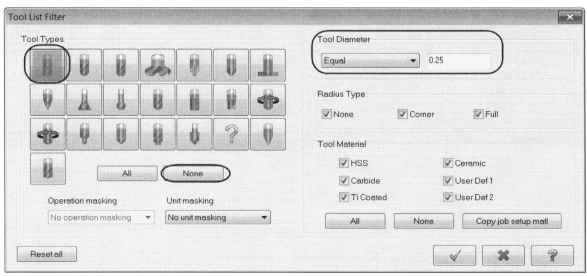

◆ Select the **OK** button to exit the **Tool List Filter.**

- In the **Tool Selection** dialog box you should only see a **1/4" Flat Endmill**.

#	Assembly Name	Tool Name	Holder Name	Dia.	Cor. rad.	Length	# Flutes	Type	Rad. Type
235	–	1/4 FLAT..	–	0.25	0.0	0.5	4	En..	None

- Select the **1/4" Flat Endmill** in the **Tool Selection** page and then select the **OK** button to exit.
- Make all the necessary changes as shown in Figure: 16.2.2.

Figure: 16.2.2

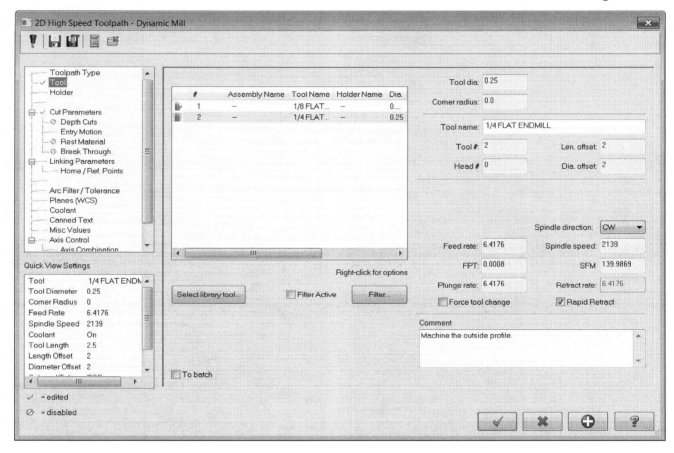

16.3 Set the Cut Parameters

◆ From the **Tree view list**, select **Cut Parameters**. Change the settings as shown in <u>Figure: 16.3.1</u>.

Figure: 16.3.1

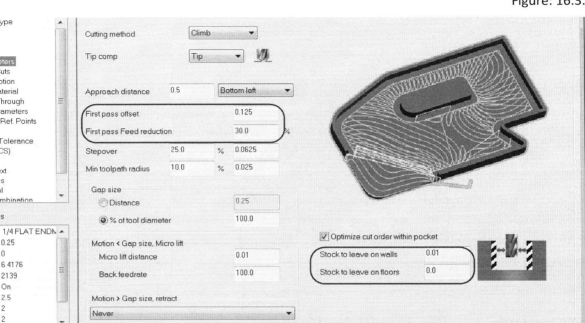

Stepover sets the distance between cutting passes in the X and Y axis.

Approach distance adds the specified absolute distance to the beginning of the toolpath's first cut.

First pass offset offsets out the machining region with a user defined distance for the tool to safely engage from the outside in the material.

First pass feed reduction allows you to slow the feed for the first passon machining region material approached from the outside.

Min toolpath radius reduces sharp corner motion between cut passes.

Micro lift distance enters the distance the tool lifts off the part on the back moves. Microlifts are slight lifts that help clear chips and minimize excessive tool heating.

Back feedrate controls the speed of the backfeed movement of the tool.

Motion > Gap Size, retract controls retracts in the toolpath when making a non-cutting move within an area where the tool can be kept down or microlifted.

Optimize cut order defines the cut order Mastercam applies to different cutting passes in the dynamic mill toolpath.

16.4 Set the Entry Motion

• Entry motion configures an entry method for the dynamic mill toolpath which determines not only how and where the tool enters the part, but the cutting method/machining strategy used by the toolpath. Set the Entry method to Helix only as shown in <u>Figure: 16.4.1</u>.

Figure: 16.4.1

Toolpath Type	Entry method
✓ Tool	Helix only ▾
Holder	
	Chain geometry
⊟ ✓ Cut Parameters	(0)
◇ Depth Cuts	
✓ Entry Motion	
◇ Rest Material	
◇ Break Through	
⊟ Linking Parameters	Helix radius 0.25
Home / Ref. Points	Trochoidal loop radius 0.0
	Additional slot width 0.0
Arc Filter / Tolerance	
Planes (WCS)	☑ Output 3D arc moves ☐ Center helix on point
Coolant	
Canned Text	
Misc Values	Z clearance 0.125
⊟ Axis Control	⦿ Plunge angle 2.0
Axis Combination	◯ Entry pitch 0.0

Quick View Settings

Tool	1/4 FLAT ENDM
Tool Diameter	0.25
Corner Radius	0
Feed Rate	6.4176
Spindle Speed	2139
Coolant	On
Tool Length	2.5
Length Offset	2
Diameter Offset	2

☐ Entry feeds / speeds
Ramp feed rate   50.0
Ramp spindle speed   3500
Dwell before cut spindle speed   0.0

Entry method set to **Helix only** creates a helical entry into the part.

16.5 Set the Break through

- From the Tree view list, select and enable **Break Through** to cut completely through the material by an amount that you specify as shown in Figure: 16.5.1.

Figure: 16.5.1

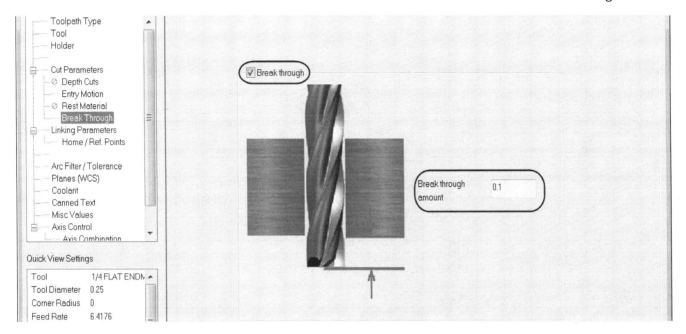

16.6 Set the Linking Parameters

• Select **Linking Parameters** and change the **Depth** to **-0.125** as shown in <u>Figure: 16.6.1</u>.

Figure: 16.6.1

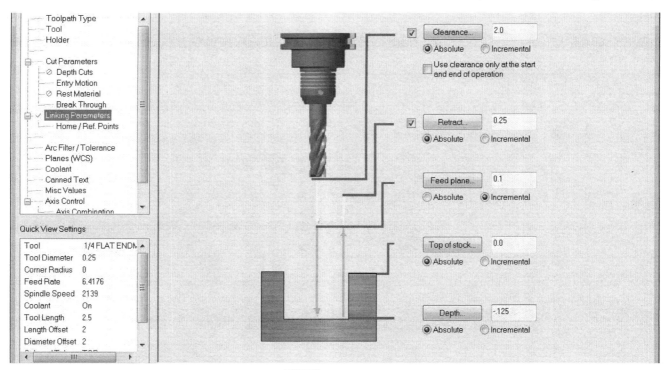

• Select the **OK** button to generate the toolpath.
• To remove the toolpath display, if needed, pres **Alt** + **T**.

16.7 Verify the toolpath

♦ From the Toolpaths Manager, click on the **Select all operations** icon.

♦ Set **Mastercam Simulation** parameters as shown on page 155.
♦ The part will appear as shown in <u>Figure: 16.7.1</u>.

Figure: 16.7.1

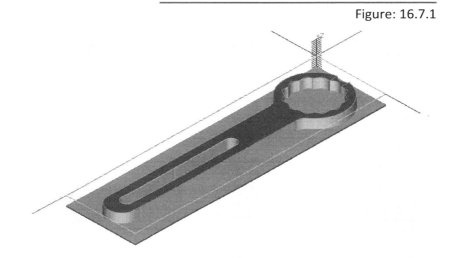

♦ To go back to Mastercam window, minimize Mastercam Simulator window as shown.

♦ To remove the toolpath display press **Alt** + **T** or click on the **Toggle display on selected operations**.

STEP 17: FINISH THE OUTSIDE PROFILE USING CONTOUR TOOLPATH

Contour toolpaths remove material along a path defined by a chain of curves. **Contour** toolpaths only follow a chain; they do not clean out an enclosed area.

Toolpath Preview:

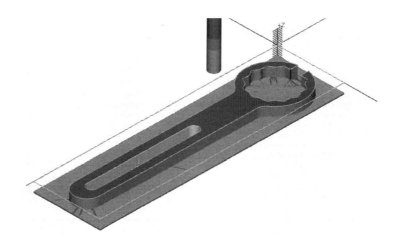

17.1 Chain selection

TOOLPATHS

* 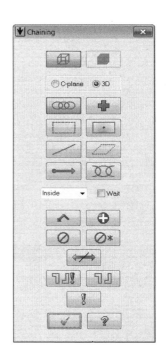 **Contour.**
* Leave the **Chain** button enabled in the **Chaining** dialog box as shown.

♦ Select the profile as shown in Figure: 17.1.1.

Figure: 17.1.1

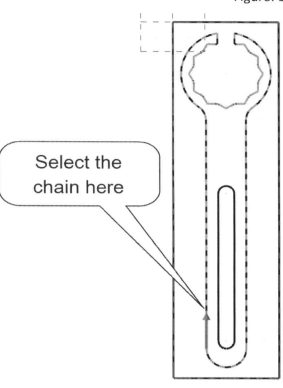

Select the chain here

♦ Select the **OK** button to exit **Chaining**.
♦ In the **Toolpath Type** page, the **Contour** icon will be selected as shown.

Contour   Pocket   Facing   Slot Mill

17.2 Select a 1/4" Flat endmill from the list and set the Tool page parameters

♦ From the Tree view list, select Tool and make all the necessary changes as shown in Figure: 17.2.1.

Figure: 17.2.1

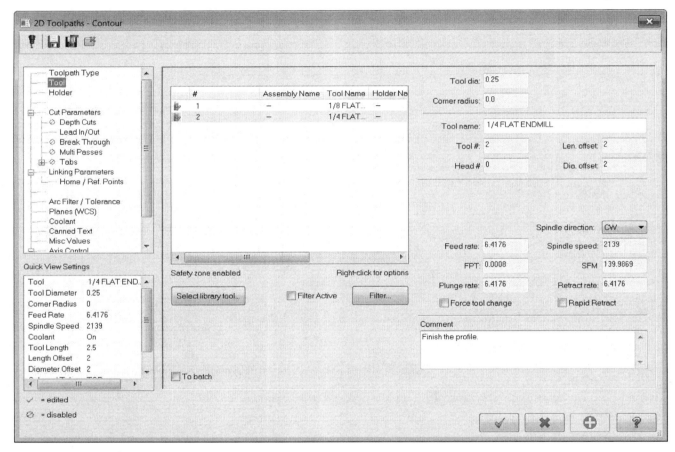

17.3 Cut Parameters

• From the **Tree view list**, select **Cut Parameters** and ensure the settings appear as shown in Figure: 17.3.1.

Figure: 17.3.1

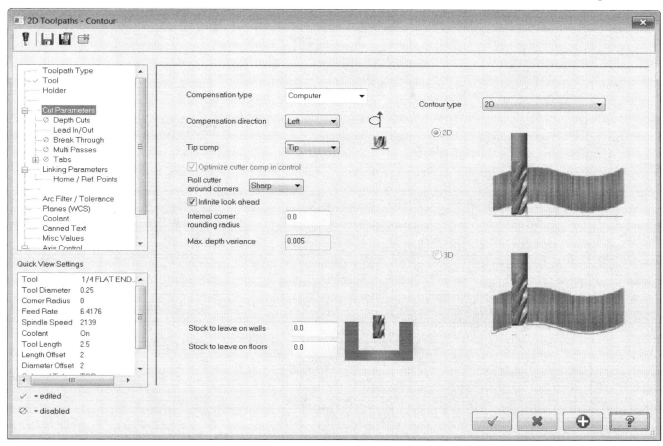

NOTE: For more information regarding these parameters please check Step 15 in Tutorial #1.

17.4 Lead In/Out

* Select **Lead In/Out** from the **Tree view list.**
* Change the parameters as shown in Figure: 17.4.1.

Figure: 17.4.1

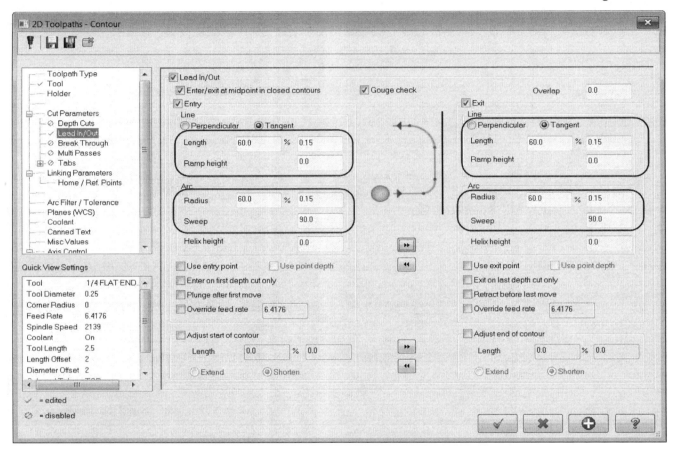

17.5 Break Through

◆ From the **Tree view list**, select **Break Through** and make the necessary changes as shown in Figure: 17.5.1.

Figure: 17.5.1

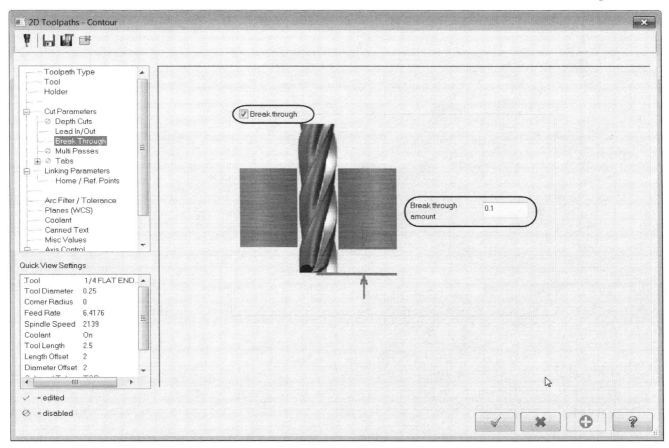

17.6 Linking Parameters

◆ Select **Linking Parameters** and input the **Depth** as shown as shown in Figure: 17.6.1.

Figure: 17.6.1

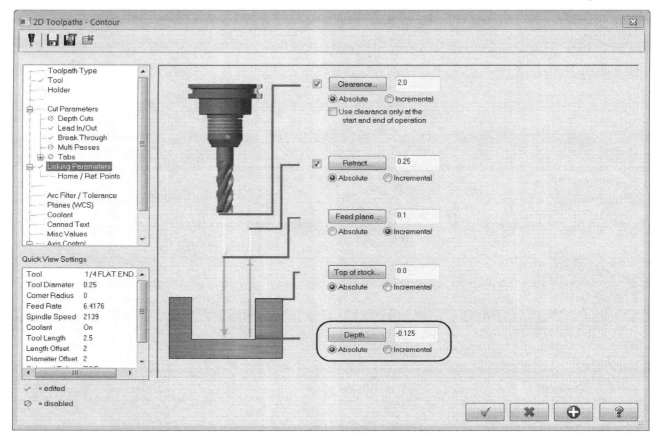

◆ Once complete pick the **OK** button to generate the toolpath.
◆ To remove the toolpath display, if needed, pres **Alt** + **T**.

17.7 Backplot and Verify the toolpaths

♦ To **Backplot** and **Verify** the toolpaths see page 152 to review the procedures.
♦ To select all the operations, from the Toolpaths Manager, click on the **Select all operations** icon.

♦ After running **Verify** the part should look as shown.

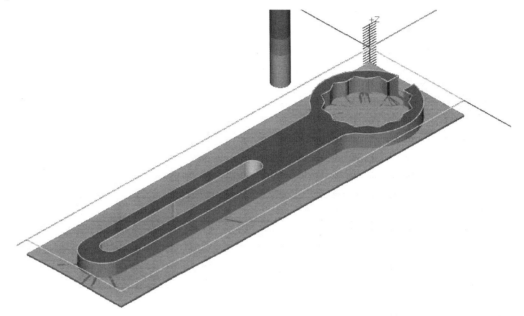

STEP 18: CLEAN THE INSIDE SHAPE USING 2D HS DYNAMIC CONTOUR

2D HS Dynamic Contour toolpath utilizes the entire flute length of the cutting tools and is used to mill material off walls. It does support both closed or open chains.

Toolpath Preview:

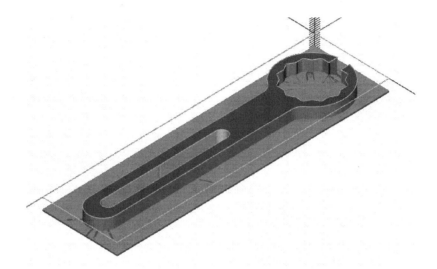

TOOLPATHS
* **2D High Speed.**

* 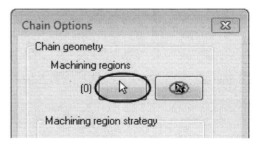 **Dynamic Contour.**

18.1 Select the Geometry

* In the **Chain Option** dialog box, in the **Machining regions**, click on the **Select** button as shown.

◆ Enable **Partial** button in the **Chaining** dialog box as shown.

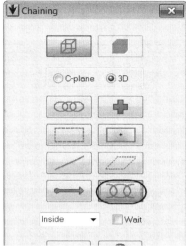

◆ Select the first entity of the chain as shown in Figure: 18.1.1. Make sure that the arrows are pointing

downwards as shown otherwise select the reverse button ⟷ from the **Chaining** dialog box.

Figure: 18.1.1

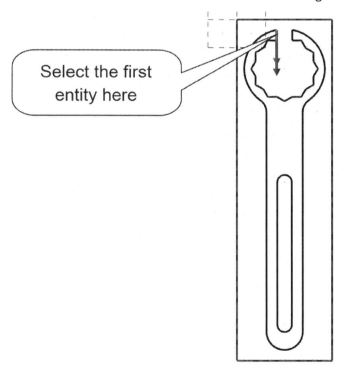

♦ Select the last entity of the chain as shown in <u>Figure: 18.1.2</u>.

Figure: 18.1.2

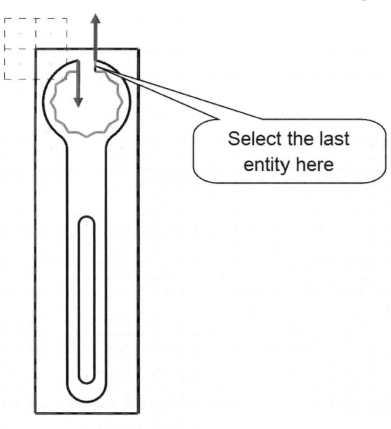

Select the last
entity here

♦ Choose the **OK** button to exit **Chaining** dialog box.

♦ Select the **OK** button to exit **Chain Options** dialog box and to continue.

♦ On the **Toolpath Type** page, **Dynamic Contour** will be picked.

18.2 Select a 1/16" Flat Endmill

- Select **Tool** from the **Tree view list**.

- Click on **Select library tool** button.
- Select the **Filter** button.

- Select the **None** button and then under **Tool Types** choose the **Flat Endmill** icon.
- Under tool diameter pick **Equal** and input a value **0.0625** as shown in Figure: 18.2.1.

Figure: 18.2.1

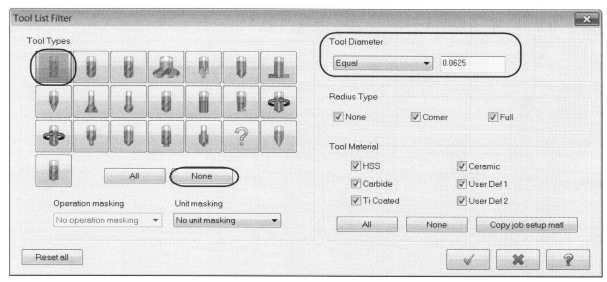

- Select the **OK** button to exit the **Tool List Filter**.
- In the **Tool Selection** dialog box you should only see a **1/16" Flat Endmill**.

#	Assembly Name	Tool Name	Holder Name	Dia.	Cor. rad.	Length	Type	# Flute
280	--	1/16 FLAT ENDMILL	--	0...	0.0	0.375	En...	4

- Select the **1/16" Flat Endmill** in the **Tool Selection** page and then select the **OK** button to exit.

♦ Make any other changes as shown in Figure: 18.2.2.

Figure: 18.2.2

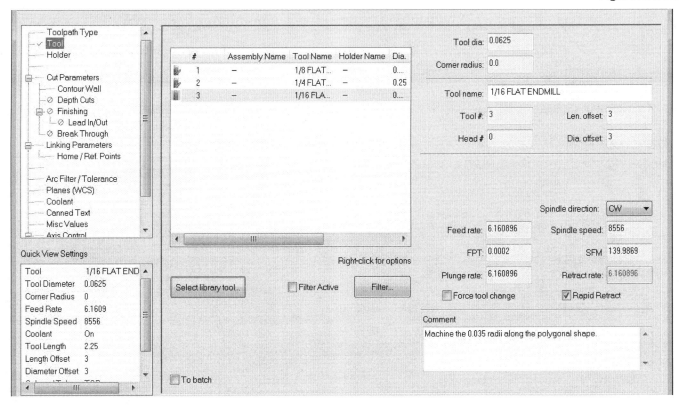

18.3 Cut Parameters

◆ From the **Tree view list** select **Cut Parameters** ensure the parameters appear the same.

Figure: 18.3.1

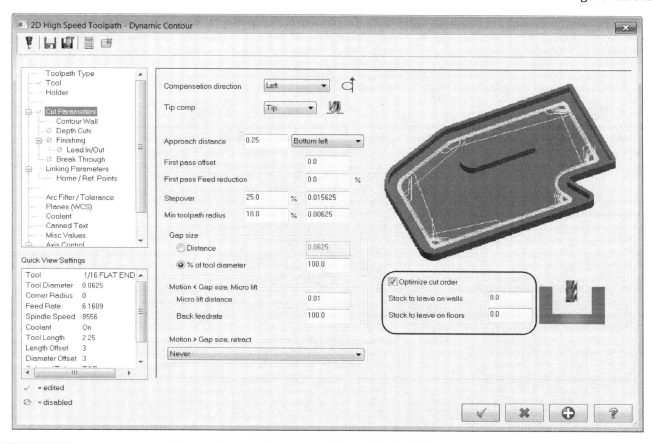

Compensation direction offsets the tool to the **Left** in our case.

Approach distance adds the specified absolute distance to the beginning of the toolpath's first cut.

First pass offset offsets out the machining region with a user defined distance for the tool to safely engage from the outside in the material.

First pass feed reduction allows you to slow the feed for the first passon machining region material approached from the outside.

Stepover sets the distance between cutting passes in the X and Y axes. Enter a percentage of the tool diameter or an absolute distance.

Min toolpath radius sets the minimum toolpath radius used in combination with the **Microlift distance** and **Back feedrate** parameters to calculate 3D arc moves between cut passes.

18.4 Contour Wall

• From the Tree view list, select **Contour Wall** and ensure your parameters appear as shown in <u>Figure: 18.4.1</u>.

Figure: 18.4.1

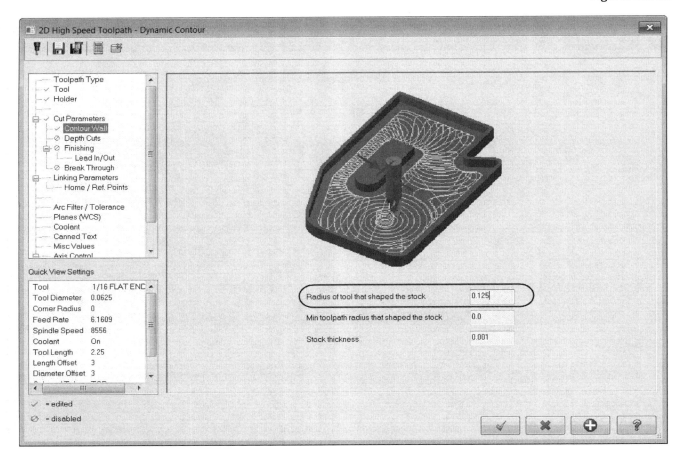

Radius of tool that shaped the stock is the radius of the tool used in a toolpath that already cut this area. Mastercam calculates the stock to remove along the contour wall using the stock thickness (required) and, if provided, the **Radius of the tool that shaped the stock** and the **Toolpath radius that shaped the stock**.

In your case, in the previous contour operation you used a 0.25 " Flat Endmill and no toolpath radius was required in the toolpath. As no stock was left in the contour the stock thickness is the value of the toolpath tolerance.

18.5 Depth Cuts

◆ From the Tree view list, choose **Depth Cuts** and enable it. Input a **Max rough step** of **0.05** as shown in
Figure: 18.5.1.

Figure: 18.5.1

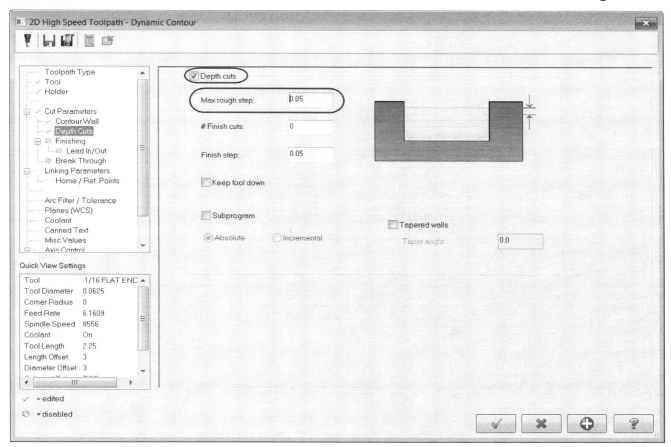

18.6 Break Through

◆ From the **Tree view list**, select **Break Through** and make the necessary changes as shown in Figure: 18.6.1.

Figure: 18.6.1

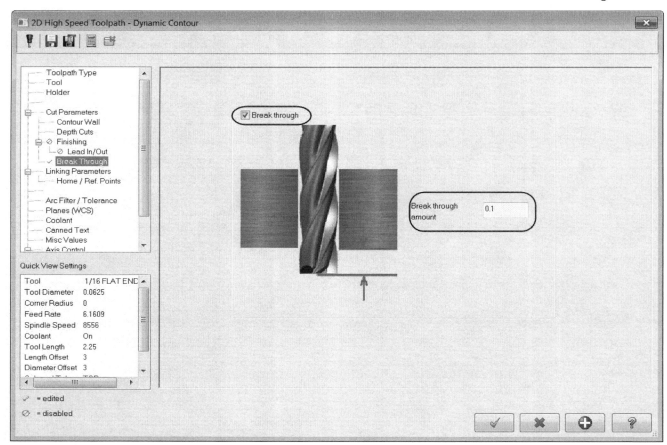

Mastercam. X

18.7 Linking Parameters

- Select **Linking Parameters** from the **Tree View** list.
- Set the **Depth** to **-0.125** as shown in <u>Figure: 18.7.1</u>.

Figure: 18.7.1

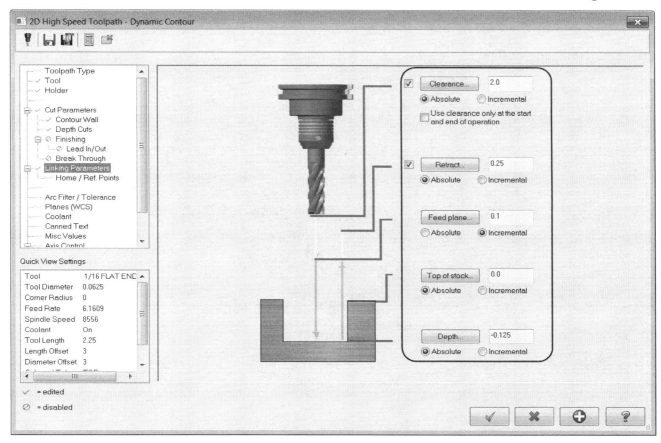

- Select the **OK** button to exit the **Dynamic Contour** parameters.

18.8 Backplot and Verify

◆ To **Backplot** and **Verify** your toolpath page 152 to review these procedures.
◆ To select all the operations, from the Toolpaths Manager, click on the **Select all operations** icon.

◆ The part should look as shown.

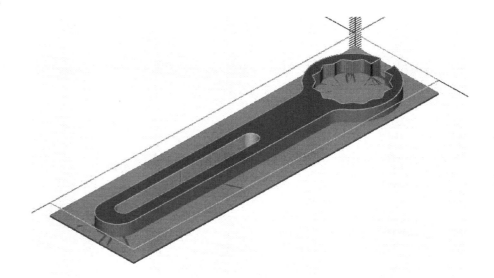

TOOLPATH CREATION - SETUP 2

SUGGESTED FIXTURE:

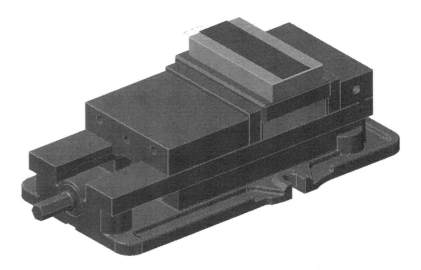

NOTE: In order to machine this part we will have 2 setups and output 2 NC files.

SETUP SHEET:

TOOL LIST

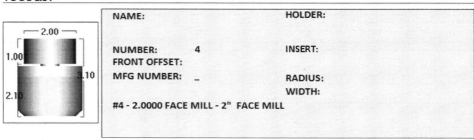

NAME:		HOLDER:
NUMBER:	4	INSERT:
FRONT OFFSET:		
MFG NUMBER:	_	RADIUS:
		WIDTH:

#4 - 2.0000 FACE MILL - 2" FACE MILL

STEP 19: CREATING AND RENAMING TOOLPATH GROUPS

To machine the part in two different setups, we will need to have two separate programs. To be able to post process separately the operations of each setup, we will create them under different toolpath groups with different NC names.

19.1 Rename the current Toolpath Group - 1 and NC file

◆ Click once on the Toolpath Group - 1 to highlight it and then click again on it to rename it "Setup #1" as shown in Figure: 19.1.1.

Figure: 19.1.1

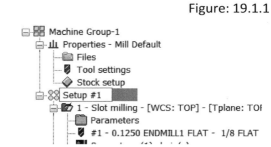

◆ Right mouse click on the **Setup #1 Toolpath group** and select **Edit selected operations** and then, select **Change NC file name.**

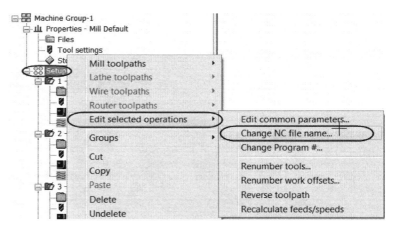

◆ Enter the new NC name: **Setup #1.**

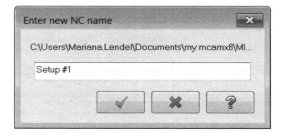

◆ Select the **OK** button to accept the new **NC name**.

19.2 Create a new Toolpath Group

◆ Right mouse click on the **Machine Group-1** and select **Groups** and then **New Toolpath group** as shown.

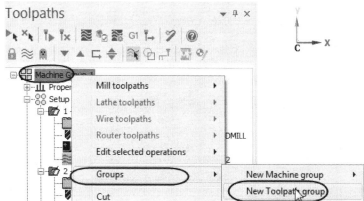

◆ Rename the toolpath group "**Setup #2**" as shown.

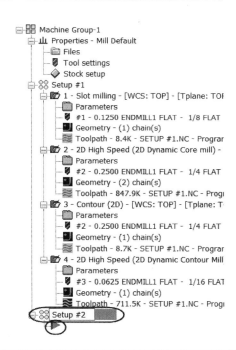

NOTE: The red insert arrow controls where the new operation will be inserted. In our case should be located below the Setup #2 group.

◆ If the insert arrow needs to be moved, from the Toolpaths Manager, click on the **Move insert arrow down** icon.

STEP 20: SET WCS TO BOTTOM

Work coordinate system (WCS) is the active coordinate system in use by Mastercam at any given time. The WCS contains the orientation of the X-Y-Z axes plus the location of the zero point (the origin). This tells Mastercam how your part is positioned or orientated in the machine.

◆ Select **WCS** located in the status bar.

◆ When the **WCS** menu appears select **"Plane Manager"** from it.

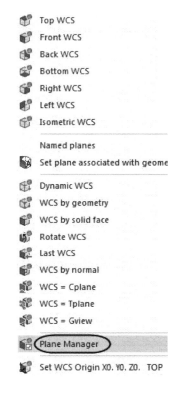

• When the **Plane Manager** dialog box appears pick **Geometry** to set the new view based on existing geometry as shown.

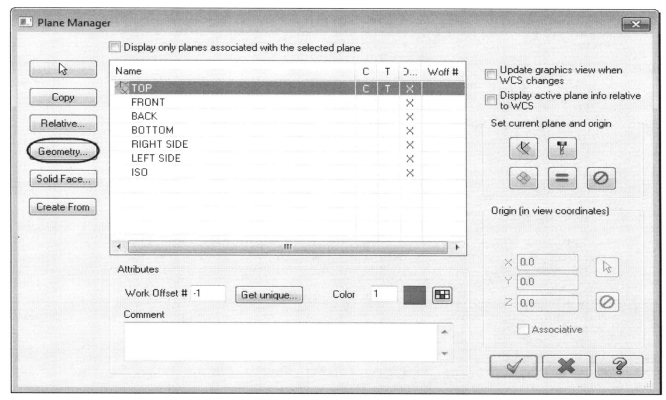

• Change the graphic view to **Isometric**.

♦ Pick first the line along the X-axis of the new view and then the second select the line along the Y-axis of the new view as shown in <u>Figure: 20.0.1</u>.

Figure: 20.0.1

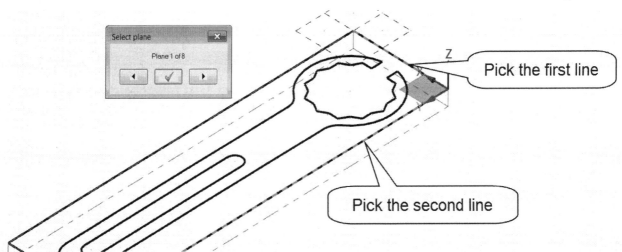

♦ In the **Select plane**, click on the **Next plane** button until the axes are oriented as shown in <u>Figure: 20.0.2</u>.

Figure: 20.0.2

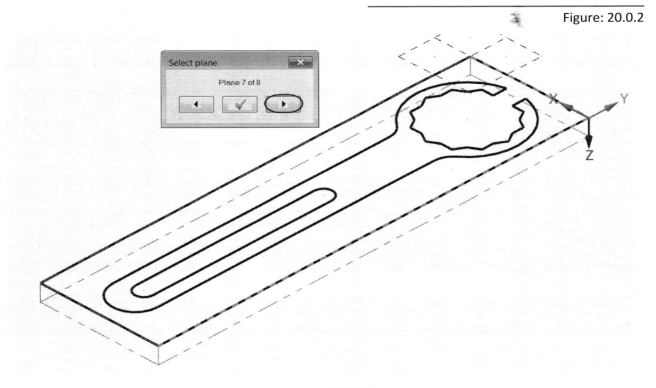

♦ From the **Select view** click on the **OK** button to continue.

- In the **New Plane** named the view **Bottom Plane** as shown.

- Select the **OK** button to continue. ✓
- Set the **Work Coordinate System (WCS)**, **Tool plane**, **Construction plane** to the **Bottom View,** by selecting the equal icon as shown in <u>Figure: 20.0.3</u>.
- Enable and set the **Origin** as shown in <u>Figure: 20.0.3</u>.

Figure: 20.0.3

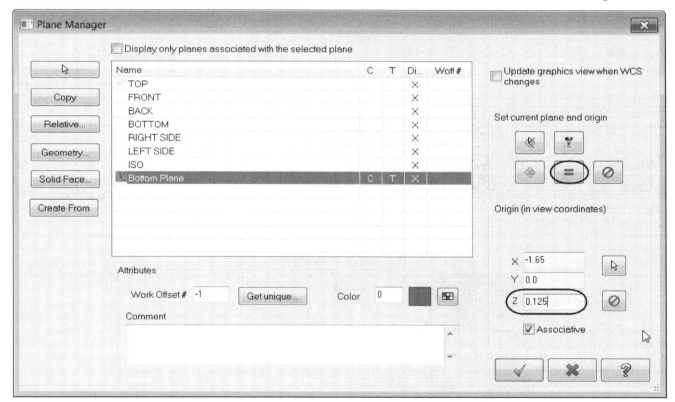

- Select the **OK** button to exit the **View Manager.** ✓

- Pick the **Isometric graphics view** to see the part in its new orientation.

- Select **Fit** screen icon.

• The part should look as shown.

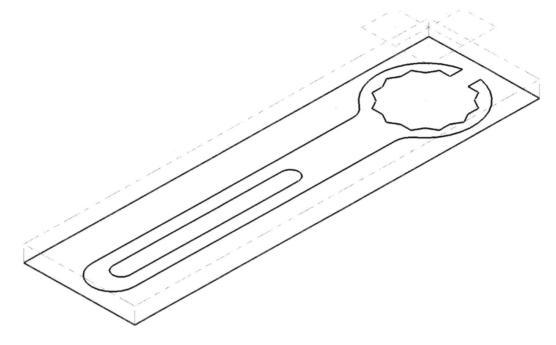

NOTE: Z zero is at **0.125** below the stock.

STEP 21: FACE THE PART

A **Facing** toolpath quickly removes material from the top of the part to create an even surface.

Toolpath Preview:

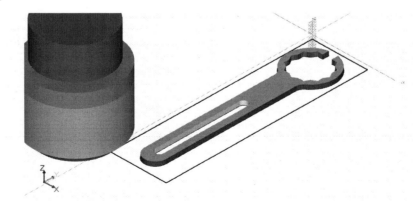

Mastercam. X

TOOLPATHS

- **Face.**
- When the chaining dialog box appears choose the **OK** button to use defined stock and exit the **Chaining** dialog box.

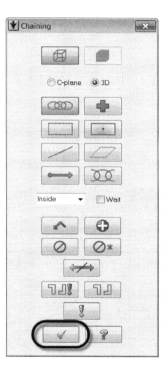

> **NOTE:** Mastercam will create the Facing toolpath defined from the stock setup.

- In the **Toolpath Type** page, the **Facing** icon will be automatically selected.

Contour   Pocket   Facing   Slot Mill

21.1 Select a 2.0" Face Mill from the library and set the Tool parameters

- Select **Tool** from the **Tree view list.**

- Click on the **Select library tool** button. Select library tool...
- To be able to see all the tools from the library disable **Filter Active**.
- Pick the **2" Face Mill (#316)** as shown.

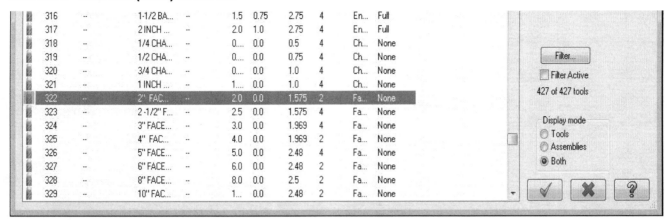

316	--	1-1/2 BA...	--	1.5	0.75	2.75	4	En...	Full
317	--	2 INCH ...	--	2.0	1.0	2.75	4	En...	Full
318	--	1/4 CHA...	--	0....	0.0	0.5	4	Ch...	None
319	--	1/2 CHA...	--	0....	0.0	0.75	4	Ch...	None
320	--	3/4 CHA...	--	0....	0.0	1.0	4	Ch...	None
321	--	1 INCH ...	--	1....	0.0	1.0	4	Ch...	None
322	--	2" FAC...	--	2.0	0.0	1.575	2	Fa...	None
323	--	2-1/2" F...	--	2.5	0.0	1.575	4	Fa...	None
324	--	3" FACE...	--	3.0	0.0	1.969	4	Fa...	None
325	--	4" FAC...	--	4.0	0.0	1.969	2	Fa...	None
326	--	5" FACE...	--	5.0	0.0	2.48	4	Fa...	None
327	--	6" FACE...	--	6.0	0.0	2.48	2	Fa...	None
328	--	8" FACE...	--	8.0	0.0	2.5	2	Fa...	None
329	--	10" FAC...	--	1...	0.0	2.48	2	Fa...	None

Filter...

☐ Filter Active

427 of 427 tools

Display mode
○ Tools
○ Assemblies
◉ Both

- Select the tool in the **Tool Selection** page and then select the **OK** button to exit.

- Make all the necessary changes as shown in Figure: 21.1.1.

Figure: 21.1.1

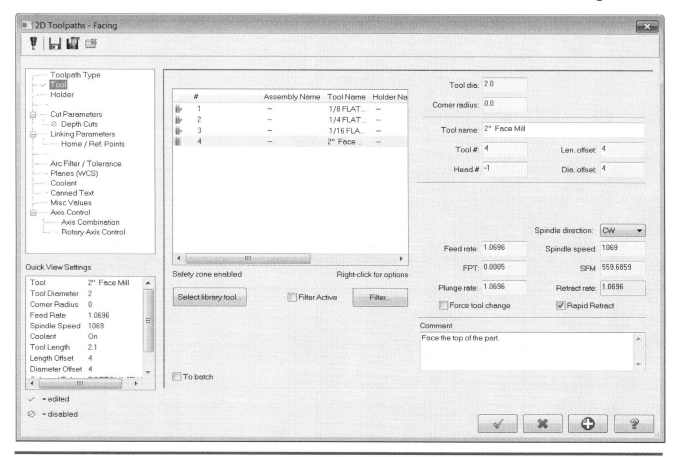

The **Feed rate, Plunge rate, Retract rate** and **Spindle speed** are based on the tool definition as set in the **Tool Settings**. You may change these values as per your part material and tools.

In the **Comment** field enter a comment to help identify the toolpath in the **Toolpaths/ Toolpaths Manager** such as the one shown above.

♦ Select **Cut Parameters** and make the necessary changes as shown in <u>Figure: 21.1.2</u>.

Figure: 21.1.2

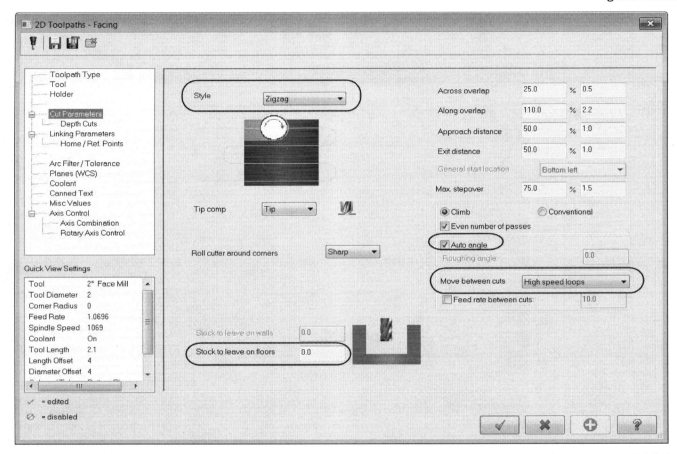

The **Style** (facing cutting method) **Zigzag** creates a back and forth cutting motion.

Auto angle determines the angle to machine along the larger side of the stock.

Move between cuts determines how the tool moves between each cut. This is only available if you select the zigzag cutting method.

♦ Select the **Linking Parameters** page and make the necessary changes as shown in <u>Figure: 21.1.3</u>.

Figure: 21.1.3

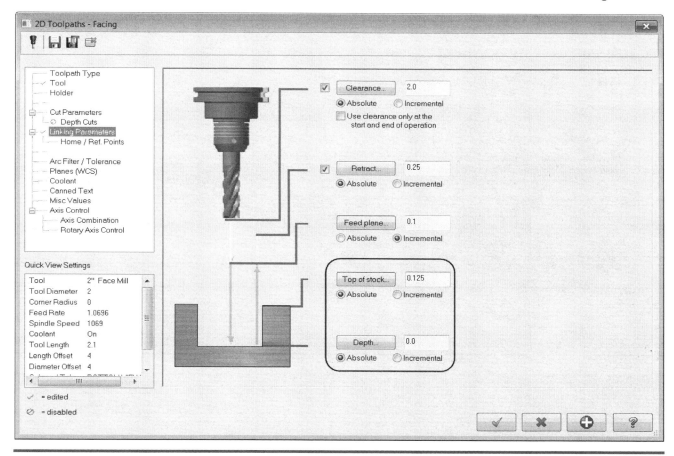

Clearance sets the height at which the tool moves to and from the part.

Retract sets the height that the tool moves up to before the next tool pass.

Feed Plane sets the height that the tool rapids to before changing to the plunge rate to enter the part.

Top of stock sets the height of the material in the Z axis.

Depth determines the final machining depth that the tool descends into the stock.

♦ Select the **OK** button to exit the **Facing Parameters**.

NOTE: The top of stock is set to **0.125"** because in our **Bottom view** we have **Origin Z** value set to **0.125"** above the first setup origin. The depth is set to **0.0"** because this is the depth of the finish part we want the tool to go to.

- To **Backplot** and **Verify** your toolpath page 152 to review these procedures.
- To select all the operations, from the Toolpaths Manager, click on the **Select all operations** icon.

- The toolpaths should look as shown.

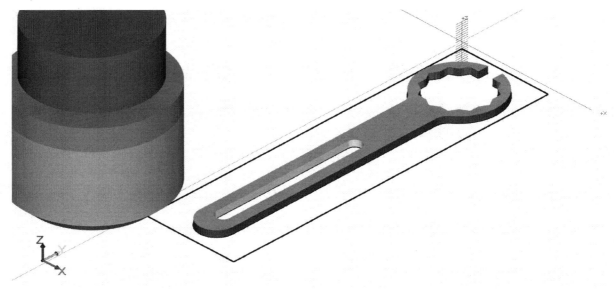

- To exit Mastercam Simulator click on the **Close** icon.

STEP 22: RENAME THE NC FILE

The Facing operation in Setup #2 kept the NC name from Setup #1. We need to rename this operation.

• Right click on Setup #2 group, choose the option **Edit selected operations** and then pick **Change NC file name**.

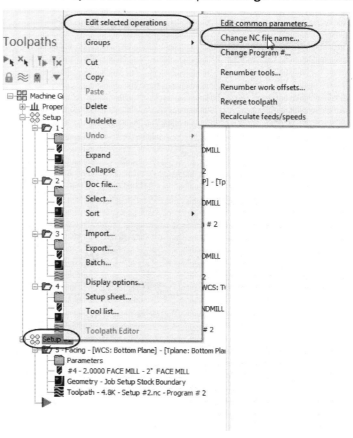

• When the **Enter new NC name** dialog box appears select **"Setup #2"**.

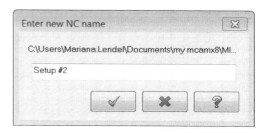

• Select the **OK** button apply the changed **NC name** to **Operation #5**.

• The result you should see **Setup #2.NC** in the last item of text for Operation #5.

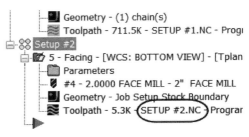

STEP 23: POST THE FILE

• Ensure all operations are selected, if they are not use the button **Select all operations** in the **Toolpaths Manager.**

• Select the **Post selected operations**  button from the **Toolpaths Manager.**
• In the **Post processing** window make the necessary changes as shown in Figure: 23.0.1.

Figure: 23.0.1

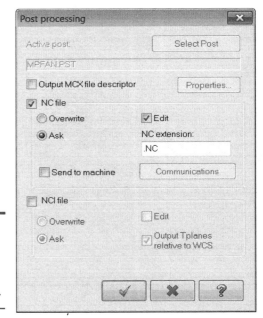

NC File enabled allows you to keep the NC file and to assign the same name as the MCX file.

Edit enabled allows you to automatically launch the default editor.

• Select the **OK** button to continue.
• Save Setup #1 NC file.
• Save Setup #2 NC file.

◆ A window with Mastercam Code Expert will be launched and the NC program will appear as shown in <u>Figure: 23.0.2</u>.

Figure: 23.0.2

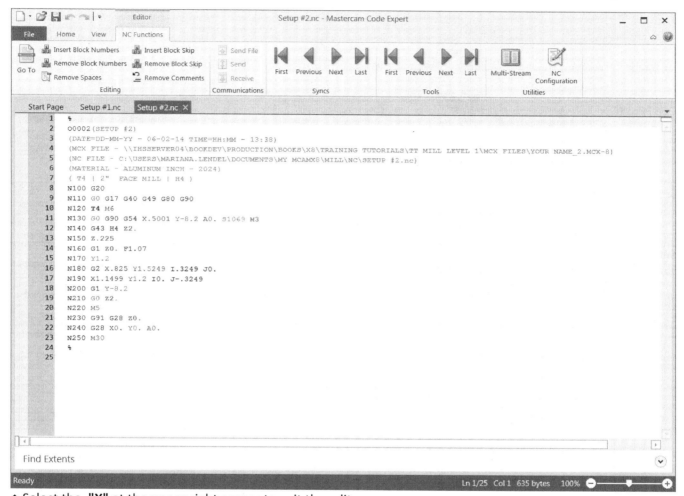

◆ Select the **"X"** at the upper right corner to exit the editor.

STEP 24: SAVE THE UPDATED MCX FILE

REVIEW EXERCISE -STUDENT PRACTICE

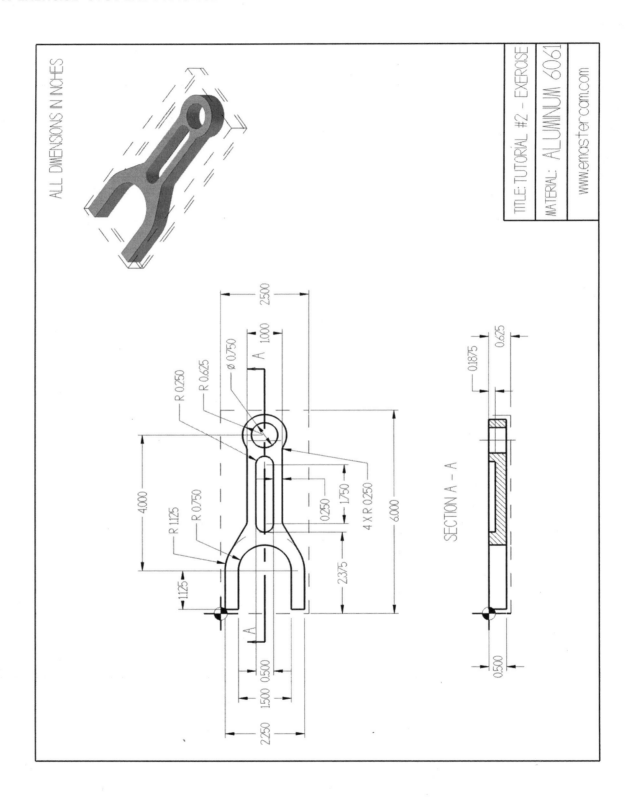

CREATE THE GEOMETRY FOR TUTORIAL #2 EXERCISE

Use these commands to create the geometry:
- Create 1/2 of the geometry.
- Create circle center point.
- Fast Point to locate arcs.
- Create Vertical and Horizontal lines.
- Create Tangent Lines.
- Edit Trim/Break Two Pieces.
- Create Line Parallel.
- Create fillet entities.

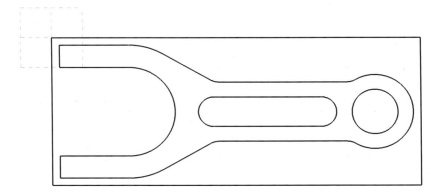

CREATE THE TOOLPATHS FOR TUTORIAL #2 EXERCISE

Create the Toolpaths for Tutorial #2 Exercise as per the instructions below.

Setup #1
Set the machine properties including the stock setup.
- Remove the material in the slot.
- Use a 1/4" Flat Endmill.
- Set the Depth according to the drawing.

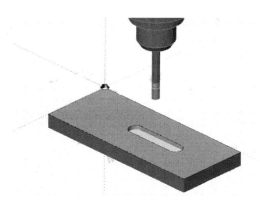

Circle Mill the 1/4" Hole.
- Choose a 1/4" Drill.
- Enable Roughing.
- Set appropriate Depth of cuts and Break through amount.
- Input a Depth according to the drawing.

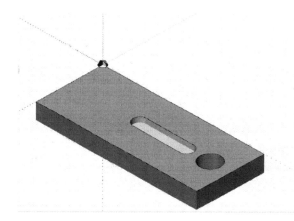

Rough the outside profile using 2D HS Dynamic.
- Select the outside rectangle in the **Machining regions**.
- Enable **From outside**.
- Select the profile in the **Avoidance regions**.
- Use a 1/2" Flat Endmill.
- Leave stock on the wall only.
- Enable **Break through**.
- Set the **Depth** according to the drawing.

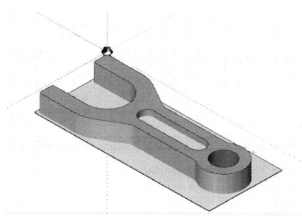

Finish the outside profile using Contour.
- Use a 1/2" Flat Endmill.
- Enable **Break through**.
- Set the final **Depth** according to the drawing.

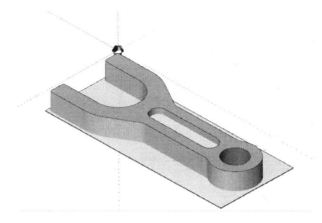

Setup #2.
- Rename the previous Toolpath Group.
- Rename all the existing operation NC file
- Create a new Toolpath Group and rename it.

Use WCS View Manager and set the Bottom plane
- Use Geometry to define the plane.
- Set WCS, Cplane and Tplane to the new view.
- Set the z origin to 0.125

Face the part the part (Contour 2D).
- Select the 2"Face Mill from the Tool page.
- Set the Depth according to the drawing.

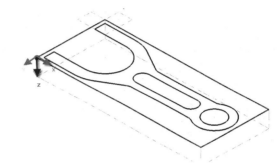

NOTES:

TUTORIAL #2 QUIZ

• What does Slot mill toolpath do?

• What does 2D HS Dynamic Mill do?

• What does the 2D HS Dynamic Contour mill do?

• What is the process used to be able to post different operations as different programs?

TUTORIAL #3

OVERVIEW OF STEPS TAKEN TO CREATE THE FINAL PART:

From Drawing to CAD Model:
- The student should examine the drawing on the following page to understand what part is being created in the tutorial.
- From the drawing we can decide how to go about creating the geometry in Mastercam.

Create the 2D CAD Model used to generate Toolpaths from:
- The student will create the Top 2D geometry needed to create the toolpaths.
- Geometry creation commands such as arc polar, circle center point, line tangent at an angle, mirror, arc tangent, ellipse, letters, bounding box and translate will be used.

Create the necessary Toolpaths to machine the part:
- The student will set up the stock size to be used and the clamping method used.
- A 2D High Speed Area Mill toolpath will be created to remove the material from the outside step.
- A 2D High Speed Dynamic Mill toolpath will be created to remove the outside material.
- A Pocket Island Facing toolpath will be created to machine the and face the letters.
- A Pocket Remachining toolpath will be used to machine the remaining material.

Backplot and Verify the file:
- The Backplot will be used to simulate a step by step process of the tool's movements.
- The Verify will be used to watch a tool machine the part out of a solid model.

Post Process the file to generate the G-code:
- The Student will then post process the file to obtain an NC file containing the necessary code for the machine.

 This tutorial takes approximately two hours to complete.

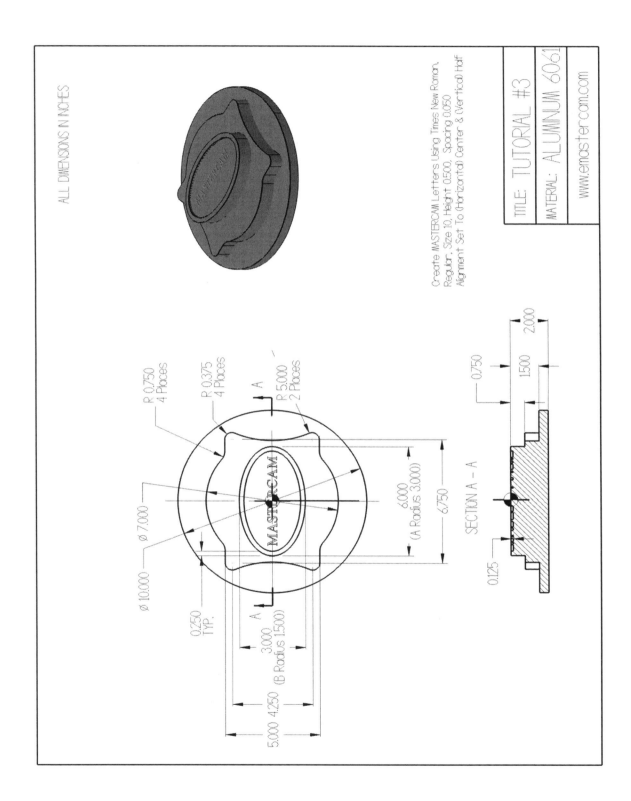

ALL DIMENSIONS IN INCHES

Create MASTERCAM Letters Using Times New Roman,
Regular. Size 10, Height 0.500, Spacing 0.050
Alignment Set To (Horizontal) Center & (Vertical) Half

TITLE: TUTORIAL #3

MATERIAL: ALUMINUM 6061

www.emastercam.com

R 0.750
4 Places

R 0.375
4 Places

A

R 5.000
2 Places

6.000

(A Radius 3.000)

6.750

Ø 7.000

MASTERCAM

Ø 10.000

0.250
TYP.

A

3.000

5.000 4.250

(B Radius 1.500)

SECTION A – A

0.750

1.500

2.000

0.125

GEOMETRY CREATION

STEP 1: SETTING UP THE GRAPHIC USER INTERFACE

Please refer to the **Getting Started** section to set up the graphics user interface.

> **NOTE:** In the next steps you will create a quater of the entire geometry. You will use the Mirror command to generate the rest.

STEP 2: CREATE TWO POLAR ARCS

In this step you will create two arcs using arc polar command. To create an arc polar you need to know the Radius, the Start Angle, the End Angle and the center point of the arc.

Step Preview:

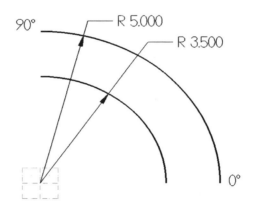

2.1 Create the 10.0" diameter arc

CREATE
* **Arc.**

*  **Arc Polar.**
* Enter the radius in the **Ribbon bar** as shown, and then press the **Tab key** to move through all the fields and enter the rest of the values.

◆ [Enter the center point]: Select the Origin as shown in <u>Figure: 2.1.1</u>.

Figure: 2.1.1

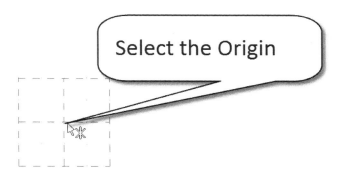

◆ Make sure that when selecting the origin, the visual cue of the cursor changes as shown.

◆ Use the **Fit** icon to fit the drawing to the screen.

◆ Your drawing will appear as shown.

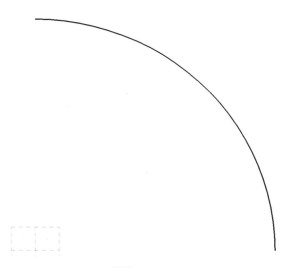

◆ Choose the **Apply** button to continue in the same command.

NOTE: During the geometry creation of this tutorial, if you make a mistake you can undo the last step using the

Undo icon. ⤺ You can undo as many steps as needed. If you delete or undo a step by mistake, just use the

Redo icon. ⤻ To delete unwanted geometry, select it first and then press **Delete** from the keyboard.

2.2 Create the 7.0" diameter arc

◆ Enter the values in the **Ribbon bar** as shown.

◆ [Enter the center point]: Select the Origin as shown in Figure: 2.1.1.

Figure: 2.2.1

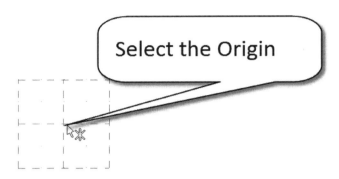

Select the Origin

◆ The drawing will appear as shown.

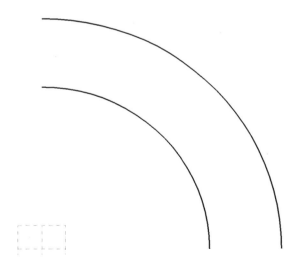

◆ Choose the **OK** button to continue.

STEP 3: CREATE A CIRCLE

In this step you will learn how to create a crcle knowing the radius and the center point.

Step Preview:

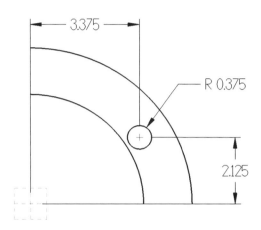

CREATE
+ **Arc.**

+  **Circle Center Point.**

+ Enter the **Radius** of **0.375** then pick the **Fast Point** command.
+ Enter the coordinates of **3.375, 2.125** as shown and then hit **Enter** on your keyboard.

3.375,2.125

+ Select the **OK** button to exit the command.

• The drawing should look as shown.

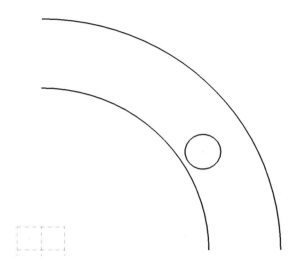

STEP 4: CREATE A LINE TANGENT TO THE CIRCLE

In this step you will use **Create Line Endpoint** command to create a line tangent to the circle at a 180 degree angle. Mastercam angles are measured counter clockwise and will always total 360 degrees.

Step Preview:

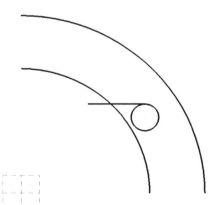

CREATE
• **Line.**

•  **Endpoint.**

• In the **Ribbon bar** make sure that only the **Tangent** icon is enabled and none of the other icons are selected as shown.

• [Specify the first point]: Select the arc approximatelly as shown in Figure: 4.0.1. For this exercise purpose, make

sure that the quadrant point does not appear while selecting the arc.

Figure: 4.0.1

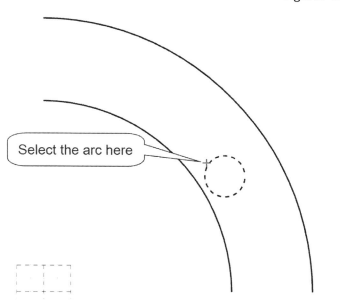

Select the arc here

• Sketch the line by moving the cursor to the left of the arc and click to select the second endpoint as shown in Figure: 4.0.2.

Figure: 4.0.2

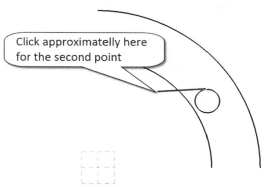

Click approximatelly here
for the second point

• In the **Ribbon bar** type the angle **180** as shown and press **Enter**.

NOTE: Once you enter the angle the line will be updated.

- Select the **OK** button to exit the command.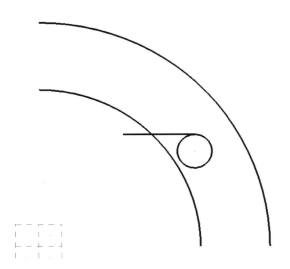
- The geometry should look as shown.

STEP 5: CREATE A FILLET

In this step you will use **Create Fillet Entities** command to create a fillet with the radius 0.75. Fillets are used to round sharp corners.

Step Preview:

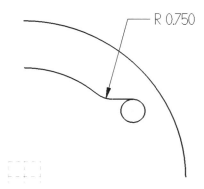

CREATE
- **Fillet.**

- **Entities.**
- Enter a fillet radius of **0.75**. Ensure the fillet style is set to **Normal** and **Trim** is enabled as shown.

- [Select an entity]: Select Entity A as shown in Figure: 5.0.1.
- [Select another entity]: Select Entity B as shown in Figure: 5.0.1.

Figure: 5.0.1

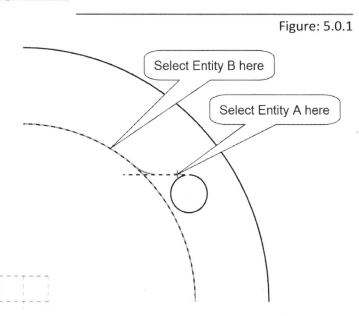

* Select the **OK** button to exit the command. ☑
* The geometry should look as shown.

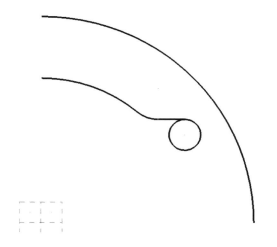

STEP 6: MIRROR THE GEOMETRY

In this step you will Mirror the inside geometry about the X-axis.

Step Preview:

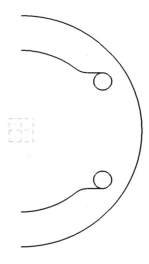

XFORM

* Mirror.

◆ [Mirror: select entities to mirror]: Make a Window around the entire geometry as shown in Figure: 6.0.1.

Figure: 6.0.1

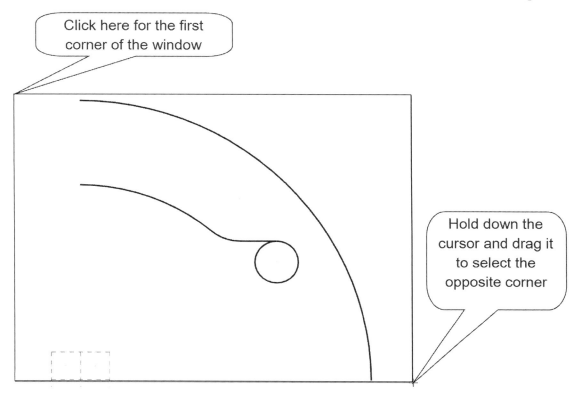

◆ Press **Enter** or choose the **End Selection** button to continue.

◆ Pick the option to mirror the entities about the **X Axis** as shown in Figure: 6.0.2.

Figure: 6.0.2

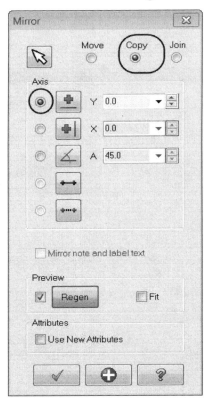

◆ Pick the **OK** button to exit the **Mirror** dialog box.

◆ Select the **Fit** icon to fit the drawing to the screen.

◆ The geometry should look as shown.

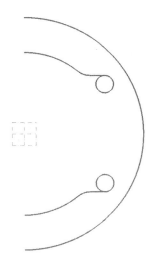

• Choose the **Clear Colors** icon from the toolbars to reset the colours back to the original colours.

STEP 7: CREATE AN ARC TANGENT TO TWO ENTITIES

In this step you will learn how to create an arc tangent to 2 arcs.

Step Preview:

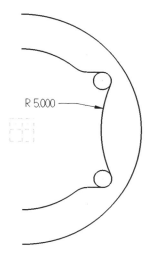

R 5.000

CREATE

• **Arc.**

• **Arc Tangent.**

• Select the **Arc Tangent 2 Entities** icon and enter the radius as shown.

NOTE: To see an explanation of the other options select the help icon [?] and then click on the **Button definitions** tab. Click on each item and a short description will appear on the screen.

- ◆ [Select the entity that the arc is to be tangent]: Select Entity A as shown in Figure: 7.0.1.
- ◆ [Select the entity that the arc is to be tangent]: Select Entity B as shown in Figure: 7.0.1.

Figure: 7.0.1

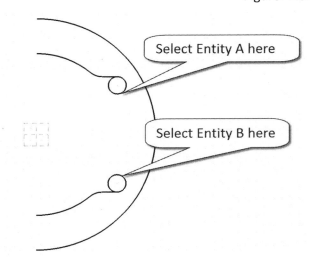

- ◆ [Select the fillet to use]: Select the arc as shown in Figure: 7.0.2.

Figure: 7.0.2

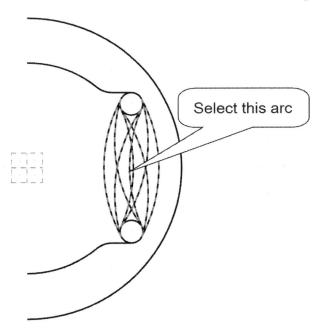

- ◆ Select the **OK** button to exit the **Create Arc Tangent** function. ✓

◆ The geometry should look as shown.

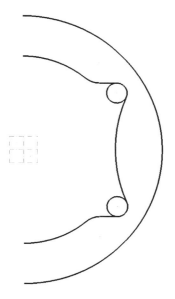

STEP 8: TRIM THE GEOMETRY USING TRIM 3 ENTITIES COMMAND

In this step you will use trim three entities command to clean the geometry. The first two entities that you select are trimmed to the third, which acts as a trimming curve. The third entity is then trimmed to the first two.
This function is useful for trimming two lines to a circle that is tangent to both lines. The arc is selected last, and the results vary depending on whether you select to keep the top or the bottom of the arc.

Step Preview:

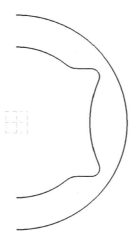

EDIT

◆ **Trim/Break.**

◆  **Trim/Break/Extend.**

◆ Select the option to **Trim 3 Entities**.

◆ [Select the first entity to trim/extend]: Select Entity A as shown in Figure: 8.0.1.
◆ [Select the first second to trim/extend]: Select Entity B as shown in Figure: 8.0.1.
◆ [Select the entity to trim/extend to]: Select Entity C as shown in Figure: 8.0.1.

Figure: 8.0.1

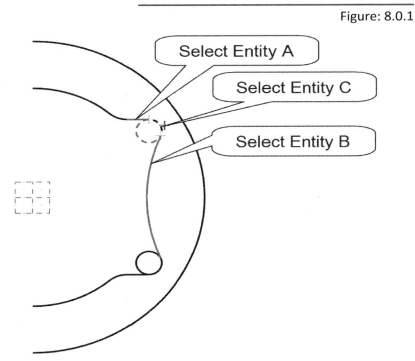

Select Entity A

Select Entity C

Select Entity B

◆ The geometry should look as shown.

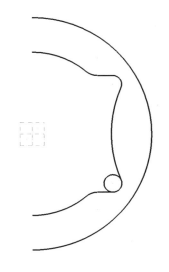

• Repeate the steps to clean the second circle as shown.

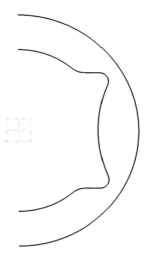

• Select the **OK** button to exit the command.

STEP 9: MIRROR THE GEOMETRY

In this step you will Mirror the inside geometry about the Y-axis.

Step Preview:

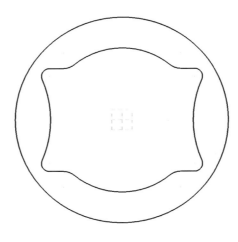

XFORM

- 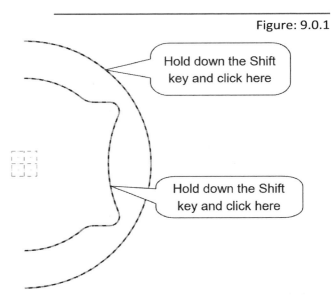 **Mirror.**

- ◆ **Mirror.**
- ◆ [Mirror: select entities to mirror]: To select the entire geometry, hold down the Shift key and click on both contours as shown in Figure: 9.0.1.

Figure: 9.0.1

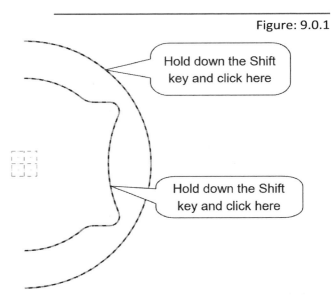

Hold down the Shift key and click here

Hold down the Shift key and click here

NOTE: By holding the **Shift** key and selecting one entity of a chain, Mastercam selects all the other entities that are in the chain.

- ◆ Choose the **End Selection** button.

Mill Level 1 Training Tutorial
Mastercam. X⁸

◆ Pick the option to mirror the entities about the **Y Axis** as shown in Figure: 9.0.2.

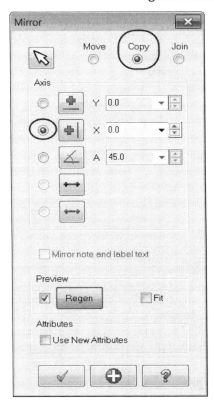

◆ Pick the **OK** button to exit the **Mirror** dialog box.

◆ Select the **Fit** icon to fit the drawing to the screen.
◆ The geometry should look as shown.

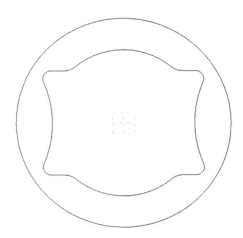

◆ Select the **Clear Colors** icon from the toolbars to reset the colours back to the original colours.

STEP 10: CREATE THE ELLIPSES

In this step you will learn how to create an ellipse knowing the point of origin, A radius and B radius.

Step Preview:

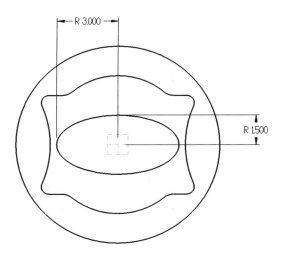

CREATE

- ◆ ⬭ **Ellipse.**
- ◆ Pick the **Origin** as the position of base point.
- ◆ Enter a **A radius** of **3.0**, a **B radius** of **1.5** and press **Enter** as shown in <u>Figure: 10.0.1</u>.

Figure: 10.0.1

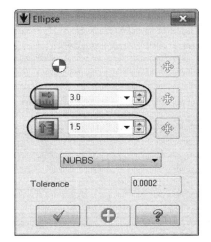

- ◆ Pick the **OK** button to exit the **Ellipse** command.

STEP 11: OFFSET THE ELLIPSE

In this step you will offset the ellipse with a given distance.

Step Preview:

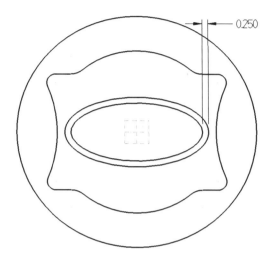

XFORM

- ◆ |→| **Offset.**
- ◆ [Select the line, arc, spline or curve to offset]: Select the ellipse as shown in <u>Figure: 11.0.1</u>.

Figure: 11.0.1

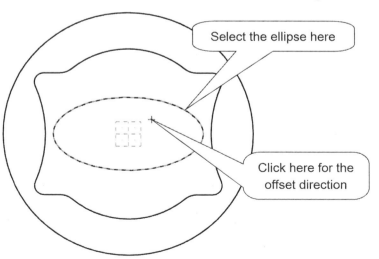

Select the ellipse here

Click here for the offset direction

• [Indicate the offset direction]: Click inside of the ellipse as shown in Figure: 11.0.1.
• Change the distance in the **Offset** dialog box to **0.25** and leave **Copy** enabled as shown in Figure: 11.0.2.

Figure: 11.0.2

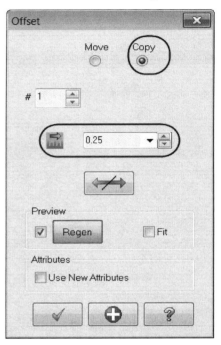

• Select the **OK** button to exit **Offset** dialog box.

• Pick the **Clear Color** icon to return the colours to the original colours.
• The geometry should look as shown.

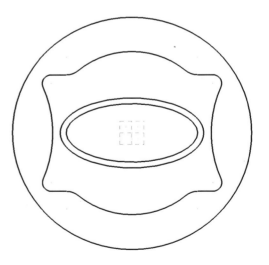

STEP 12: ADD THE TEXT

In this step we will create the **Letters,** then using **Bounding box** you will create a point at their center and then you will use **Translate** command to move them in the center of the part.

Creating letters uses lines, arcs and **NURBS** splines. There are various fonts found in this command as well. When using **TrueType** fonts the height of the letters may not match the value you entered for the letter height because Mastercam scales the letters based on all the information encoded into the **TrueType** font.

Step Preview:

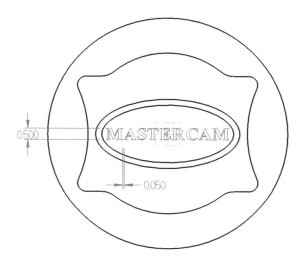

12.1 Change the wireframe color to red

♦ From the **Status bar**, click on the **Wireframe color** as shown.

• Select the **red color no. 12** as shown.

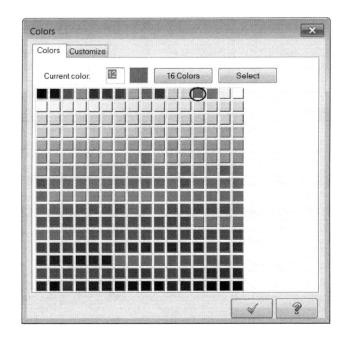

• Select the **OK** button to continue.

12.2 Create the letters

CREATE

• A **Letters.**
• When the **Create Letters** dialog box appears select the **TrueType(R)** button as shown in Figure: 12.2.1.

Figure: 12.2.1

• Scroll down the font list and find the font **Times New Roman**.

◆ Select **Bold** for the **Font style** as shown in Figure: 12.2.2.

Figure: 12.2.2

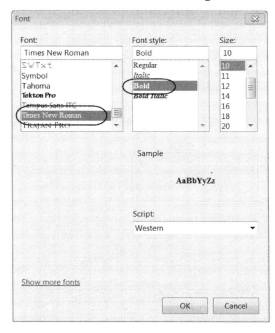

◆ Select the **OK** button.
◆ Input the word **Mastercam** under the area titled **Letters** as shown in Figure: 12.2.3.

Figure: 12.2.3

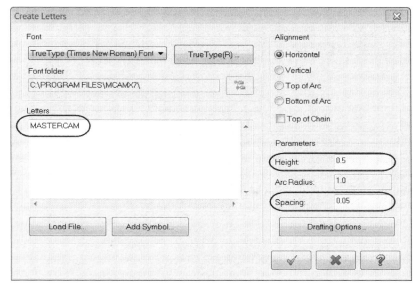

◆ Change the **Height** to **0.50** and the **Spacing** to **0.05**.

◆ Select the **OK** button.

◆ [Enter the starting location]: Pick a point to the right of the part as the text starting location as shown in <u>Figure: 12.2.4</u>.

Figure: 12.2.4

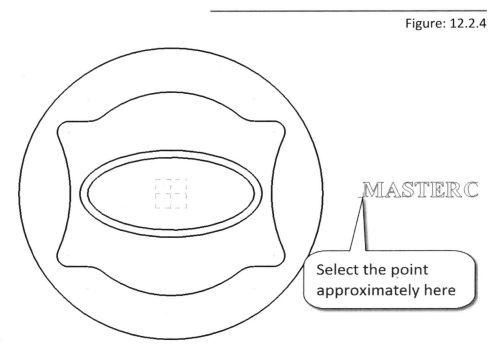

MASTERC

> Select the point approximately here

◆ Press your Esc key on your keyboard to exit the command.

> **NOTE:** Next we will move the text within the part.

◆ Select the **Fit** icon.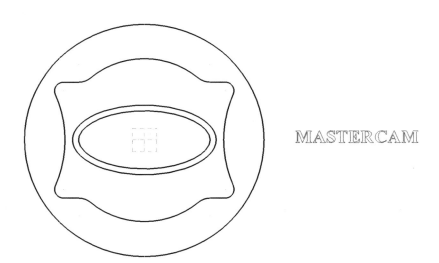

MASTERCAM

12.3 Create a point at the center of the letters using Bounding Box

CREATE

- ⬠ **Bounding Box.**
- When the **Bounding Box dialog** box appears disable the option to create **Lines Arcs** and enable only the **Center Point.**
- Uncheck **All Entities** as shown in Figure: 12.3.1.

Figure: 12.3.1

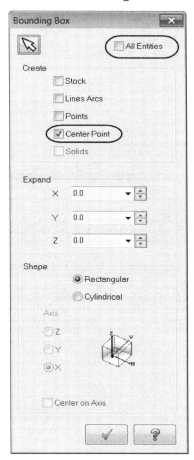

NOTE: Once you unchecked All Entities, Mastercam brings you to the graphics window where you can select the letters.

◆ [Select entities]: Click on the **QM Color** icon located to the right of the graphics window as shown.

◆ From the **Select All** dialog box click on the red color as shown.

☐		1
☑		12

◆ Select the **OK** button to exit **Select All** dialog box.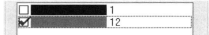

◆ Press **Enter** or pick the **End Selection** button.

◆ Select the **OK** button to exit **Bounding box** dialog box.

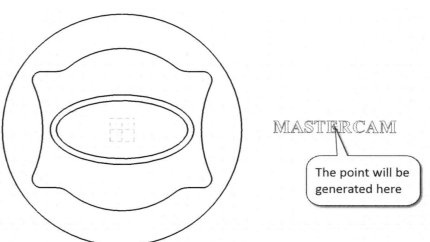

MASTERCAM

The point will be generated here

NOTE: A point should appear in the middle of the letters. This is the center point of the text and will be used to center the letters inside of the inner ellipse.

Mastercam **X**

12.4 Move the letters using Translate

XFORM

- 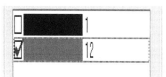 **Translate.**
- [Translate: select entities to translate]: Click on the **QM Color** icon as shown.

- Select the red color again as shown.

- Select the **OK** button to exit **Select All** dialog box.

- Choose the **End Selection** button to finish the selection.

- When the **Translate dialog** box appears, select the **Move** button and then choose the **From Point** icon +1 as shown in <u>Figure: 12.4.1</u>.

Figure: 12.4.1

- Choose the **Zoom Window** icon and create a window around the letters as shown in <u>Figure: 12.4.2</u>.

Figure: 12.4.2

◆ Select the point inside the "**E**" as shown in Figure: 12.4.3.

Figure: 12.4.3

Select the point

◆ Pick the **Fit** icon.
◆ From the **Autocursor** flyout menu select the option **Origin**.

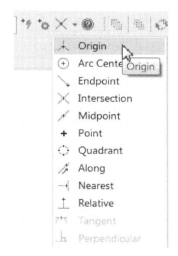

◆ Select the **OK** button in the **Translate** dialog box.

◆ Select **Fit** screen to see the geometry.

◆ Pick the **Clear Color** icon to return the colours to the original colours.

♦ Once complete the geometry should look as shown.

STEP 13: DELETE THE POINT

In this step you will use QM Point selection to select the center point and then you will delete it.

♦ From the **Quick Mask** toolbar select **QM Point** as shown to select all the existing point.

♦ Select the **Delete** key from your keyboard or select the **Delete entities** icon.

STEP 14: SAVE THE FILE

FILE

♦ 🖫 **Save As.**
♦ File name: "Your Name_3".

Mastercam. X⁸

TOOLPATH CREATION

SUGGESTED FIXTURE:

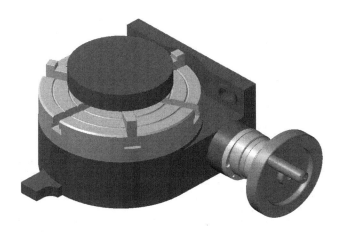

SETUP SHEET:

TOOL LIST

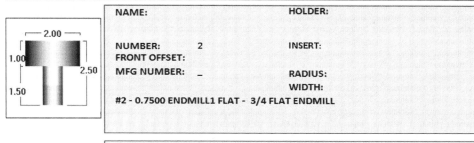

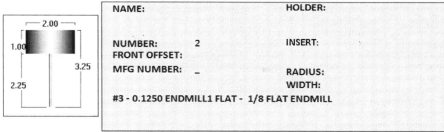

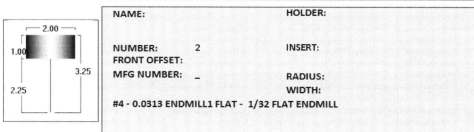

STEP 15:   SELECT THE MACHINE AND SET UP THE STOCK

In Mastercam, you select a **Machine Definition** before creating any toolpaths. The **Machine Definition** is a model of your machines capabilities and features. It acts like a template for setting up your machine. The machine definition ties together three main components. The schematic model of your machines components. The control definition that models your control capabilities and the post processor that will generate the required machine code (G-code). For a Mill Level 1 exercise (2D toolpaths) we need just a basic machine definition.

> **NOTE:** For the purpose of this tutorial, we will be using the Default milling machine.

◆ To display the **Toolpaths Manager** press **Alt + O**.

◆ Use the **Fit** icon to fit the drawing to the screen.

MACHINE TYPE
◆ **Mill.**
◆ **Default.**

◆ Select the plus sign in front of **Properties** in the **Toolpaths Manager** to expand the **Toolpaths Group Properties.**

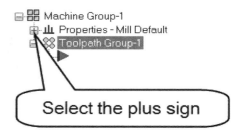

◆ Select **Tool Settings** to set the tool parameters.

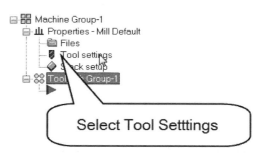

◆ Change the parameters to match the screenshot as shown in Figure: 15.0.1.

Figure: 15.0.1

Program # is used to enter a number if your machine tool requires a number for a program name.

Assign tool numbers sequentially allows you to overwrite the tool number from the library with the next available tool number. (First operation tool number 1; Second operation tool number 2, etc.)

Warn of duplicate tool numbers allows you to get a warning if you enter two tools with the same number.

Override defaults with modal values enables the system to keep the values that you enter.

Feed Calculation set From tool uses feed rate, plunge rate, retract rate and spindle speed from the tool definition.

◆ Select the **Stock Setup** tab to define the stock.
◆ Select the **Cylindrical Shape** and enter the values as shown in Figure: 15.0.2.

Figure: 15.0.2

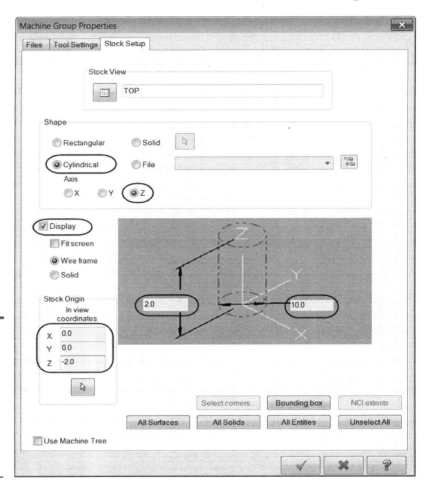

The **Stock Origin** values adjust the positioning of the stock, ensuring that you have equal amount of extra stock around the finished part.

Display options allow you to set the stock as Wireframe and to fit the stock to the screen. (Fit Screen)

◆ Select the **OK** button to exit the **Machine Group Properties**.

◆ Select the **Isometric** view from the graphics view toolbar to see the stock.

◆ Use the **Fit** icon to fit the drawing to the screen.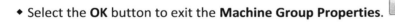

◆ The stock model will appear as shown.

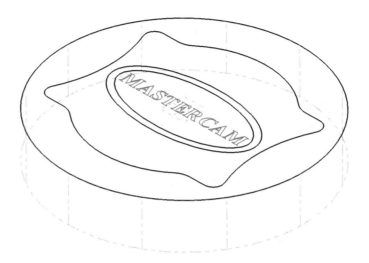

NOTE: The stock is not geometry and can not be selected.

◆ Select the **Top** view from the view toolbar to see the part from the top.

NOTE: There will not be facing toolpath because the stock is already to size.

STEP 16: 2D HIGH SPEED AREA MILL

2D High Speed Area Mill generates the free-flowing motion needed to machine features, such as standing bosses and cores or pockets in a single operation. With **Area Mill High Speed** smaller depth of cuts are recommended versus **Dynamic Mill** in which the depth cuts can be the size of the flute.

The toolpath depends on the **Machining strategy** that you choose in the **Chain Options**. If the strategy choosed is **From outside**, the toolpaths starts at the outmost chain and works its way in taking on the final shape of the part as it approaches the final pass. You can also machine pockets in which case the strategy selected is Start inside which keeps the tool inside the machining regions.

Toolpath Preview:

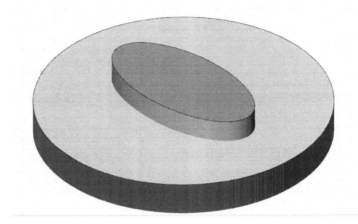

TOOLPATHS

♦ **2D High Speed.**

♦ **Area.**

♦ If a prompt appears, enter new **NC name**, select the **OK** button to accept the default.

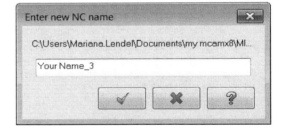

- In the **Chain Options** enable **From outside** and click on the **Select** button in the **Machining regions** as shown.

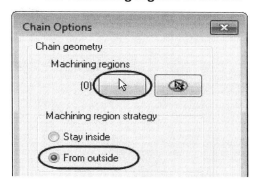

- Leave the default settings in the **Chaining** dialog box.

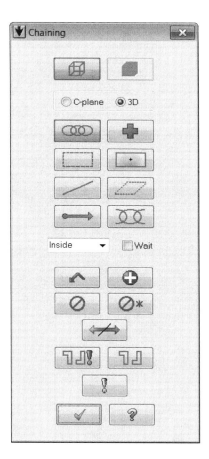

◆ [2D HST machining chain 1]: Select the first chain as shown in <u>Figure: 16.0.1</u>.

Figure: 16.0.1

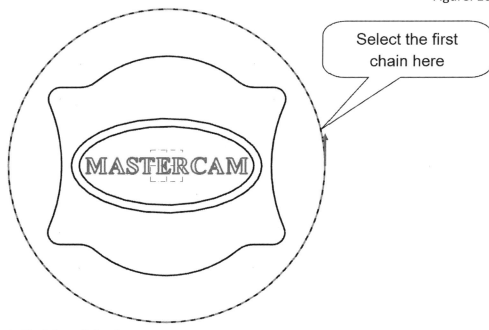

Select the first chain here

◆ Select the **OK** button to exit **Chaining** dialog box.
◆ From the **Chain Options**, click on the **Select** button in the **Avoidance regions** as shown.

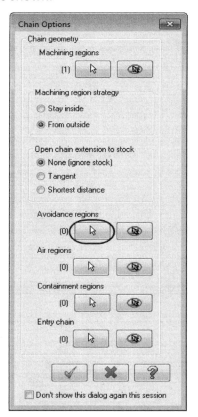

Mastercam X⁸

- [Select 2d HST avoidance chain1]: Select the chain as shown in Figure: 16.0.2.

Figure: 16.0.2

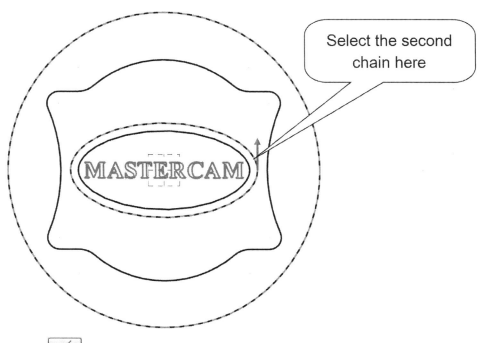

Select the second chain here

- Choose the **OK** button to continue.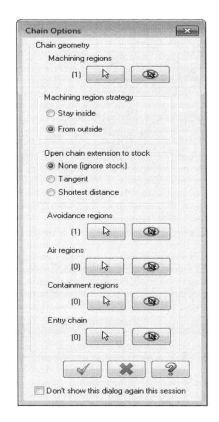

- Select the **OK** button to exit the **Chain Options** dialog box.
- In the **Toolpath Type** page, **Area Mill** will be selected as shown.

Dynamic Mill   Area Mill   Dynamic Contour   Peel Mill   Blend Mill

NOTE: Mastercam updates the pages as you modify them and then marks them, in the **Tree view** list, with a green check mark. Pages that are not changed are marked with a red circle and slash.

16.1 Select a 3/4" Flat Endmill from the Tool Library and set the Tool Parameters

- From the **Tree view list**, select **Tool**.

- Click on **Select library tool** button. `Select library tool...`
- Select the **Filter** button.

-
- Select the **None** button and then under **Tool Types** choose the **Flat Endmill** Icon.
- Under tool diameter pick **Equal** and input a value of **0.75** as shown in Figure: 16.1.1.

Figure: 16.1.1

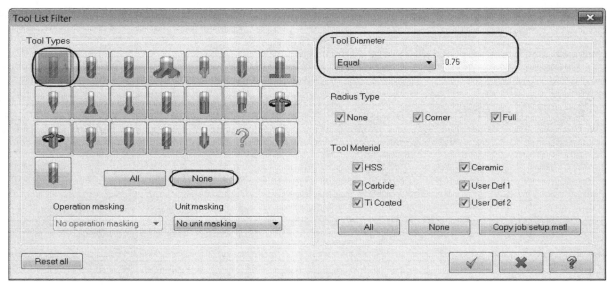

- Select the **OK** button to exit the **Tool List Filter.**

◆ In the **Tool Selection** dialog box you should only see a **3/4" Flat Endmill**.

#	Assembly Name	Tool Name	Holder Name	Dia.	Cor. rad.	Length	# Flutes	Type	Rad. Type
241	–	3/4 FLAT...	–	0.75	0.0	2.0	4	En...	None

◆ Select the **3/4" Flat Endmill** in the **Tool Selection** page and then select the **OK** button to exit.
◆ Make all the necessary changes as shown in Figure: 16.1.2.

Figure: 16.1.2

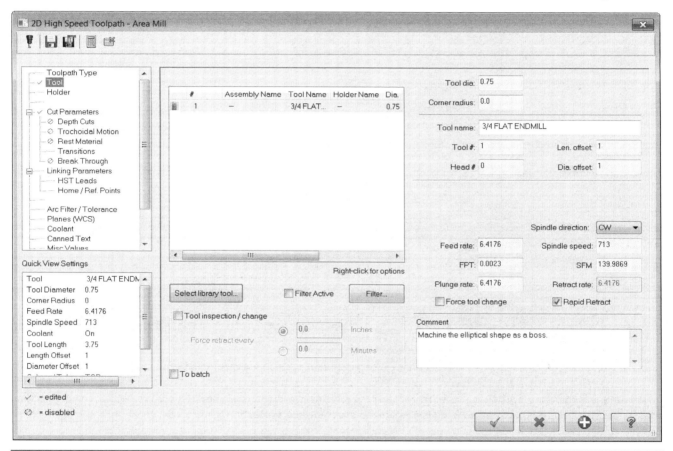

Tool Inspection/change forces a retract move at set intervals so that your machine operator can inspect the tool. When the tool reaches an inspection point, it retracts and rapid off the part to the clearance plane.

16.2 Set the Cut Parameters

◆ Select **Cut Parameters** and enable **Corner rounding** as shown in Figure: 16.2.1.

Figure: 16.2.1

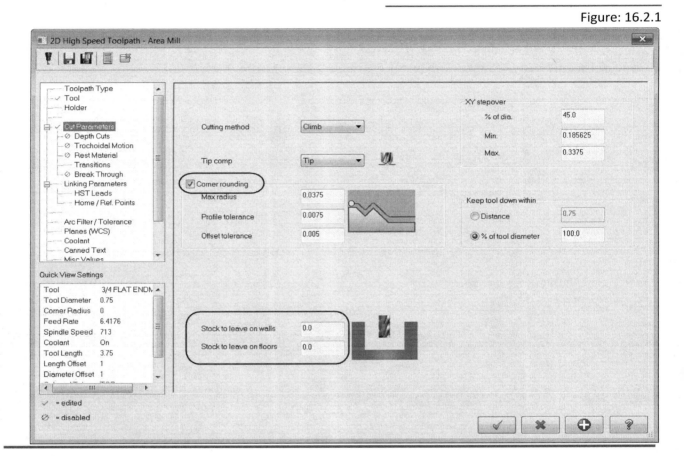

Corner Rounding replaces sharp corners with arcs for faster and smoother transitions in tool direction.

Max Radius is the largest arc that you allow Mastercam to insert to replace a corner. Larger arcs will create a smoother toolpath but with greater deviation from the originally programmed toolpath.

Profile Tolerance represents the maximum distance that the outermost profile of a toolpath created a corner with a corner rounding can deviate from the original toolpath.

Offset Tolerance represents the maximum distance that a profile of a toolpath created with corner rounding can deviate from the original toolpath. This is the same measurement as the profile tolerance but is applied to all the profiles except the outermost one.

XY Stepover expresses the maximum XY stepover as a percentage of the tool diameter. Mastercam will use the largest value possible that does not leave unwanted upstands of material between the passes.

Keep Tool Down Within keeps the tool down if the distance from the end pass to the start of the next pass is less than the value here. Mastercam will not create a retract move as defined on the linking parameters page. Instead the tool will stay down and move directly between the passes at the feed rate.

16.3 Set the Depth Cuts Parameters

♦ Select **Depth cuts** and make the necessary changes as shown in Figure: 16.3.1.

Figure: 16.3.1

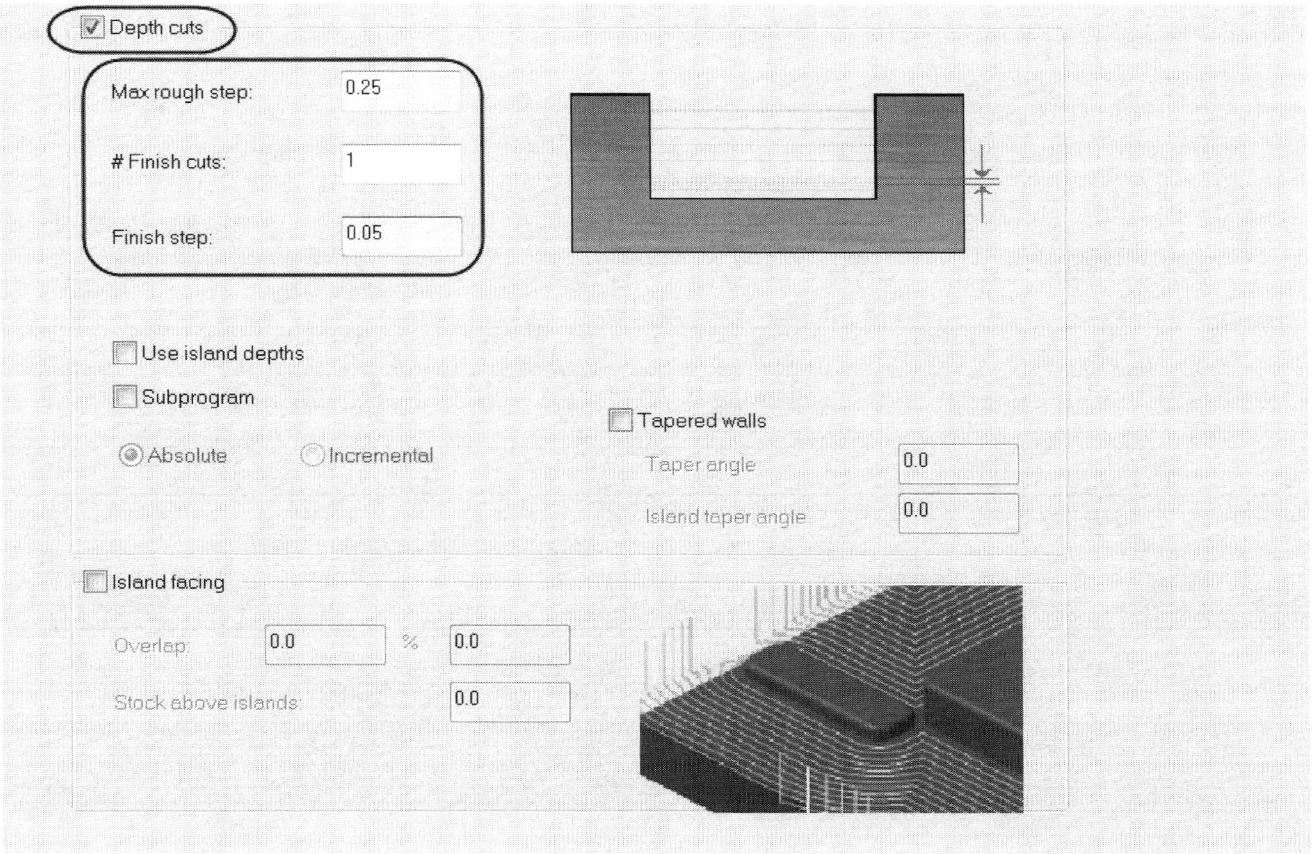

☑ Depth cuts

Max rough step: 0.25

Finish cuts: 1

Finish step: 0.05

☐ Use island depths
☐ Subprogram

◉ Absolute   ◯ Incremental

☐ Tapered walls

Taper angle   0.0

Island taper angle   0.0

☐ Island facing

Overlap: 0.0   %   0.0

Stock above islands: 0.0

16.4 Set the Transitions Parameters

- ◆ Select **Transitions**, choose the **Entry method Entry helix** and enter a **Radius** of **0.25**.
- ◆ Enable **Output 3D arc moves** and ensure the value set in **Skip pockets smaller than** is **0.55** as shown in <u>Figure: 16.4.1</u>.

Figure: 16.4.1

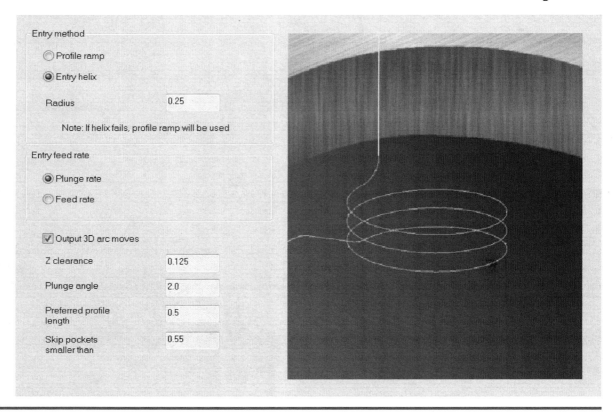

Entry method sets the entry move that the tool makes as it transitions to new Z depths. If you choose to create a helical entry and there is not enough room, Mastercam creates a ramp entry instead.

Entry feed rate sets the rate that the tool feeds into the material.

Output 3d arc moves using this option Mastercam creates the helix with arc (G2/G3) moves. If this option is disabled the helix will be created with many small linear moves.

Z clearance is extra height used in the ramping motion down from a top profile. It ensures the tool has fully slowed down from the rapid speeds before touching the material.

16.5 Set the Linking Parameters

♦ Select **Linking Parameters** and make the necessary changes as shown in Figure: 16.5.1.

Figure: 16.5.1

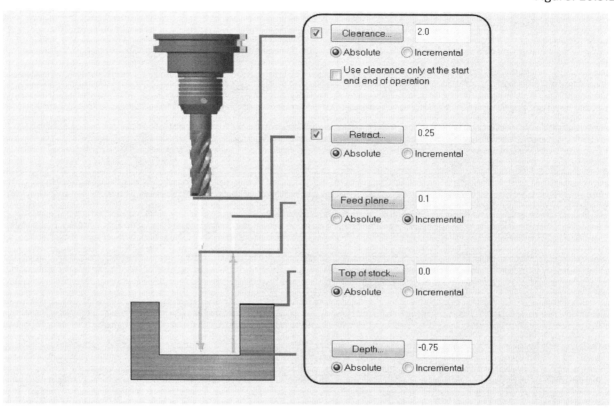

16.6 Set the HST Leads

◆ From the Tree view list, select HST Leads and make any necessary changes as shown in <u>Figure: 16.6.1</u>.

Figure: 16.6.1

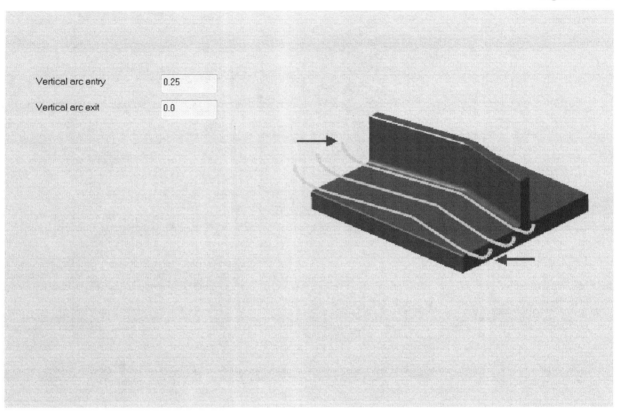

Vertical arc entry   0.25

Vertical arc exit   0.0

HST Leads page allows you to specify an entry and exit arc radius value for the **2D High Speed Toolpaths**. The arc is created vertically to lead on and off the material.

16.7 Set the Arc Filter / Tolerance

◆ Choose **Arc Filter / Tolerance** from the **Tree view list.**
◆ Select **OK** button to accept the warning and make the necessary changes as shown in Figure: 16.7.1.

Figure: 16.7.1

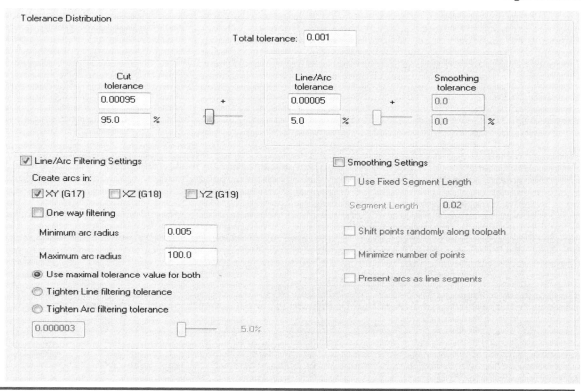

Tolerance Distribution allows you to dynamically adjust the toolpath's total tolerance. Total tolerance is the sum of the cut tolerance and the line/arc and smoothing tolerances. Move the sliders between the **Cut tolerance**, **Line/Arc tolerance** and/or **Smoothing tolerance** fields, the ratios update in 5% increments and the toolpath's total tolerance remains at its current value.

Line/Arc Filtering Settings allows you to activate Line/Arc filtering for the toolpath and apply the settings you define in this section to the toolpath refinement. Toolpath filtering lets you replace multiple very small linear moves — within the filter tolerance — with single arc moves to simplify the toolpath. Smoothing distributes a toolpath's node points, avoiding the clustering and grouping of points that can cause marks and other imperfections.

Create arcs in creates arcs in the selected plane. Your post processor must be able to handle arcs and output the code G17, G18, G19 to select this option.

◆ Select the **OK** button once the parameters have been set.

STEP 17: BACKPLOT THE TOOLPATHS

◆ Make sure that the toolpaths are selected (signified by the green check mark on the folder icon). If the operation is not selected choose the **Select all operations** icon.

◆ Select the **Backplot selected operations** button.

NOTE: Mastercam launches a new window that allows you to check the part using **Backplot** or **Verify**. For more information on how to set and use **Backplot** and **Verify** please check Tutorial 2 page 152.

◆ Select the **Play** button in the **VCR** bar to run **Backplot**.
◆ After Backplot is completed the toolpath should look as shown.

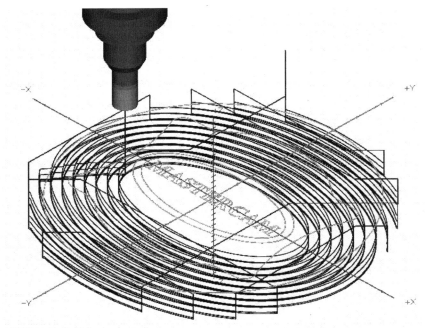

STEP 18: SIMULATE THE TOOLPATH IN VERIFY

◆ From **Mastercam Backplot Home** tab, switch to **Verify** and change the settings for the **Visibility** and **Focus** as shown in Figure: 18.0.1.

Figure: 18.0.1

◆ Select the **Play** button in the **VCR** bar to run **Verify**.

◆ The part should appear as shown in Figure: 18.0.2.

Figure: 18.0.2

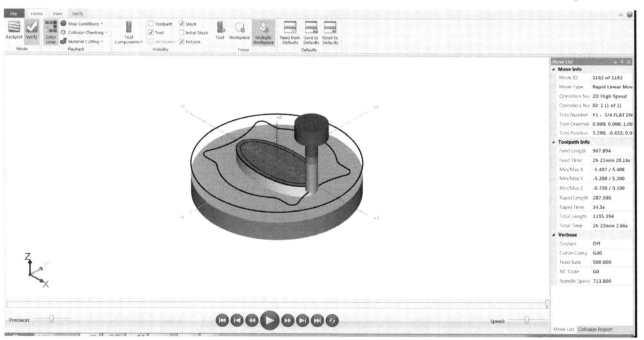

◆ To go back to Mastercam window, minimize **Mastercam Simulator** window as shown.

STEP 19: 2D HIGH SPEED DYNAMIC MILL

In this step you will machine the outside profile using **2D HS Dynamic Mill** toolpath which machines pockets, material that other toolpaths left behind, and standing bosses or cores using the entire flute length.

The toolpath supports many powerful entry methods, including a custom entry method. Entry methods and micro lifts support custom feeds and speeds to optimize and generate safe tool motion.

The toolpath depends on the **Machining strategy** that you choose in the **Chain Options.** If the strategy choosed is From outside, the toolpaths starts at the outmost chain and works its way in taking on the final shape of the part as it approaches the final pass. You can also machine pockets in which case the strategy selected is Start inside which keeps the tool inside the machining regions.

Toolpath Preview:

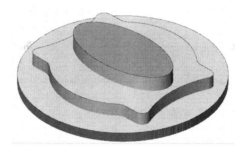

19.1 Chain Selection

- To remove the toolpath display press **Alt + T** or click on the **Toggle display on selected operations** in the **Toolpaths Manager.**

TOOLPATHS
- **2D High speed.**

- 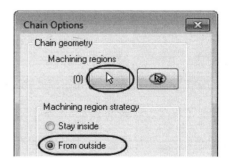 **Dynamic Mill.**

- In the **Chaining Options** dialog box, **Machining regions**, enable **From outside** and click on the **Select** button as shown.

◆ Leave the default setting in the **Chaining** dialog box.

◆ [2D HST machining chain 1]: Pick the first chain as shown in Figure: 19.1.1.

Figure: 19.1.1

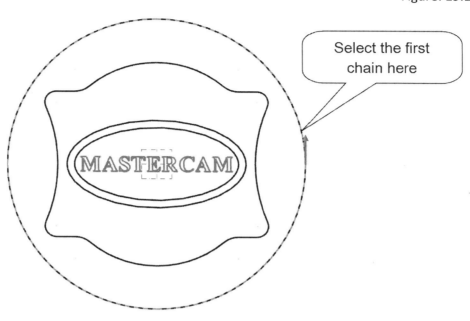

Select the first
chain here

◆ Select the **OK** button to exit the **Chaining** dialog box.

◆ In the **Chain Options** dialog box, **Avoidance regions**, click on the **Select** button as shown.

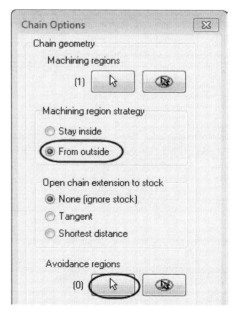

• [Select 2D HST avoidance chain 1]: Select the chain as shown in <u>Figure: 19.1.2</u>.

Figure: 19.1.2

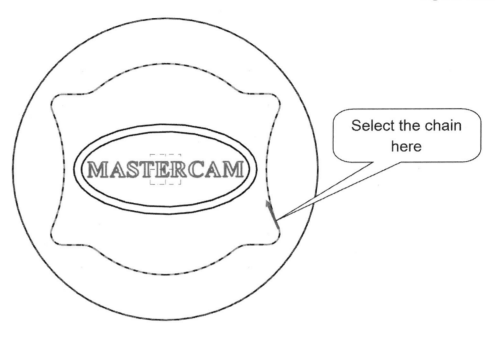

Select the chain here

• Select the **OK** button to exit the **Chaining** dialog box.

• Select the **OK** button exit the **Chain Options** dialog box.

• In the **Toolpath Type** page, the **Dynamic Mill** should already be selected as shown.

 Dynamic Mill   Area Mill   Dynamic Contour   Peel Mill   Blend Mill

19.2 Select the existing 3/4" Flat endmill from the list and set the Tool Parameters

◆ Make all the necessary changes as shown in Figure: 19.2.1.

Figure: 19.2.1

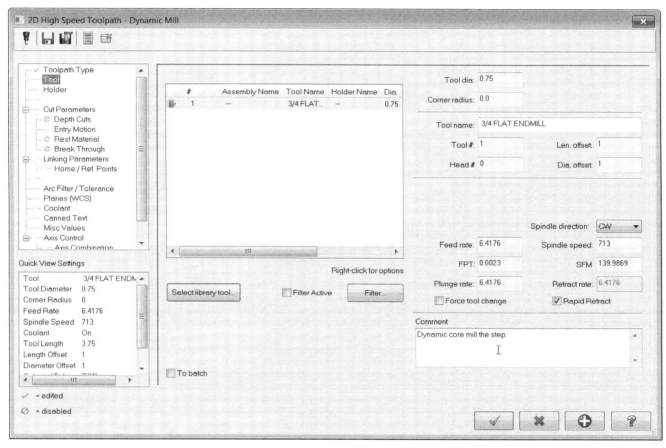

19.3 Set the Cut Parameters

♦ From the **Tree view list**, select **Cut Parameters**. Input a **Stepover** value of **25%** as shown in Figure: 19.3.1.

Figure: 19.3.1

Approach Distance available only when open pocket machining is selected. Adds the specified absolute distance to the beginning of the toolpaths first cut.

First pass offset offsets out the machining region with a user defined distance for the tool to safely engage from the outside in the material.

First pass feed reduction allows you to slow the feed for the first pass on machining region material approached from the outside.

Stepover sets the distance between cutting passes in the X and Y axis.

Toolpath Radius reduces sharp corner motion between cut passes.

Micro Lift Distance enter the distance the tool lifts off the part on the back moves. Microlifts are slight lifts that help clear chips and minimize excessive tool heating.

Back Feedrate controls the speed of the backfeed movement of the tool.

Retract controls retracts in the toolpath when making a non-cutting move within an area where the tool can be kept down or microlifted.

19.4 Disable the Depth cuts parameters

◆ From the **Tree view list**, select the **Depth Cuts** and make sure is disabled as shown.

☐ Depth cuts

19.5 Set the Entry Motion

◆ From the **Tree view** list, select **Entry Motion**.
◆ Input a **Z clearance** of **0.05** and a **Plunge angle** of **2.0** degrees.
◆ Enable **Entry feeds / speeds** and set a **Ramp feed rate** of **10.0** Inches per minute, a **Ramp spindle speed** of **4000** RPM and **Dwell before cut spindle speed** of **3.0** seconds as shown in Figure: 19.5.1.

Figure: 19.5.1

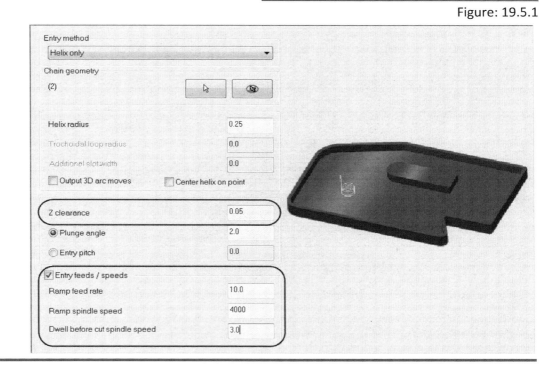

Entry method defines the entry point and cutting strategy used to create the toolpath.

Z clearance adds an extra height used in the ramping motion down from a top profile. It ensures that the tool has fully slowed down from rapid speeds before touching the material.

Plunge angle sets the angle of descent for the entry move, and determines the pitch.

Rapid feed rate overrides the feed rate set on the tools page and uses the specified feed rate for entry ramps into the material.

Ramp spindle speed overrides the spindle speed set in the tools page and uses the specified spindle speed for entry ramps into the material.

19.6 Set the Linking Parameters

◆ Select **Linking Parameters** and input the **Depth** as shown in Figure: 19.6.1.

Figure: 19.6.1

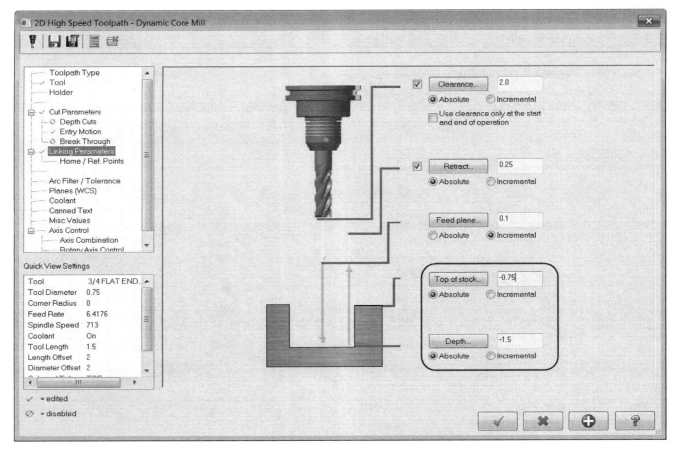

◆ Once complete pick the **OK** button to generate the toolpath.

19.7 Backplot the toolpath

• To **Backplot** the toolpath see page 152 to review this procedure.

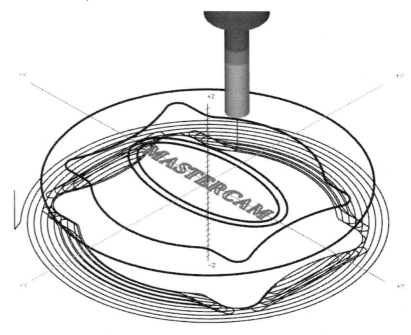

• To go back to Mastercam window, minimize **Mastercam Simulator** window as shown.

19.8 Simulate the toolpaths using Verify

• To select all operations, in the **Toolpaths Manager**, click on the **Select all operation** icon.

• To **Verify** the toolpath see page 155.

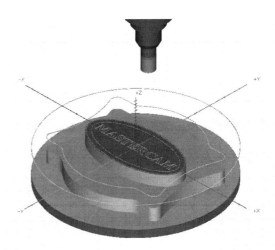

• To go back to Mastercam window, minimize Mastercam Simulator window as shown.

STEP 20: POCKET

Toolpath Preview:

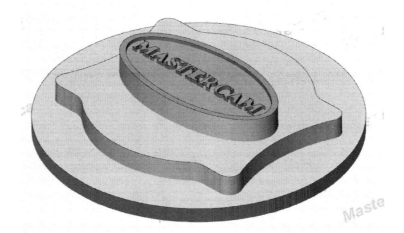

• Press **Alt + T** to remove the toolpath display.

TOOLPATHS

• 🔲 **Pocket.**

20.1 Select the Geometry

• Choose the **Top** graphics view from the toolbars.

• When the chaining dialog box appears select the **Window** chaining option.

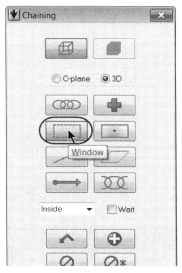

• Create a window around the letters and the inner ellipse as shown in <u>Figure: 20.1.1</u>.

NOTE: Make sure that the window is big enough to include the inside ellipse completed but avoid the outside ellipse.

Figure: 20.1.1

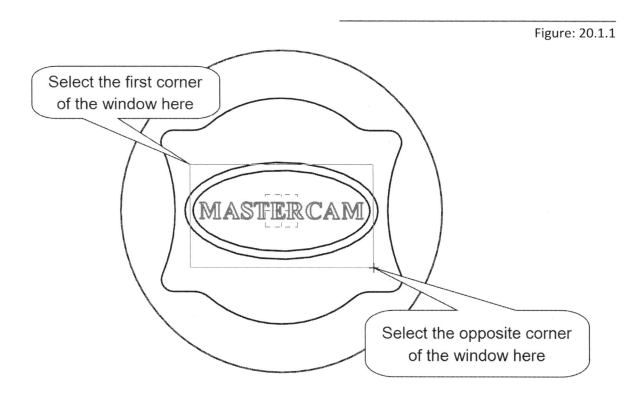

Select the first corner of the window here

Select the opposite corner of the window here

◆ [Sketch approximate start point]: Pick an approximate starting point near the bottom of the letter "M" as shown in Figure: 20.1.2.

Figure: 20.1.2

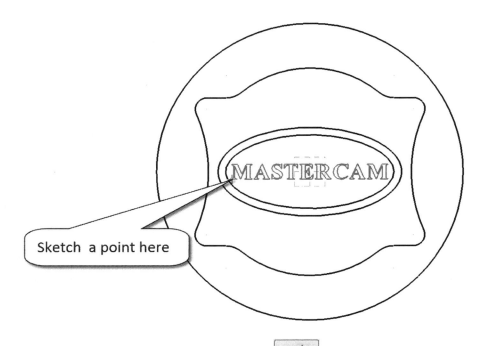

Sketch a point here

◆ Choose the **OK** button to exit the **Chaining** dialog box.
◆ On the **Toolpath Type** page **Pocket** will be picked.

Contour   Pocket   Facing   Slot Mill

20.2 Select a 1/8" Flat endmill from the library and set the Tool Parameters

◆ Select **Tool** from the **Tree view** list.

◆ Click on **Select library tool** button.
◆ Select the **Filter** button.

Mastercam. X

◆ Select the **None** button and then under **Tool Types** choose the **Flat Endmill** icon.
◆ Under tool diameter pick **Equal** and input a value **0.125** as shown in <u>Figure: 20.2.1</u>.

Figure: 20.2.1

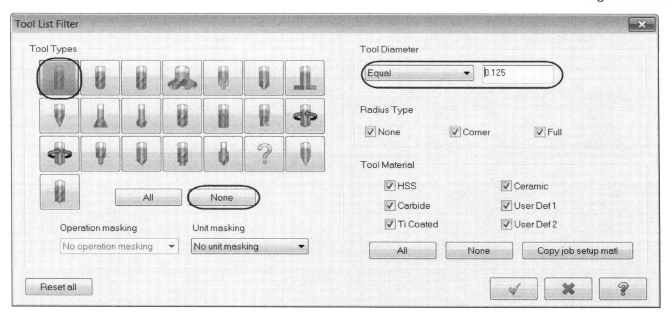

◆ Select the **OK** button to exit the **Tool List Filter.**
◆ In the **Tool Selection** dialog box you should only see a **1/8" Flat Endmill**.

#	Assembly Name	Tool Name	Holder Name	Dia.	Cor. rad.	Length	# Flutes	Type	Rad. Type
232	--	1/8 FLAT...	--	0...	0.0	0.375	4	En...	None

◆ Select the **1/8" Flat Endmill** in the **Tool Selection** page and then select the **OK** button to exit.

◆ Make all the necessary changes as shown in Figure: 20.2.2.

Figure: 20.2.2

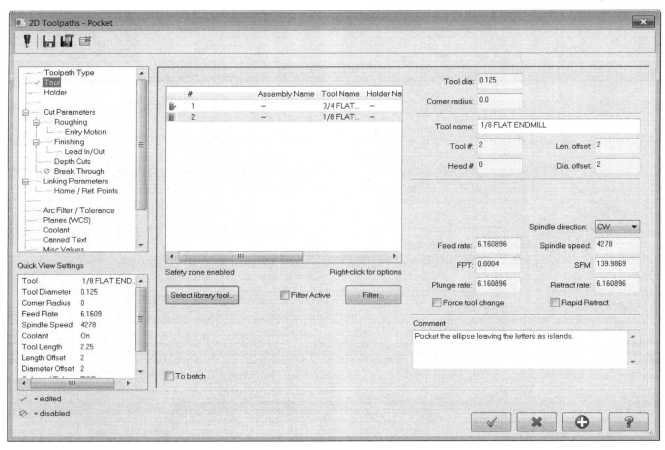

20.3 Set the Cut Parameters

- From the **Tree view** list select **Cut Parameters,** and ensure **Pocket type** is set to **Standard** as shown in Figure: 20.3.1.

Figure: 20.3.1

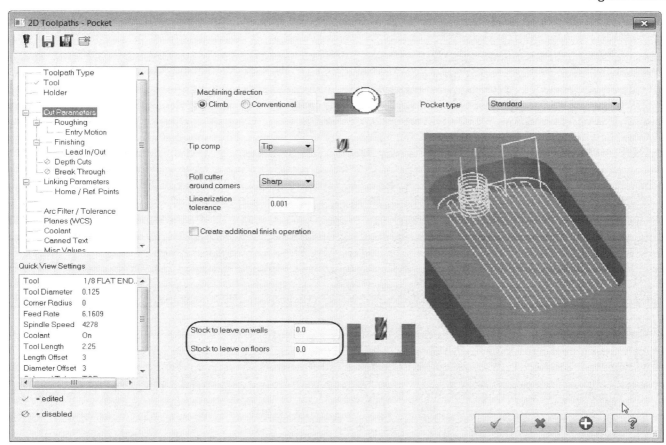

NOTE: Pocket set to Standard will machine the inside of the ellipse leaving the letters as islands with heights at the same level as the top of the pocket.

20.4 Set the Roughing Parameters

• Enable **Roughing** and ensure your parameters appear as shown in Figure: 20.4.1.

Figure: 20.4.1

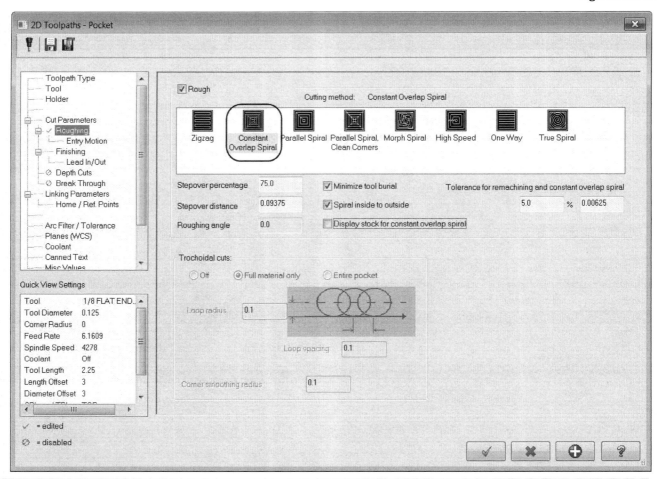

Constant Overlap Spiral creates one roughing pass, determines the remaining stock and recalculates based on the new stock amount. This process repeats until the pocket is cleared.

20.5 Set the Entry Motion

◆ Choose **Entry Motion** from the **tree view list.** Ensure your settings appear as shown in Figure: 20.5.1.

Figure: 20.5.1

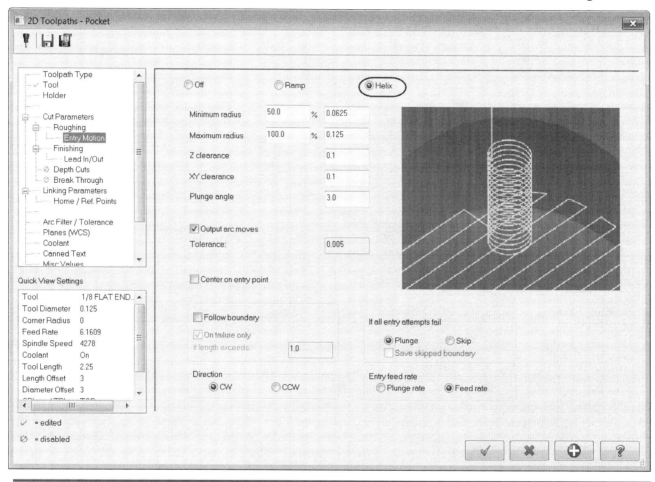

Minimum Radius sets the smallest possible radius for the entry helix.

Maximum Radius sets the largest possible radius for the entry helix.

20.6 Set the Finishing Parameters

♦ Select **Finishing** and ensure you options appear as shown in Figure: 20.6.1.

Figure: 20.6.1

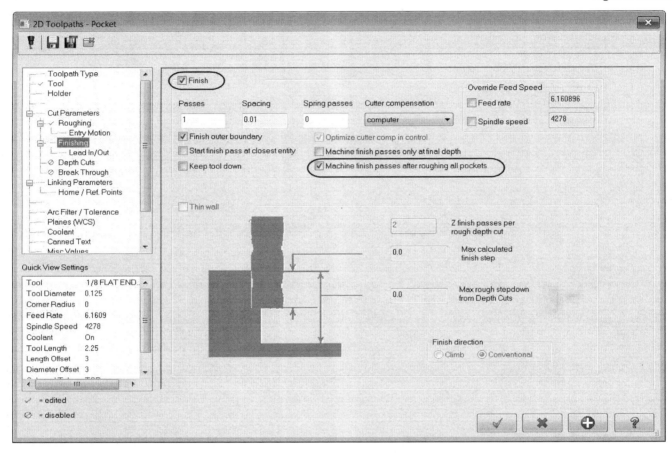

20.7 Set the Lead In/Out Parameters

◆ Select **Lead In/Out** from the **Tree view list.** Set the length and arc percentage to **60%** and input an **Arc Sweep** of **90** degrees as shown in <u>Figure: 20.7.1</u>.

Figure: 20.7.1

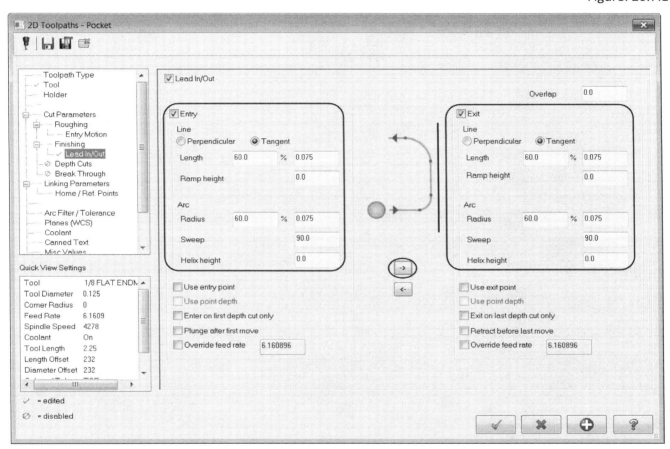

20.8 Setup Depth Cuts Parameters

♦ Pick **Depth Cuts** and enable this option. Set the **Max rough step** to **0.05** as shown in <u>Figure: 20.8.1</u>.

Figure: 20.8.1

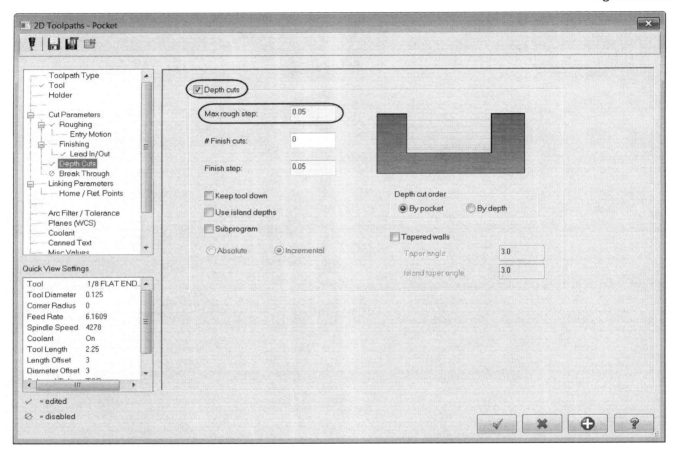

Mill Level 1 Training Tutorial **Mastercam. X⁸**

20.9 Set the Linking Parameters

• Choose **Linking Parameters** and input a final **Depth** of **-0.125** as shown in Figure: 20.9.1.

Figure: 20.9.1

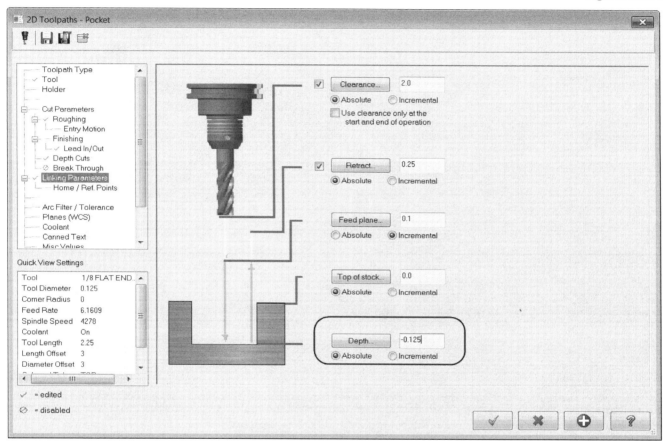

• Select the **OK** button to exit the **Pocket** parameters.

20.10 Backplot and Verify the toolpath

♦ To **Backplot** and **Verify** your toolpath see page 152 to review these procedures.

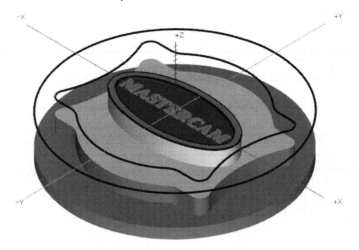

NOTE: To better see the machined part make the tool invisible by clicking twice on the square in front of the **Tool** in the **Visibility** area.

STEP 21: POCKET REMACHINING

Pocket Remachining is only used with closed chains. It calculates areas where the pocket roughing tool could not machine the stock and creates a remachining pocket toolpath to clear the remaining material.

Toolpath Preview:

21.1 Select the Geometry

TOOLPATHS

* **Pocket.**
* When the **Chaining** dialog box appears choose the **Last** button to reselect the chains used in the previous toolpath.

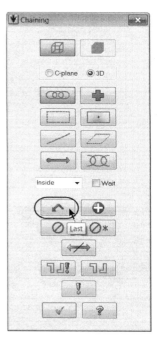

* Select the **OK** button to exit the chaining dialog box.
* On the **Toolpath Type** page **Pocket** will be picked.

Contour   Pocket   Facing   Slot Mill

21.2 Select a 1/32" Flat endmill from the library and set the Tool Parameters

* Select **Tool** from the **Tree view list**.

* Click on **Select library tool** button. `Select library tool...`
* Select the **Filter** button.

- Select the **None** button and then under **Tool Types** choose the **Flat Endmill** Icon.
- Under tool diameter pick **Equal** and input a value **0.03125** as shown in Figure: 21.2.1.

Figure: 21.2.1

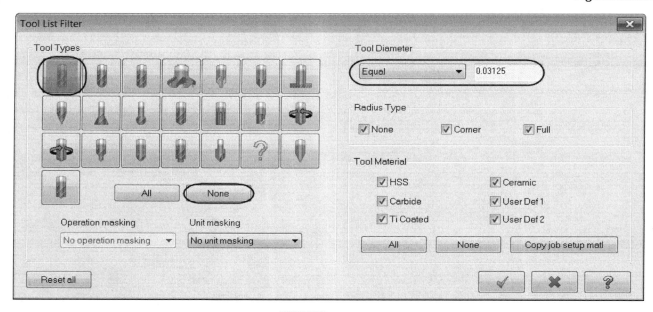

- Select the **OK** button to exit the **Tool List Filter.**
- In the **Tool Selection** dialog box you should only see a **1/32" Flat Endmill**.

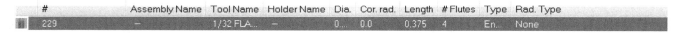

#	Assembly Name	Tool Name	Holder Name	Dia.	Cor. rad.	Length	# Flutes	Type	Rad. Type
229	—	1/32 FLA...	—	0...	0.0	0.375	4	En...	None

- Select the **1/32" Flat Endmill** in the **Tool Selection** page and then select the **OK** button to exit.

◆ Make all the necessary changes as shown in <u>Figure: 21.2.2</u>.

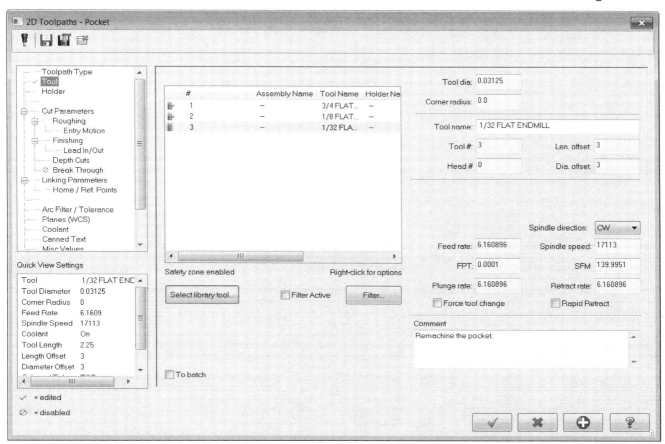

21.3 Set the Cut Parameters

◆ Select **Cut Parameters** and change the **Pocket Type** to **Remachining.**

NOTE: The standard pocket removes the material inside of a closed boundary while the remachining pocket removes only the remaining material that a previous toolpath could not clean due to the tool size.

◆ Ensure your settings appear as shown in <u>Figure: 21.3.1</u>.

Figure: 21.3.1

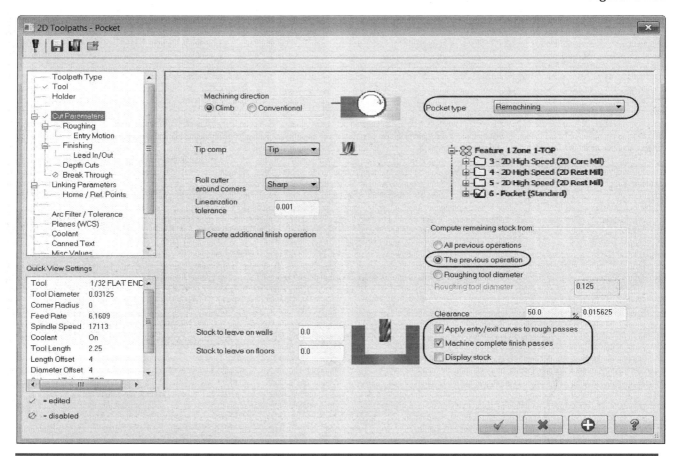

Compute remaining stock from The previous operation determines remaining stock for remachining by calculating stock removed during the previous toolpath.

Clearance extends the remachining toolpath at the beginning and end to prevent cusps of material from being left behind.

21.4 Set the Roughing Parameters

♦ Choose **Roughing** and change the **Stepover percentage** to **55** as shown in <u>Figure: 21.4.1</u>.

Figure: 21.4.1

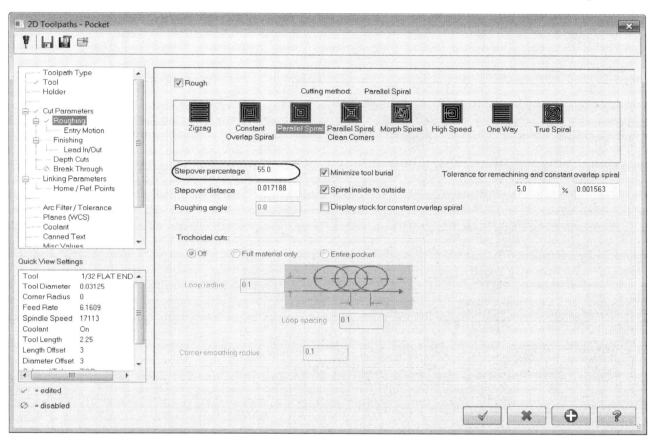

NOTE: The **Cutting method** is defined by the **Pocket type** and can not be modified for **Remachining**. The **Finishing**, **Lead In/Out** and **Depth Cuts** parameters are the same as the previous toolpath therefore we do not need to view them.

21.5 Set the Linking Parameters

* Choose **Linking Parameters**, and set the **Depth** to **-0.125** as shown in <u>Figure: 21.5.1</u>.

Figure: 21.5.1

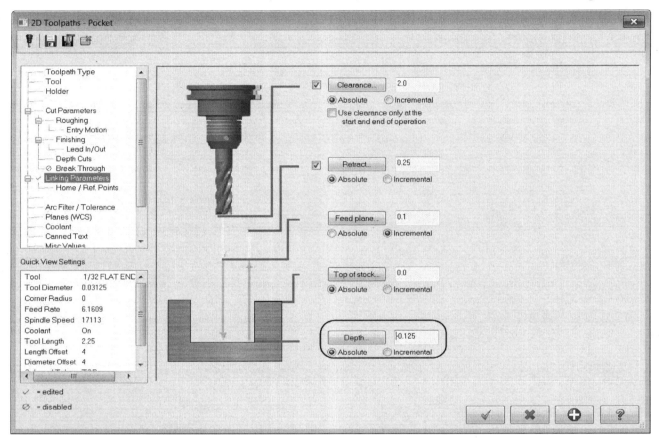

* Select the **OK** button to exit the pocket parameters.

21.6 Backplot and Verify the toolpaths

♦ To **Backplot** and **Verify** your toolpath page 152 to review these procedures.

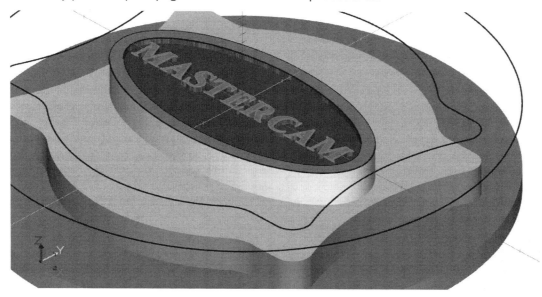

♦ To exit exit **Mastercam Simulator** select the close button as shown.

STEP 22: POST THE FILE

◆ Ensure all operations are selected, if they are not use the button **Select all operations** in the **Toolpaths Manager.**

◆ Select the **Post selected operations** button from the **Toolpaths Manager.**

◆ In the **Post processing** window make the necessary changes as shown in Figure: 22.0.1.

Figure: 22.0.1

NC File enabled allows you to keep the NC file and to assign the same name as the MCX file.

Edit enabled allows you to automatically launch the default editor.

◆ Select the **OK** button to continue.

◆ Save the NC file.

♦ A window with **Mastercam Code Expert** will be launcheded and the NC program will appear as shown in Figure: 22.0.2.

Figure: 22.0.2

```
D · 🖉 🖫 ↶ ↷ | ╤          Editor          Your Name_3.nc - Mastercam Code Expert                    — □ ×
File    Home    View    NC Functions                                                                      ⌃ ●

        Insert Block Numbers      Insert Block Skip      Send File      ◄◄  ◄  ►  ►►   ◄◄  ◄  ►  ►►   □□      ▭
Go To   Remove Block Numbers      Remove Block Skip      Send        First Previous Next Last  First Previous Next Last  Multi-Stream   NC
        Remove Spaces             Remove Comments        Receive                                                        Configuration
                Editing                  Communications                Syncs              Tools          Utilities

  Start Page    Setup #1.nc    Setup #2.nc    Your Name_3.nc ×
   1    %
   2    O0003(YOUR NAME_3)
   3    (DATE=DD-MM-YY - 07-02-14 TIME=HH:MM - 10:01)
   4    (MCX FILE - \\IHSSERVER04\BOOKDEV\PRODUCTION\BOOKS\X8\TRAINING TUTORIALS\TT MILL LEVEL 1\MCX FILES\YOUR NAME_3.MCX-8)
   5    (NC FILE - C:\USERS\MARIANA.LENDEL\DOCUMENTS\MY MCAMX8\MILL\NC\YOUR NAME_3.nc)
   6    (MATERIAL - ALUMINUM INCH - 2024)
   7    ( T1 |   3/4 FLAT ENDMILL | H1 )
   8    ( T2 |   1/8 FLAT ENDMILL | H2 )
   9    ( T3 |   1/32 FLAT ENDMILL | H3 )
  10    N100 G20
  11    N110 G0 G17 G40 G49 G80 G90
  12    ( MACHINE THE ELLIPTICAL SHAPE AS A BOSS. )
  13    N120 T1 M6
  14    N130 G0 G90 G54 X2.0118 Y-5.0152 A0. S713 M3
  15    N140 G43 H1 Z.1
  16    N150 G1 Z-.2333 F6.42
  17    N160 G3 X1.9718 Y-4.9924 I-.04 J-.0236
  18    N170 X1.962 Y-4.9934 I0. J-.0464
  19    N180 G2 X.0273 Y-5.2001 I-1.9347 J8.9494
  20    N190 G1 X.0002
  21    N200 X-.0221
  22    N210 G2 X-1.9622 Y-4.9936 I0. J9.2147
  23    N220 G3 X-1.972 Y-4.9926 I-.0098 J-.0453
  24    N230 X-2.0154 Y-5.0227 I0. J-.0463
  25    N240 G0 Z0.
  26    N250 Z.1
  27    N260 X3.3677 Y-4.2358
  28    N270 G1 Z-.2333
  29    N280 G3 X3.3304 Y-4.217 I-.0373 J-.0276
  30    N290 X3.3118 Y-4.221 I0. J-.0464
  31    N300 G2 X2.551 Y-4.4992 I-2.5613 J5.8234
  32    N310 X.0241 Y-4.8676 I-2.5269 J8.482

 Find Extents                                                                                                      ⌄
 Ready                                                                       Ln 1/24835  Col 1  597.33KB   100% ⊖ ── ⊕
```

♦ Select the red **"X"** box at the upper right corner to exit the editor.

STEP 23: SAVE THE UPDATED MCX FILE

REVIEW EXERCISE - STUDENT PRACTICE

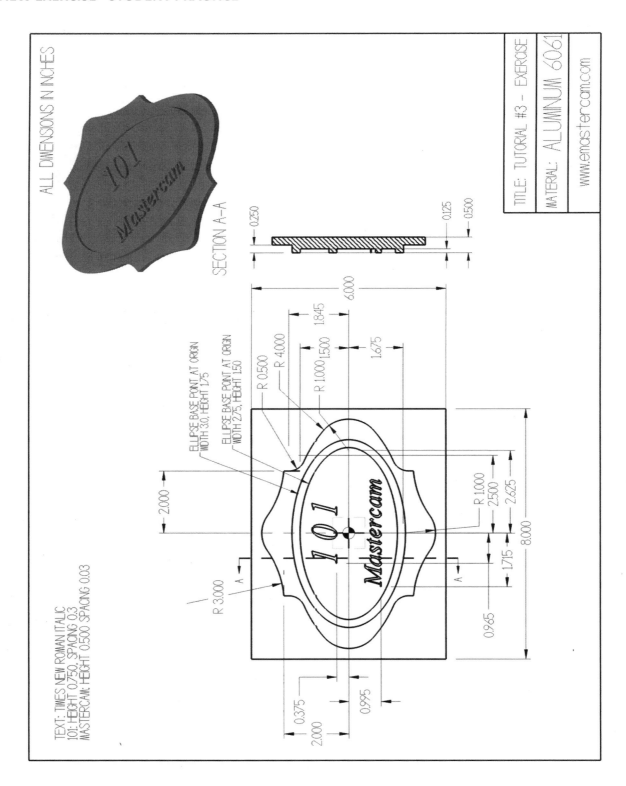

ALL DIMENSIONS IN INCHES

SECTION A-A

TITLE: TUTORIAL #3 - EXERCISE

MATERIAL: ALUMINUM 6061

www.emastercam.com

0.250

0.125
0.500

6.000

1.845

R 0.500

R 4.000

R 1.000 1.500

1.675

ELLIPSE BASE POINT AT ORIGIN
WIDTH 3.0, HEIGHT 1.75

ELLIPSE BASE POINT AT ORIGIN
WIDTH 2.75, HEIGHT 1.50

2.000

R 1.000
2.500
2.625

8.000

1.715

0.965

R 3.000

TEXT: TIMES NEW ROMAN ITALIC
101: HEIGHT 0.750, SPACING 0.3
MASTERCAM: HEIGHT 0.500 SPACING 0.03

0.375

2.000

0.995

Mastercam.X[8]

CREATE THE GEOMETRY FOR TUTORIAL #3 EXERCISE

Use these commands to create the geometry:
◆ Create Arc Circle Center Point.
◆ Create Horizontal line.
◆ Create Arc Tangent 2 Entities.
◆ Trim/Break/Extend.
◆ Xform Mirror.
◆ Create Ellipse.

CREATE THE TOOLPATHS FOR TUTORIAL #3 EXERCISE

Create the Toolpaths for Tutorial #3 Exercise as per the instructions below.

Set the machine properties including the stock setup.
- Remove the material around the part using Core Mill.
- Use a 1" Flat Endmill.
- Enable Corner Rounding.
- Set the Entry method.
- Use Depth Cuts.
- Enable Break through.
- Set the Depth according to the drawing.

Remove the material at the step using Dynamic Mill.
- Chain the outer profile in Machining regions.
- Enable **From outside**.
- Chain the outer ellipse in the Avoidance regions.
- Use the 1" Flat Endmill.
- Enable smoothing.
- Disable Depth cuts.
- Set your entry method.
- Disable Break through.
- Set the Depth according to the drawing.

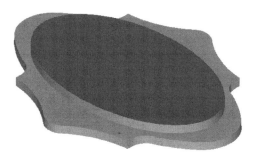

Pocket out the Center.
- Select the inner ellipse and the letters.
- Use a 1/4" Flat Endmill.
- Choose a cutting method.
- Set the Entry Motion.
- Disable Finishing.
- Enable Depth cuts and set a cut depth of 0.125".
- Set the Depth according to the drawing.

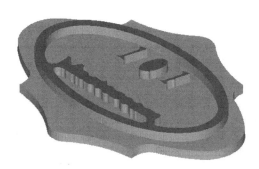

Remachine the Pocket

- Use a 1/16" Flat Endmill.
- Change the Pocket Type to Remachining.
- Disable Display stock.
- Change the Stepover Percentage to 55%.
- Set the Entry Motion.
- Enable Depth cuts and set a cut depth of 0.0625".
- Set the Depth according to the drawing.

NOTES:

TUTORIAL #3 QUIZ

◆ What does Area Mill do?

◆ What does smoothing do?

◆ What does pocket remachining do?

TUTORIAL #4

OVERVIEW OF STEPS TAKEN TO CREATE THE FINAL PART:

From Drawing to CAD Model:
* The student should examine the drawing on the following page to understand what part is being created in the tutorial.
* From the drawing we can decide how to go about creating the geometry in Mastercam.

Create the 2D CAD Model used to generate Toolpaths from:
* The student will create the Top 2D geometry needed to create the toolpaths.
* Geometry creation commands such as circle center point, line tangent, mirror, arc tangent, arc polar, trim, fillet, rotate and translate will be used.

Create the necessary Toolpaths to machine the part:
* The student will set up the stock size and the clamping method used. Two setups will be used to machine the part from the top and then from the bottom.
* A 2D High Speed Area Mill toolpath will be created to remove the material inside of the step.
* A 2D High Speed Dynamic Mill toolpath will be created to remove the material inside of the deeper pockets.
* A 2D High Speed Area Mill toolpath will be created to remove the material inside of the smaller pocket.
* Transform-Rotate toolpath is used to machine the rest of the smaller pocket.
* Two Drill toolpath will be created to machine the holes.
* A Circle Mill toolpath will be created to remove the material inside of the center hole.
* A Contour-Chamfer toolpath will be created to chamfer all edges.
* A 2D High Speed Dynamic Mill toolpath will be created to remove the material inside of the part from the bottom.

Backplot and Verify the file:
* The Backplot will be used to simulate a step by step process of the tool's movements.
* The Verify will be used to watch a tool machine the part out of a solid model.

Post Process the file to generate the G-code:
* The Student will then post process the file to obtain an NC file containing the necessary code for the machine.

 This tutorial takes approximately two hours to complete.

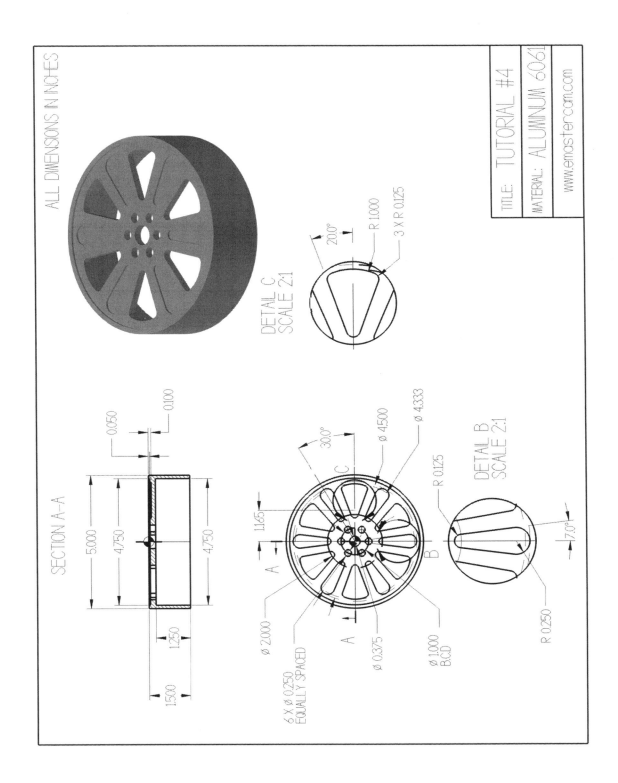

ALL DIMENSIONS IN INCHES

DETAIL C
SCALE 2:1

20.0°
R 1.000
3 X R 0.125

SECTION A-A

0.050
0.100

5.000
4.750
4.750
1.250
1.500

30.0°
Ø 4.500
Ø 4.333

1.165

C

A

A

A

R 0.125

DETAIL B
SCALE 2:1

R 0.250
7.0°

6 X Ø 0.250
EQUALLY SPACED
Ø 2.000
Ø 0.375
Ø 1.000
B.C.D

TITLE: TUTORIAL #4
MATERIAL: ALUMINUM 6061
www.emastercam.com

GEOMETRY CREATION

STEP 1: SETTING UP THE GRAPHIC USER INTERFACE

Please refer to the Getting Started section to set up the graphics user interface.

STEP 2: CREATE ARCS

In this step you will create the arcs used for the main body of the part.

Step Preview:

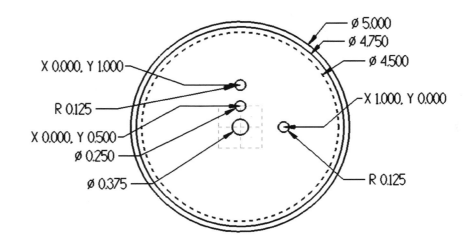

2.1 Create Circles

CREATE

◆ **Arc.**

◆ **Circle Center Point.**

◆ Enter the **Diameter** of **5.0**.

◆ [Enter the center point]: Select the **Origin** as shown in <u>Figure: 2.1.1</u>.

Figure: 2.1.1

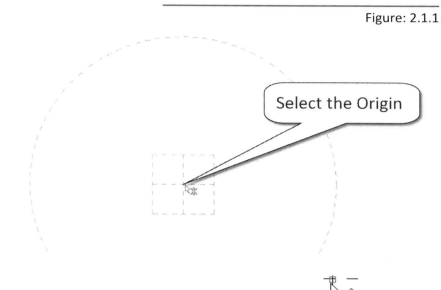

Select the Origin

◆ Make sure that when selecting the origin, the visual cue of the cursor changes as shown.

◆ Choose the **Apply** button to continue.

NOTE: During the geometry creation of this tutorial, if you make a mistake you can undo the last step using the **Undo** icon. You can undo as many steps as needed. If you delete or undo a step by mistake, just use the **Redo** icon. To delete unwanted geometry, select it first and then press **Delete** from the keyboard.

◆ Use the **Fit** icon to fit the drawing to the screen.

◆ Enter a **Diameter** value of **4.75**.
◆ [Enter the center point]: Select the **Origin**.

◆ Choose the **Apply** button to continue.

◆ Enter a **Diameter** value of **0.375**.
◆ [Enter the center point]: Select the **Origin**.

◆ Choose the **Apply** button to continue.

◆ Enter a **Diameter** value of **0.25** and lock the value by selecting the diameter icon as shown.

• [Enter the center point]: Select the **Fast Point** icon.
• Enter the coordinates as shown and hit **Enter** on your keyboard.

0,0.5

• Choose the **Apply** button to continue.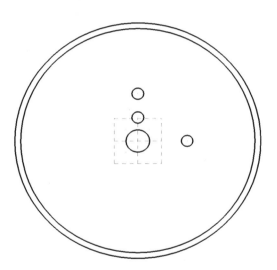

• [Enter the center point]: Select the **Fast Point** icon.
• Enter the coordinate value of **1, 0** and hit **Enter** on your keyboard.

• Choose the **Apply** button to continue.

• [Enter the center point]: Select the **Fast Point** icon.
• Enter the coordinate value of **0, 1**and hit **Enter** on your keyboard.

• Choose the **OK** button to continue.
• The geometry should look as shown.

2.2 Change the Line Style and create the 4.5"diameter circle

• Left click on the **Line Style** options in the **Status Bar** as shown in Figure: 2.2.1.

Figure: 2.2.1

• Select from the list the **hidden line style** (2nd style in the list) as shown in Figure: 2.2.2.

Figure: 2.2.2

CREATE

• **Arc.**

• 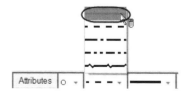 **Circle Center Point.**

• Click on the **Diameter** icon to unlock the value.

• Enter the **Diameter** of **4.5**.

• [Select position for the center of the arc]: Select the **Origin**.

• Choose the **OK** button to continue.

2.3Change the Line Style back to Solid

• Left click on the **Line Style** options in the **Status Bar** as shown in Figure: 2.3.1.

Figure: 2.3.1

• Select from the list the **solid line style** (1st style in the list) as shown in Figure: 2.3.2.

Figure: 2.3.2

◆ The geometry should look as shown.

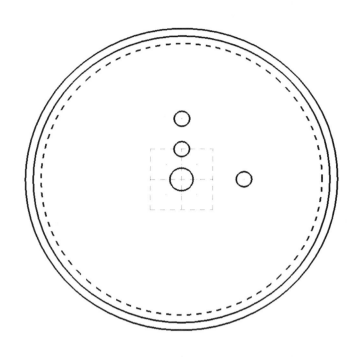

STEP 3: CREATE TANGENT LINES

In this step you will learn how to create tangent lines knowing the angle of the lines.

Step Preview:

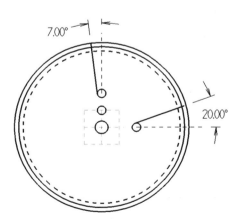

CREATE
◆ **Line.**

◆  **Endpoint.**

- In the **Ribbon Bar** ensure the **Tangent** option is on and **Vertical** or **Horizontal** are not enabled as shown.

- Select the **Zoom Window** button  and zoom in on the area as shown in Figure: 3.0.1.

Figure: 3.0.1

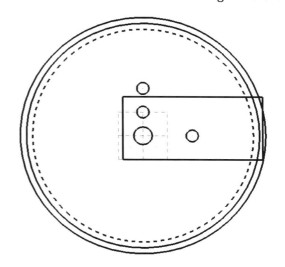

- Select the arc as shown in Figure: 3.0.2.

NOTE: Make sure that you are not selecting any endpoints, midpoints or quadrants from the arc. If you select one of these points Mastercam snaps to the points and disregards the tangent option.

Figure: 3.0.2

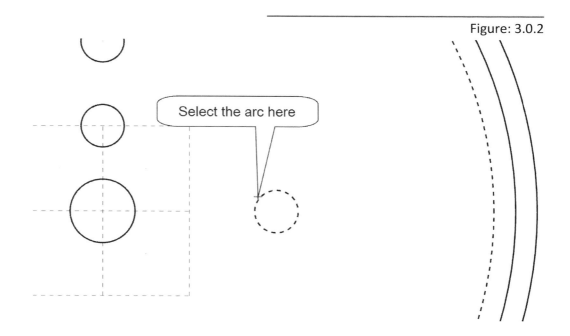

Select the arc here

◆ Sketch a line at any angle to the point as shown in Figure: 3.0.3.

Figure: 3.0.3

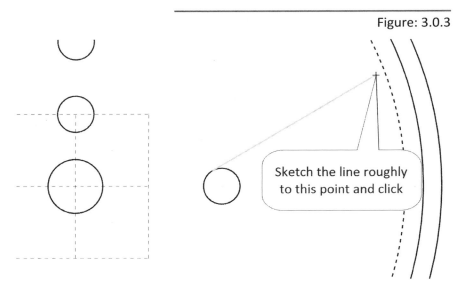

Sketch the line roughly to this point and click

◆ In the **Ribbon bar** enter a line **Length** of **1.5** and an **Angle** of **20**.

◆ Hit **Enter** on your keyboard to preview this line.

◆ Choose the **Apply** button to continue making lines.

◆ Pick the **Fit** button.

◆ Select the **Zoom Window** button and zoom in on the area as shown in Figure: 3.0.4.

Figure: 3.0.4

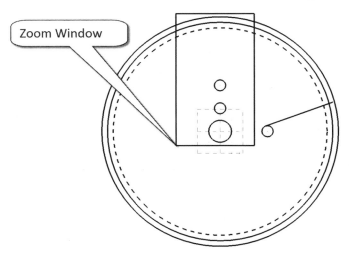

Zoom Window

Mastercam. X⁸

• Select the arc as shown in Figure: 3.0.5.

NOTE: Make sure that you are not selecting any endpoints, midpoints or quadrants from the arc. If you select one of these points Mastercam snaps to the points and disregards the tangent option.

Figure: 3.0.5

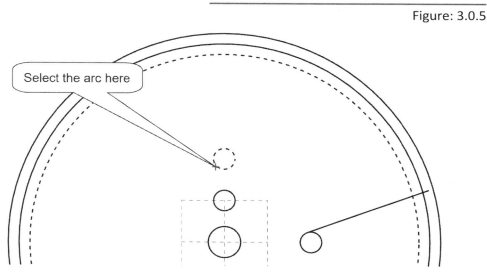

Select the arc here

• Sketch a line at any angle to the point as shown in Figure: 3.0.6.

Figure: 3.0.6

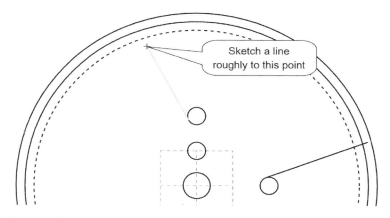

Sketch a line
roughly to this point

• In the Ribbon bar enter a line **Length** of **1.5** and an **Angle** of **7+90**.

• Hit **Enter** to preview this line.

• Choose the **OK** button exit the command.

• Pick the **Fit** button.

◆ The drawing should appear as shown.

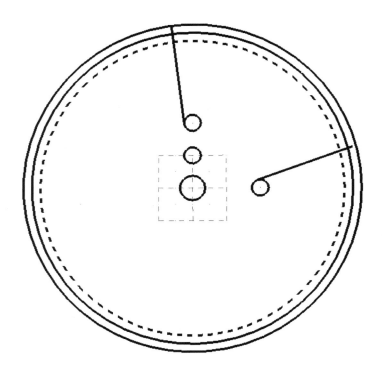

STEP 4: MIRROR THE TANGENT LINES

In this step you will learn how to Mirror the lines we created in the previous step.

Step Preview:

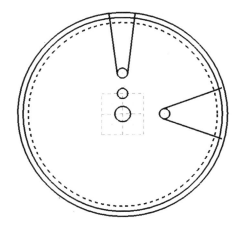

XFORM

- **Mirror.**
- Select the line to mirror it as shown in <u>Figure: 4.0.1</u>.

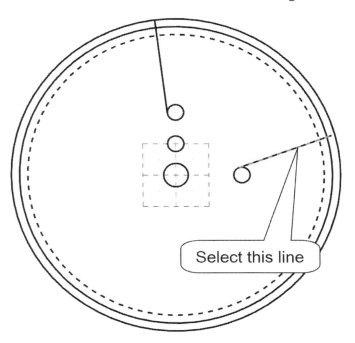

Figure: 4.0.1

Select this line

- Press Enter or select the **End Selection** button.

◆ In the **Mirror** dialog box ensure **Copy** is enabled and pick the option to **Mirror about X axis** as shown in <u>Figure: 4.0.2</u>.

Figure: 4.0.2

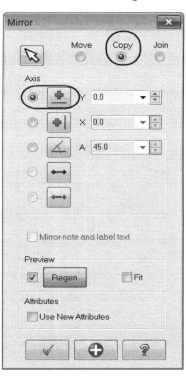

◆ Pick the **Apply** button to select the next line to mirror.
◆ Select the line to mirror as shown in <u>Figure: 4.0.3</u>.

Figure: 4.0.3

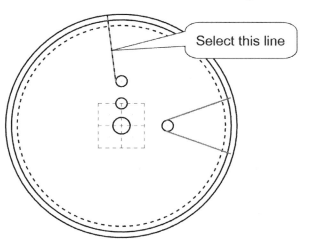

Select this line

◆ Choose the **End Selection** button.

Mastercam. X⁸

- In the **Mirror** dialog box ensure **Copy** is enabled and pick the option to **Mirror about Y axis** as shown in Figure: 4.0.4.

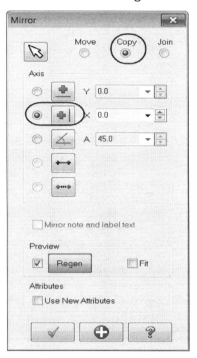

- Choose the **OK** button to exit the command.

- Pick the **Clear Colors** icon to return the colors to the original system colors.
- The geometry should look as shown.

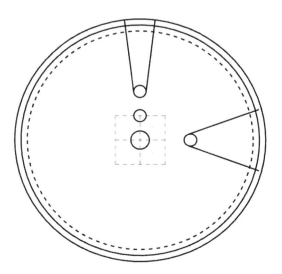

STEP 5: CREATE ARC TANGENT

In this step you will learn how to create an arc tangent to 3 entities.

Step Preview:

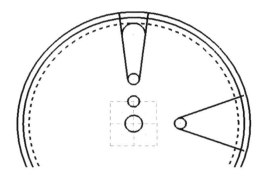

CREATE
* **Arc.**

* **Arc Tangent.**

* Choose the **Arc Tangent 3 Entities** button in the **Ribbon bar**.
* Pick the entities in the order as shown in Figure: 5.0.1.

Figure: 5.0.1

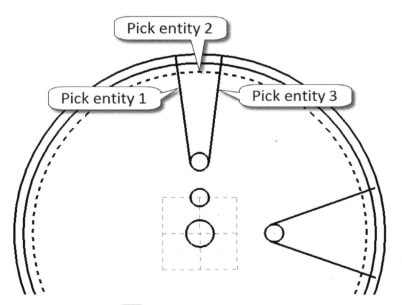

* Select the **OK** button to exit the **Create Arc Tangent** command.

STEP 6: CREATE ARC POLAR

In this step you will learn how to create an arc polar, knowing the center point, radius, start angle and end angle.

Step Preview:

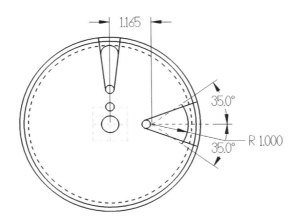

CREATE
* **Arc.**

*  **Arc Polar.**

* Choose the **Fast Point** icon to enter the center point.
* Input the coordinates **1.165, 0** as shown.

```
1.165,0
```

* Press **Enter**.

* Enter the arc **Radius** of **1.0**, a **Start Angle** of **-35.0** degrees and a **End Angle** of **35.0**.

* Select the **OK** button to exit the command.

* Select **Fit** screen.

STEP 7: TRIM THE LINES

In this step you will learn how to Trim 3 entities and use the Divide function.

Step Preview:

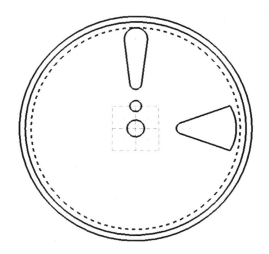

EDIT
- ◆ **Trim / Break.**

- ◆  **Trim / Break/ Extend.**

- ◆ From the Ribbon bar select the **Trim 3 Entities** button.
- ◆ Choose the entities in the order shown in <u>Figure: 7.0.1</u>.

Figure: 7.0.1

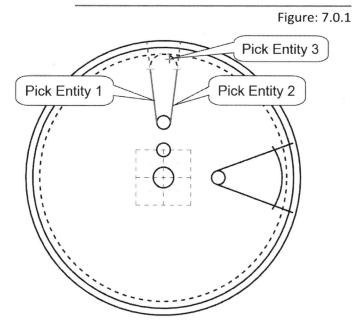

Mastercam.X[8]

• Repeat the step selecting the entities as shown in <u>Figure: 7.0.2</u>.

Figure: 7.0.2

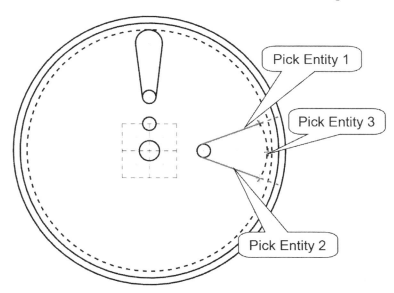

• Repeat the step selecting the entities as shown in <u>Figure: 7.0.3</u>.

Figure: 7.0.3

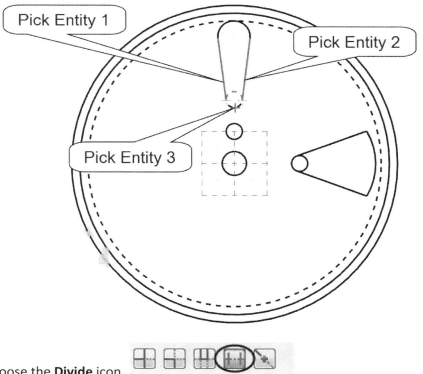

• Once the entities have been picked choose the **Divide** icon.

• Pick the arcs as shown in <u>Figure: 7.0.4</u>.

Figure: 7.0.4

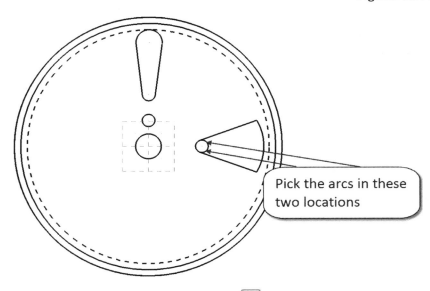

Pick the arcs in these two locations

• Once the arcs have been selected choose the **OK** button to exit the command. ✓
• Your part will appear as shown up to this point.

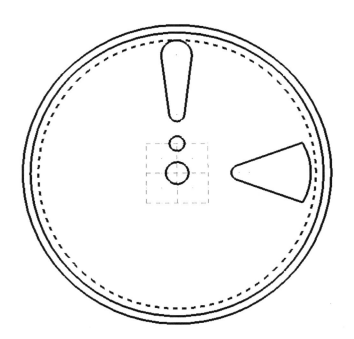

STEP 8: CREATE FILLETS

In this step you will learn how to create filleted corners. Filleted corners apply round corners to sharp corners.

Step Preview:

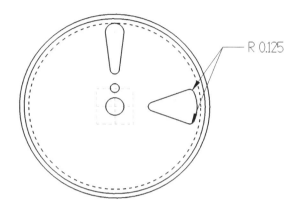

CREATE
* **Fillet.**

* **Entities.**

* Input a **Radius** value of **0.125.**
* Select the entities as shown in <u>Figure: 8.0.1</u>.

Figure: 8.0.1

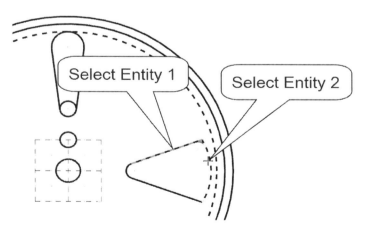

◆ Pick the entities as shown in <u>Figure: 8.0.2</u>.

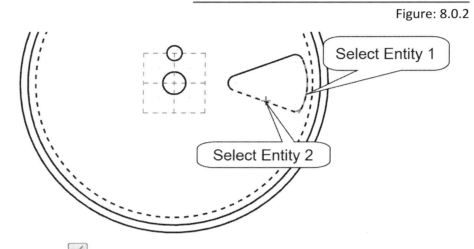

◆ Select the **OK** button to exit the command.

STEP 9: DELETE THE CONSTRUCTION ARC

In this step we will delete the arc.

Step Preview:

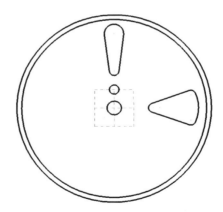

• Select the arc as shown in <u>Figure: 9.0.1</u>.

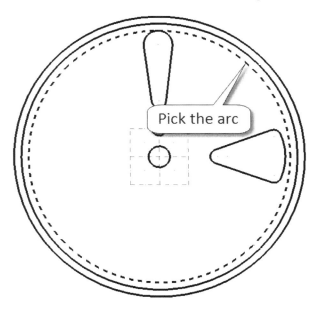

Figure: 9.0.1

Pick the arc

• Click on the **Delete** button from the keyboard.

STEP 10: XFORM ROTATE

In this step you will learn how to rotate entities around a center point by a specified angle.

Step Preview:

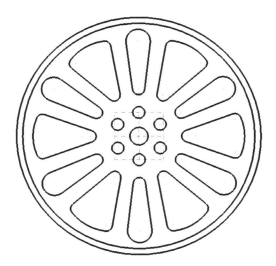

XFORM

♦ **Rotate.**

♦ Hold the **Shift** key and pick the shapes as shown in <u>Figure: 10.0.1</u>.

> **NOTE:** By holding down the **Shift** key and selecting one entity of a chain, Mastercam selects the whole chain.

Figure: 10.0.1

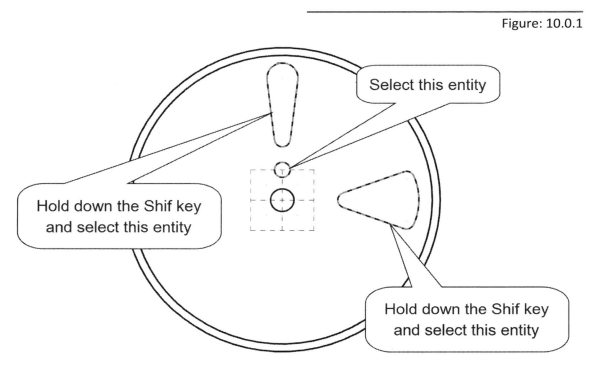

♦ Choose the **End Selection** button.

- When the **Rotate** dialog box appears ensure that **Copy** is enabled and the number of copies **#** is set to **5** as shown in Figure: 10.0.2.
- Choose the option **Angle between** and input **360.0/6** and hit **Enter**.

Figure: 10.0.2

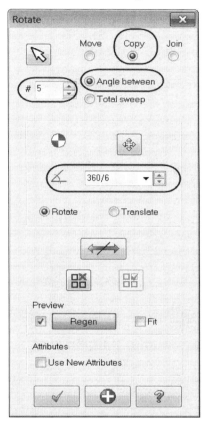

- Select the **OK** button to accept these parameters.

- Pick the **Clear Colors** icon to set the colors back to the system colors.

• The geometry will appear as shown.

STEP 11: XFORM TRANSLATE

In this step you will learn how to translate entities to a different Z depth. This geometry will be used when creating a toolpath from the bottom of the part.

Step Preview:

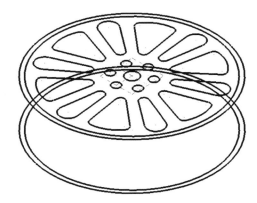

XFORM

+ Translate.

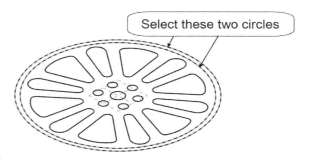

+ Select the graphic view **Isometric** from the toolbars.
+ [Translate: select entities to translate]: Select the two outer circles as shown in Figure: 11.0.1.

Figure: 11.0.1

Select these two circles

+ Choose the **End Selection** button from the ribbon bar.
+ When the **Translate** dialog box appears ensure **Copy** is enabled and input a depth of **-1.5** as shown in Figure: 11.0.2.

Figure: 11.0.2

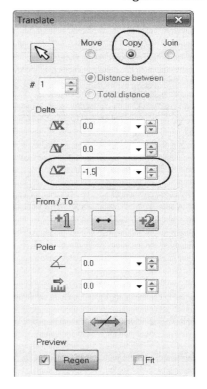

+ Choose the **Apply** button to accept these parameters.

Mastercam. X⁸

Mill Level 1 Training Tutorial

• Hold down the **Shift** key and click on all of the inside hidden lines shapes ithin those two circles as shown in Figure: 11.0.3.

Figure: 11.0.3

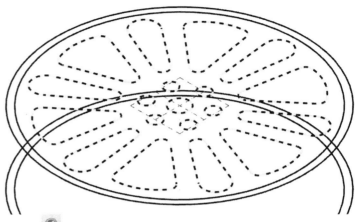

• Choose the **End Selection** button from the ribbon bar.
• When the **Translate** dialog box appears ensure **Move** is enabled and input a depth of **-0.05** as shown in Figure: 11.0.4.

Figure: 11.0.4

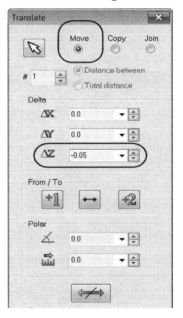

• Choose the **OK** button to accept these parameters.

• Pick the **Clear Colors** icon to set the colors back to the system colors.

◆ The geometry should look as shown.

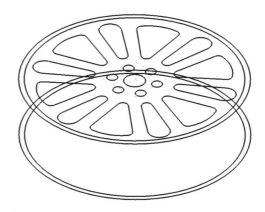

STEP 12: SAVE THE FILE

FILE

◆ **Save As.**
◆ File name: "Your Name_4".

TOOLPATH CREATION - SETUP 1

SUGGESTED FIXTURE 1:

> **NOTE:** In order to machine this part we will have 2 setups and output 2 NC files. To view the second setup see page 391.

SETUP SHEET 1:

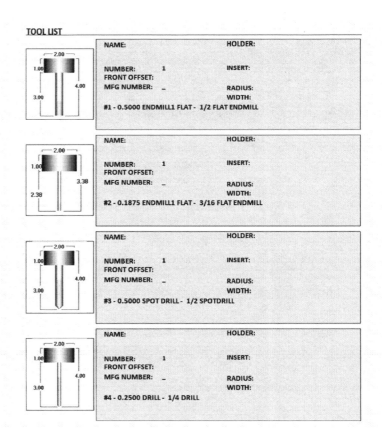

TOOL LIST

	NAME:	HOLDER:
	NUMBER: 1	INSERT:
	FRONT OFFSET:	
	MFG NUMBER: _	RADIUS:
		WIDTH:
	#1 - 0.5000 ENDMILL1 FLAT - 1/2 FLAT ENDMILL	

	NAME:	HOLDER:
	NUMBER: 1	INSERT:
	FRONT OFFSET:	
	MFG NUMBER: _	RADIUS:
		WIDTH:
	#2 - 0.1875 ENDMILL1 FLAT - 3/16 FLAT ENDMILL	

	NAME:	HOLDER:
	NUMBER: 1	INSERT:
	FRONT OFFSET:	
	MFG NUMBER: _	RADIUS:
		WIDTH:
	#3 - 0.5000 SPOT DRILL - 1/2 SPOTDRILL	

	NAME:	HOLDER:
	NUMBER: 1	INSERT:
	FRONT OFFSET:	
	MFG NUMBER: _	RADIUS:
		WIDTH:
	#4 - 0.2500 DRILL - 1/4 DRILL	

STEP 13: SELECT THE MACHINE AND SET UP THE STOCK

In Mastercam, you select a **Machine Definition** before creating any toolpaths. The **Machine Definition** is a model of your machines capabilities and features. It acts like a template for setting up your machine. The machine definition ties together three main components. The schematic model of your machines components. The control definition that models your control capabilities and the post processor that will generate the required machine code (G-code). For a Mill Level 1 exercise (2D toolpaths) we need just a basic machine definition.

> **NOTE:** For the purpose of this tutorial, we will be using the Default milling machine.

- To display the **Toolpaths Manager** press **Alt + O**.

- Use the **Fit** icon to fit the drawing to the screen.

MACHINE TYPE
- **Mill.**
- **Default.**

- Select the plus sign in front of **Properties** in the **Toolpaths Manager** to expand the **Toolpaths Group Properties.**

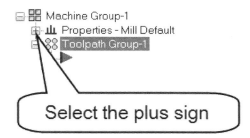

- Select **Tool Settings** to set the tool parameters.

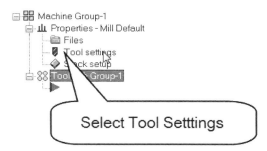

◆ Change the parameters to match the screen shot as shown in Figure: 13.0.1.

Figure: 13.0.1

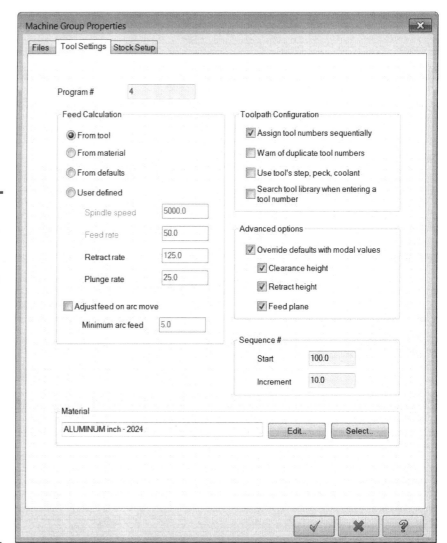

Program # is used to enter a number if your machine tool requires a number for a program name.

Assign tool numbers sequentially allows you to overwrite the tool number from the library with the next available tool number. (First operation tool number 1; Second operation tool number 2, etc.)

Warn of duplicate tool numbers allows you to get a warning if you enter two tools with the same number.

Override defaults with modal values enables the system to keep the values that you enter.

Feed Calculation set From tool uses feed rate, plunge rate, retract rate and spindle speed from the tool definition.

- Select the **Stock setup** tab to define the stock.
- Pick the **Cylindrical** shape option and the axis which the stock will be set to select **"Z."**
- Pick the **All Entities** button to define the stock size as shown in Figure: 13.0.2.

Figure: 13.0.2

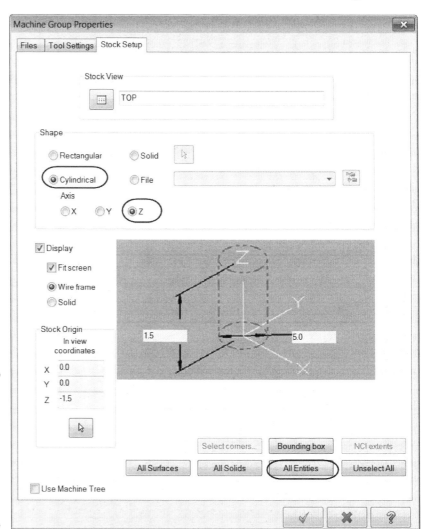

The **Stock Origin** values adjust the positioning of the stock, ensuring that you have equal amount of extra stock around the finished part.

Display options allow you to set the stock as Wireframe and to fit the stock to the screen. (Fit Screen)

NOTE: The **stock** model that you create can be displayed with the part geometry when viewing the file or the toolpaths, during backplot, or while verifying toolpaths.

- Select the **OK** button to exit **Machine Group Properties**.
- Select the **Isometric** view from the graphics view toolbar to see the stock.
- Use the **Fit** icon to fit the drawing to the screen.

◆ The stock model will appear as shown in Figure: 13.0.3.

Figure: 13.0.3

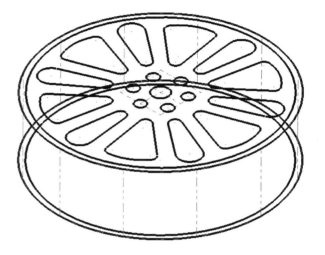

NOTE: The stock is not geometry and can not be selected.
There will not be a facing toolpath because the stock is already to size.

STEP 14: 2D HIGH SPEED AREA MILL

2D High Speed Area Mill toolpath allows you to machine pockets, material that other toolpaths left behind, and standing bosses or cores using a smooth clean motion. Helical entries and tangent stepovers create efficient motion for your machine tools. Cut parameters let you control corner rounding to create the best toolpath, avoiding sharp corners or direction changes. You will machine the pocket keeping the tool inside the machining region by selecting as strategy **Start inside**.

Toolpath Preview:

14.1 Chain Selection

TOOLPATHS
◆ **2D High Speed.**

◆ **Area.**

◆ When the new NC name dialog box appears select the **OK** button to accept the name.

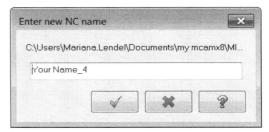

◆ In the **Chain Options** make sure that Stay inside is enabled and click on the **Select** button in the **Machining regions** as shown.

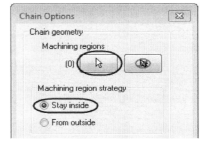

◆ Leave the default setting in the chaining dialog box and chain the inner circle as shown in Figure: 14.1.1.

Figure: 14.1.1

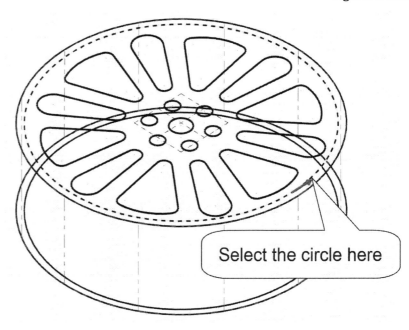

Select the circle here

◆ Select the **OK** button to exit the **Chaining** dialog box.

◆ Select the **OK** button to exit the **Chain Options** dialog box.
◆ In the **Toolpath Type** page, **Area Mill** should be already selected as shown.

Dynamic Mill   Area Mill   Dynamic Contour   Peel Mill   Blend Mill

14.2 Select a 1/2" Flat Endmill from the Library and set the Tool Parameters

◆ Select **Tool** from the **Tree view** list.

◆ Click on **Select library tool** button. | Select library tool... |
◆ Select the **Filter** button.

◆ Select the **None** button and then under **Tool Types** choose the **Flat Endmill** icon.
◆ Under tool diameter pick **Equal** and input a value of **0.5** as shown in Figure: 14.2.1.

Figure: 14.2.1

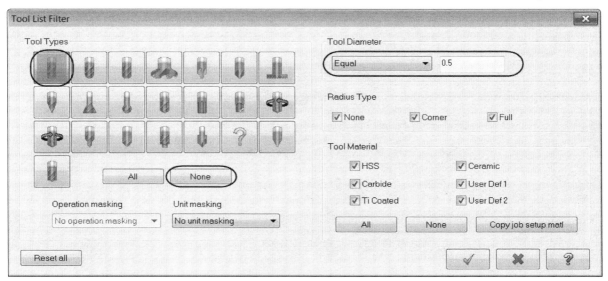

◆ Select the **OK** button to exit the **Tool List Filter.** | ✓ |
◆ In the **Tool Selection** dialog box you should only see a **1/2" Flat Endmill**.

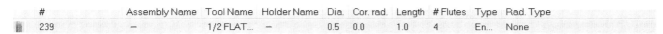

#	Assembly Name	Tool Name	Holder Name	Dia.	Cor. rad.	Length	# Flutes	Type	Rad. Type
239	—	1/2 FLAT...	—	0.5	0.0	1.0	4	En...	None

◆ Select the **1/2" Flat Endmill** in the **Tool Selection** page and then select the **OK** button to exit.

◆ Make all the necessary changes as shown in <u>Figure: 14.2.2</u>.

Figure: 14.2.2

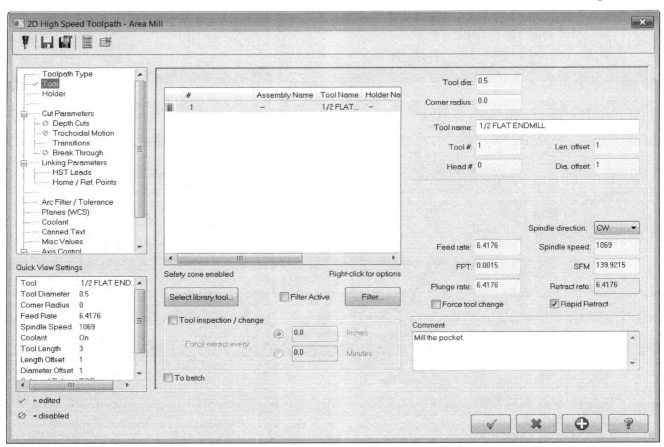

14.3 Set the Cut Parameters

◆ From the **Tree view list**, select **Cut Parameters**.
◆ Set the parameters as shown in Figure: 14.3.1.

Figure: 14.3.1

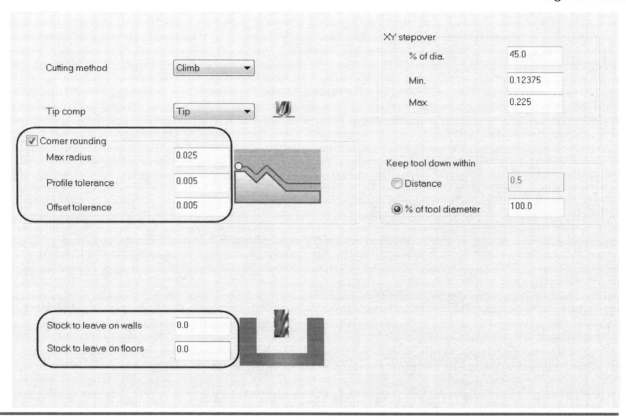

Cutting method set to **Climb** cuts in one direction with the tool rotating in the opposite direction of the tool motion.

XY stepover sets the distance between cutting passes in the X and Y axis.
% of diameter expresses the maximum XY stepover as a percentage of the tool diameter. The Max. XY stepover field will update automatically when you enter a value in this field. The actual stepover is calculated by Mastercam between the Min. and Max. values.

Corner rounding activates toolpath corner rounding, which replaces sharp corners with arcs for faster and smoother transitions in tool direction.

Profile tolerance represents the maximum distance that the outermost profile of a toolpath created with corner rounding can deviate from the original toolpath.

Offset tolerance represents the maximum distance that a profile of a toolpath created with corner rounding can deviate from the original toolpath. This is the same measurement as the profile tolerance but is applied to all the profiles except the outermost one.

14.4 Set the Depth Cuts Parameters

◆ From the **Tree view list**, select the **Depth Cuts** and disable it as shown.

☐ Depth cuts

14.5 Set the Transitions

◆ From the Tree view list, select Transitions and make sure the parameters are set as shown in Figure: 14.5.1.

Figure: 14.5.1

Entry method	
○ Profile ramp	
◉ Entry helix	
Radius	0.25

Note: If helix fails, profile ramp will be used

Entry feed rate	
◉ Plunge rate	
○ Feed rate	

☑ Output 3D arc moves

Z clearance	0.125
Plunge angle	2.0
Preferred profile length	0.5
Skip pockets smaller than	0.55

Entry helix creates a helical entry move.

Output 3D arc moves generates the g-code of the helix with arc (G2/G3) moves. Otherwise, the helix will be rendered with many small linear moves. This can be useful for some types of machines:Many machines have built-in "look ahead" capabilities. Using small linear moves with these capabilities can be more efficient than arc moves.

Z clearance adds an extra height used in the ramping motion down from a top profile. It ensures that the tool has fully slowed down from rapid speeds before touching the material.

Plunge angle sets the angle of descent for the entry move, and determines the pitch.

Skip pockets smaller than allows you to specify a minimum pocket size that Mastercam will consider creating a cutting pass for.

14.6 Set the Linking Parameters

♦ Select **Linking Parameters** and input a **Depth** of **-0.05** as shown in <u>Figure: 14.6.1</u>.

Figure: 14.6.1

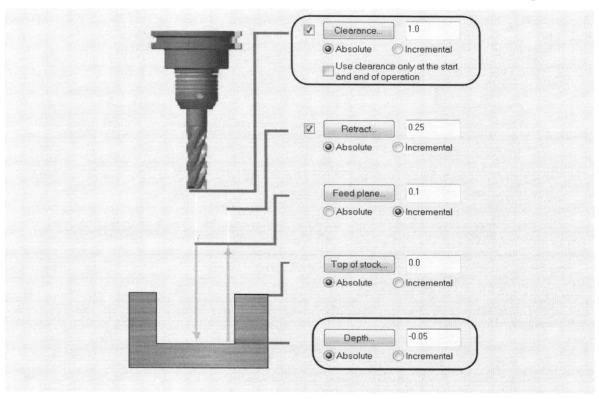

♦ Once complete pick the **OK** button to generate the toolpath.

STEP 15: BACKPLOT THE TOOLPATHS

♦ Make sure that the toolpaths are selected (signified by the green check mark on the folder icon). If the operation is not selected choose the **Select all operations** icon.

♦ Select the **Backplot selected operations** button.

> **NOTE:** Mastercam launches a new window that allows you to check the part using **Backplot** or **Verify**. For more information on how to set and use **Backplot** and **Verify** please check Tutorial 2 page 152.

♦ Select the **Play** button in the **VCR** bar to run **Backplot**.
♦ After Backplot is completed the toolpath should look as shown.

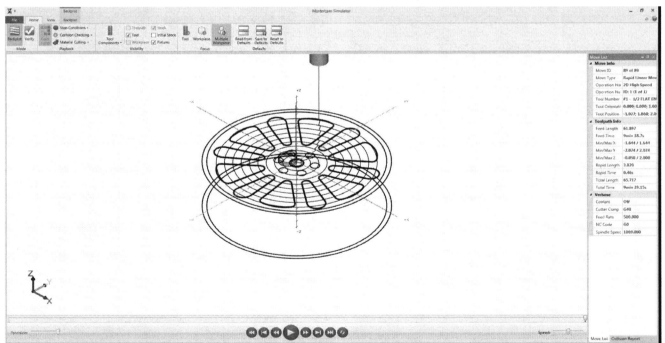

STEP 16: SIMULATE THE TOOLPATH IN VERIFY

◆ From **Mastercam Backplot Home** tab, switch to **Verify** and change the settings for the **Visibility** and **Focus** as shown in Figure: 16.0.1.

Figure: 16.0.1

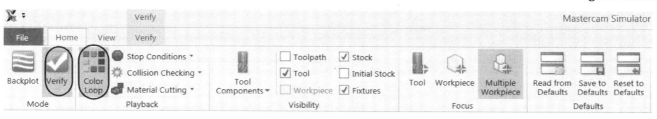

◆ Select the **Play** button in the **VCR** bar to run **Verify**.

◆ The part will appear as shown.

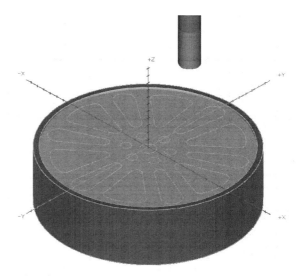

◆ To go back to Mastercam window, minimize **Mastercam Simulator** window as shown.

STEP 17: 2D HIGH SPEED DYNAMIC MILL

2D High Speed Dynamic Mill utilizes the entire flute length of their cutting tools to produce the smoothest, most efficient tool motion for high speed pocketing. The toolpath supports a custom entry method and many others. Micro lifts further refine the dynamic milling motion and avoid excessive heat build up. Custom feeds and speeds optimize and generate safe tool motion. Dynamic Mill machines pockets using one or more chains to drive the toolpath. The outside chain contains the toolpah; all inside chains are considered islands.

In this step you will machine the six bigger pockets using 2D HS Dynamic Mill toolpath. To select all chains, you will use the **Chain Feature** option.

Toolpath Preview:

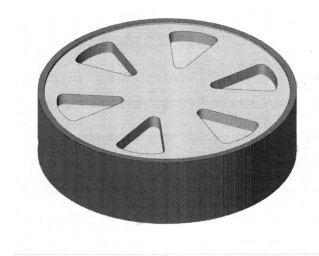

17.1 Chain selection using Chain Feature Option

◆ Press **Alt** + **T** to remove the toolpath display.

TOOLPATHS
◆ **2D High speed.**

◆ 🔲 **Dynamic Mill.**

◆ In the **Chain Options** make sure that Stay inside is enabled as strategy and click on the **Select** button in the **Machining regions** as shown.

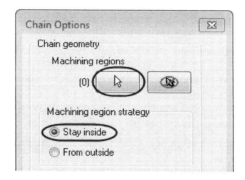

◆ Leave the default setting in the chaining dialog box and pick the chain as shown in <u>Figure: 17.1.1</u>.

Figure: 17.1.1

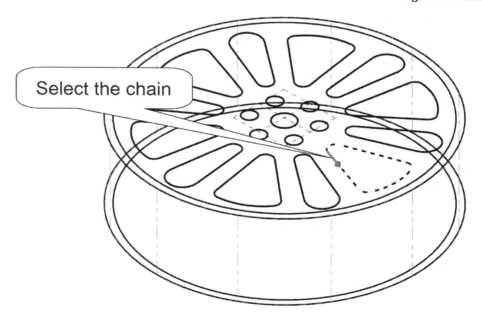

• From the **Chaining** dialog box select the **Chain Feature** button.

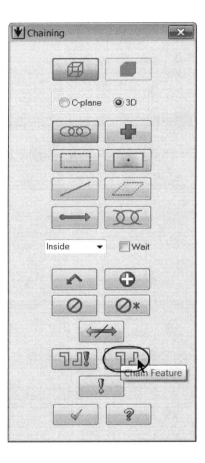

NOTE: Chain Feature allows you to automatically select chains based on the initial chain. Chain Feature is most useful when you have a large number of chains in a part with groups of similar shapes and window chaining is not an option.

• Select the **OK** button to exit the **Chaining** dialog box.

Mastercam. X

♦ In the **Chain Options** dialog box, **Machining regions** will have 6 chains as shown.

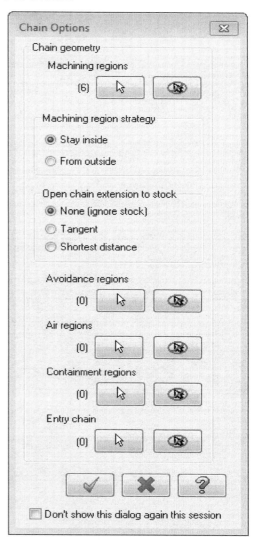

♦ Select the **OK** button to exit the **Chain Options** dialog box.
♦ In the **Toolpath Type** page, **Dynamic Mill** will be already selected as shown in <u>Figure: 17.1.2</u>.

Figure: 17.1.2

17.2 Select a 3/16" Flat endmill from the library and set the Tool Parameters

• Select **Tool** from the Tree view list.

• Click on **Select library tool** button. Select library tool...
• Select the **Filter** button.

• Select the **None** button and then under **Tool Types** choose the **Flat Endmill** icon.
• Under tool diameter pick **Equal** and input a value **0.1875** as shown in Figure: 17.2.1.

Figure: 17.2.1

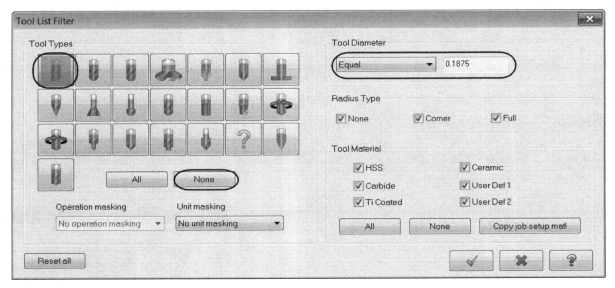

• Select the **OK** button to exit the **Tool List Filter.** ✓
• In the **Tool Selection** dialog box you should only see a **3/16" Flat Endmill**.

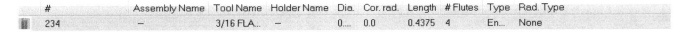

#	Assembly Name	Tool Name	Holder Name	Dia.	Cor. rad.	Length	# Flutes	Type	Rad. Type
234	–	3/16 FLA...	–	0....	0.0	0.4375	4	En...	None

• Select the **3/16" Flat Endmill** in the **Tool Selection** page and then select the **OK** button to exit.

• Make all the necessary changes as shown in Figure: 17.2.2.

Figure: 17.2.2

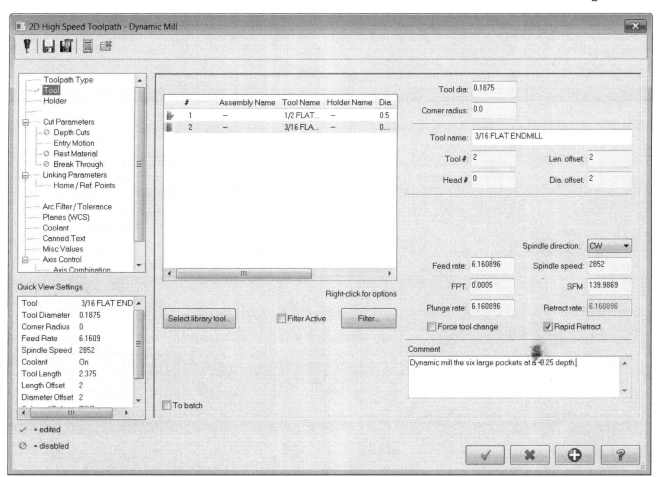

Mastercam.X

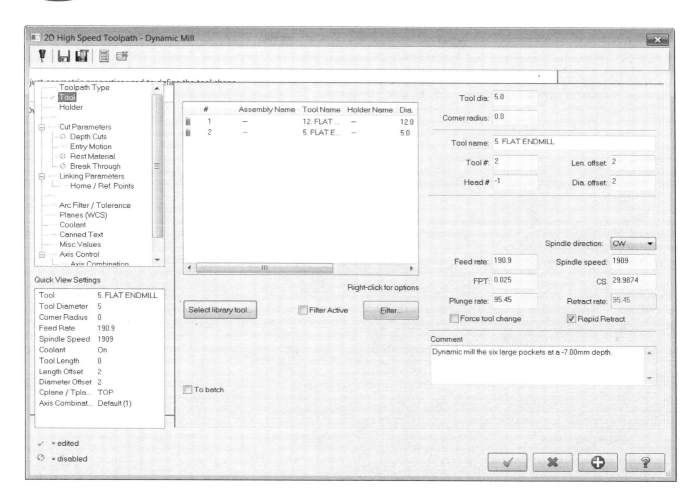

17.3 Set the Cut Parameters

◆ From the **Tree view list**, select **Cut Parameters**. The previously used settings will still be there.
◆ Change the settings for this second toolpath as shown in <u>Figure: 17.3.1</u>.

Figure: 17.3.1

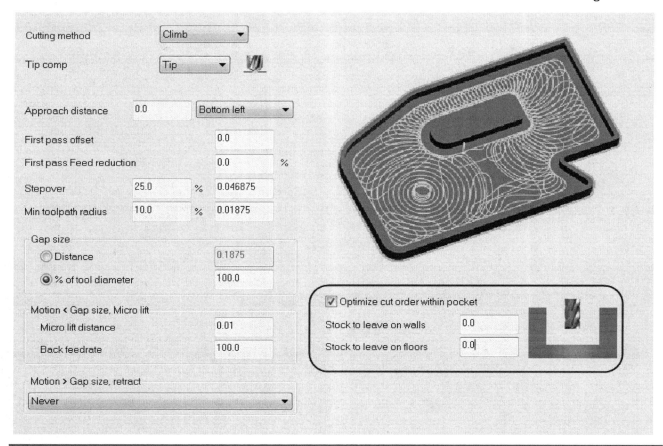

Stepover sets the distance between cutting passes in the X and Y axis.

Toolpath radius reduces sharp corner motion between cut passes.

Micro lift distance enters the distance the tool lifts off the part on the back moves. Microlifts are slight lifts that help clear chips and minimize excessive tool heating.

Back feedrate controls the speed of the backfeed movement of the tool.

Motion > Gap Size, retract controls retracts in the toolpath when making a non-cutting move within an area where the tool can be kept down or microlifted.

Optimize cut order defines the cut order Mastercam applies to different cutting passes in the dynamic mill toolpath.

17.4 Set the Entry Motion

- Entry motion configures an entry method for the dynamic mill toolpath which determines not only how and where the tool enters the part, but the cutting method/machining strategy used by the toolpath. The previous settings will be saved.
- All we want to do is change the **Entry method** to **Profile** as shown in Figure: 17.4.1.

Figure: 17.4.1

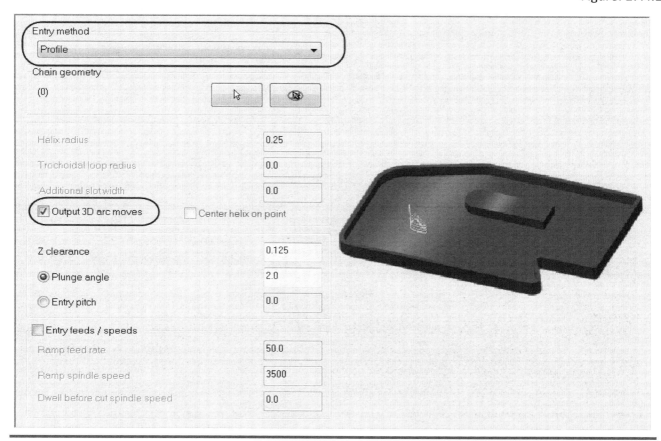

Entry method set to **Profile** creates a boundary based on the shape of the selected chain and uses the tool to ramp into the part. The slot is cleared by taking lighter cuts in the Z axis until the tool reaches the full depth.

Z clearance adds an extra height used in the ramping motion down from a top profile. It ensures that the tool has fully slowed down from rapid speeds before touching the material.

Plunge angle sets the angle of descent for the entry move, and determines the pitch.

17.5 Set the Linking Parameters

♦ Select **Linking Parameters** and change the **Top of Stock** value to **Incremental 0.0** and the **Depth** to **-0.25 Incremental** as shown in Figure: 17.5.1.

Figure: 17.5.1

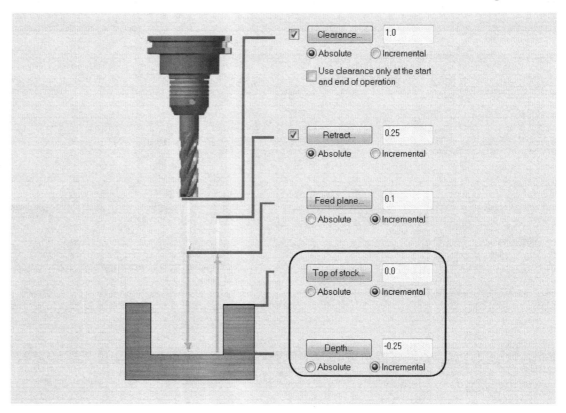

Incremental values are relative to other parameters or chained geometry. In this tutorial the pocket chains were moved **0.05** along Zaxis, below zero. The **Top of stock** and the the **Depth** set to **Incremental** is measure from the z depth of the chains. If you want to set the **Top of stock** and the **Depth** to **Absolute**, the values should be **- 0.05** and **-0.3** respectively .

♦ Select the **OK** button to generate the toolpath.

*Mastercam. X*⁸

- To **Backplot** the toolpath see page 152 to review this procedure.

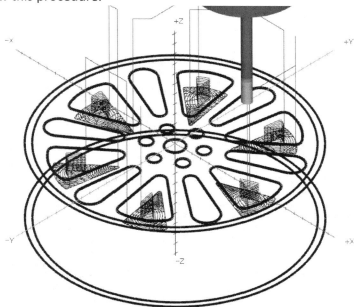

- To go back to Mastercam window, minimize **Mastercam Simulator** window as shown.

- To **Verify** the toolpaths see page 155.
- To select both toolpaths click on the **Select all operations** icon.

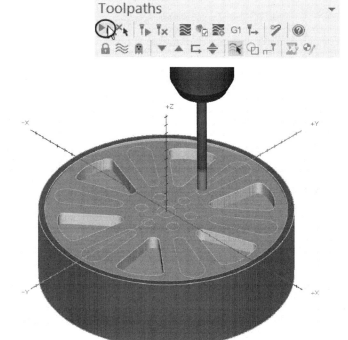

- To go back to Mastercam window, minimize **Mastercam Simulator** window as shown.

STEP 18: MACHINE ONE SMALLER POCKET USING 2D HIGH SPEED AREA MILL

In this step you will machine one smaller pocket using 2D HS Area Mill.

Toolpath Preview:

18.1 Chain Selection

◆ Press **Alt + T** to remove the toolpath display.

◆ **2D High Speed.**
◆ 🔲 **Area.**
◆ In the **Chain Options** click on the **Select** button in the **Machining regions** as shown.

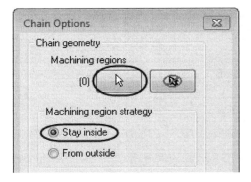

Mill Level 1 Training Tutorial

- Leave the default setting in the chaining dialog box and pick the chain as shown in Figure: 18.1.1.

Figure: 18.1.1

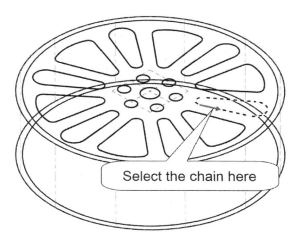

Select the chain here

- Select the **OK** button to exit the **Chaining** dialog box.

- Select the **OK** button to exit the **Chain Options** dialog box.
- In the **Toolpath Type**, **Area Mill** should be already selected as shown.

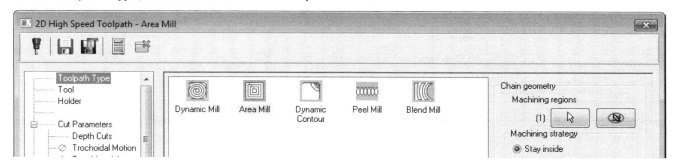

◆ Fom the **Tree view list** select **Tool**.

◆ Select the **3/16" Flat Endmill** and make all the necessary changes as shown in <u>Figure: 18.1.2</u>.

Figure: 18.1.2

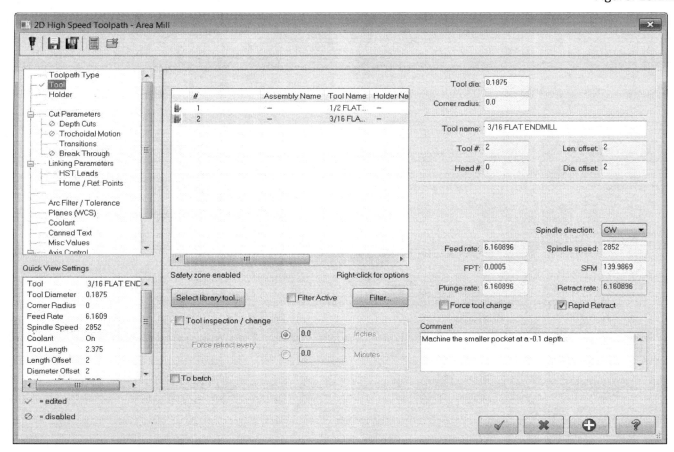

Mastercam. X⁸

18.2 Set the Cut Parameters

◆ From the **Tree view list**, select **Cut Parameters**. The previously used settings will still be there. Use these settings for this third toolpath as shown in Figure: 18.2.1.

Figure: 18.2.1

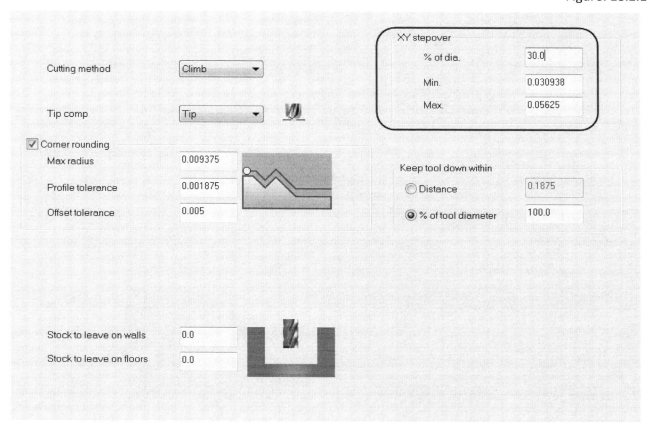

18.3 Set the Depth Cuts parameters

♦ From the **Tree view list**, select **Depth Cuts** and set the parameters as shown in.

Figure: 18.3.1

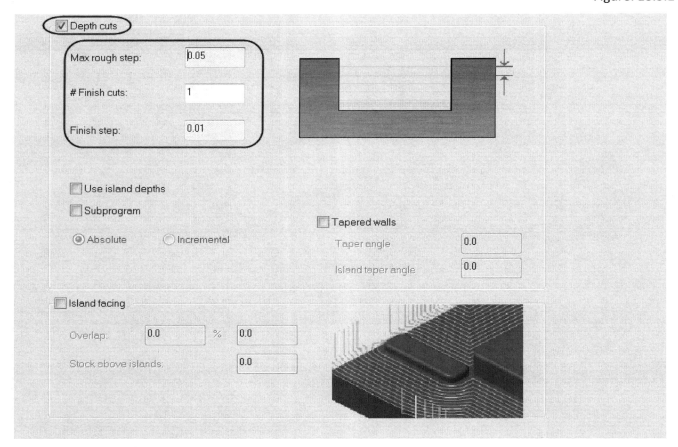

Mill Level 1 Training Tutorial
Mastercam.X

18.4 Set the Transitions

- From the **Tree view list**, select **Transitions** and leave the **Entry method** set to **Entry helix** as shown in Figure: 18.4.1.

Figure: 18.4.1

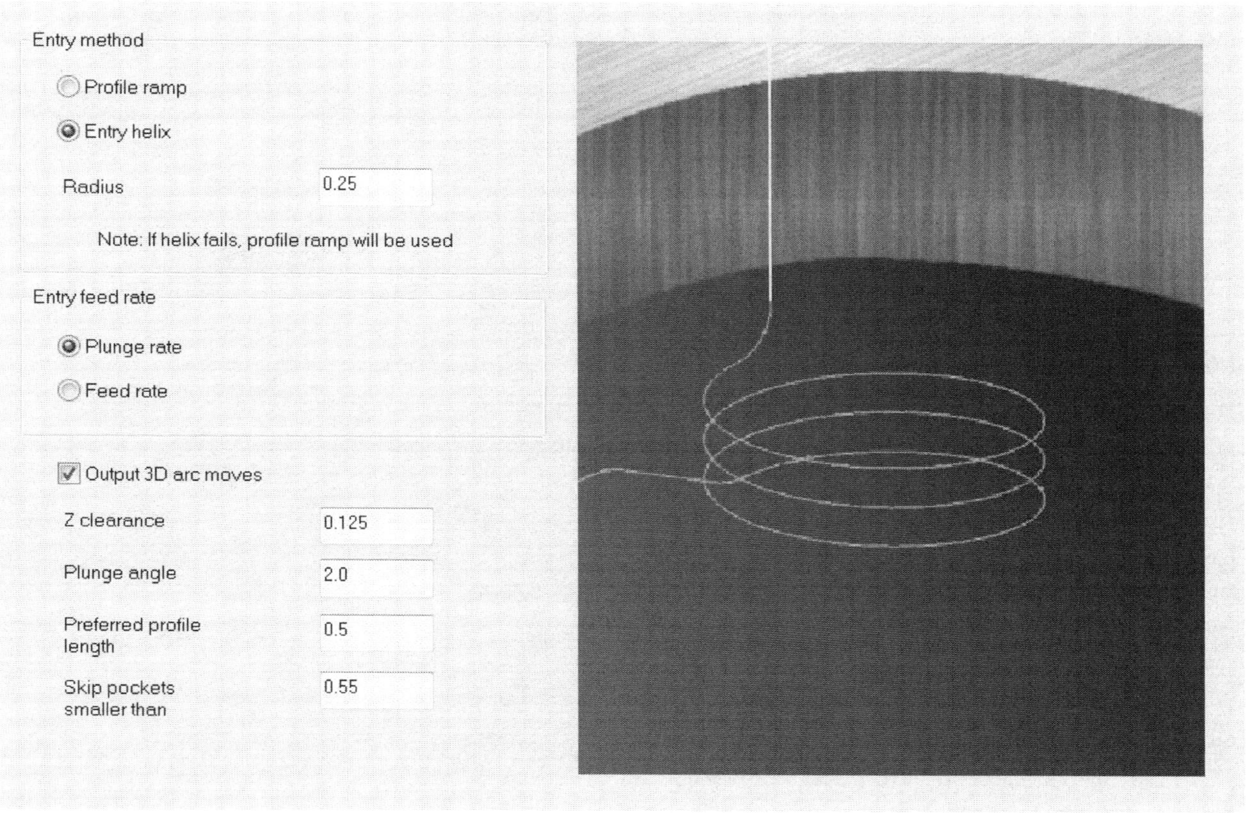

Entry method

- ○ Profile ramp
- ● Entry helix

Radius   0.25

Note: If helix fails, profile ramp will be used

Entry feed rate

- ● Plunge rate
- ○ Feed rate

☑ Output 3D arc moves

Z clearance	0.125
Plunge angle	2.0
Preferred profile length	0.5
Skip pockets smaller than	0.55

18.5 Set the Linking Parameters

♦ Select **Linking Parameters** and input the **Depth** as shown in Figure: 18.5.1.

Figure: 18.5.1

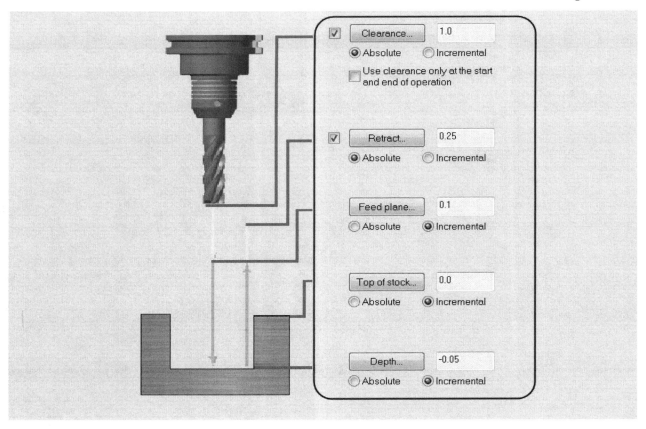

♦ Once complete pick the **OK** button to generate the toolpath.
♦ **Backplot** the toolpath as shown at page 152.

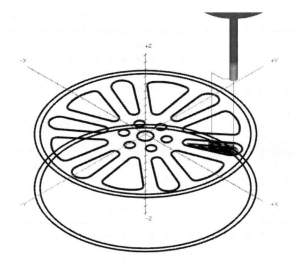

• Minimize **Mastercam Simulator** window, select all toolpaths and then **Verify** them as shown at page 155.

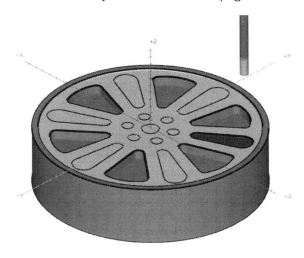

STEP 19: TRANSFORM TOOLPATHS

Transform toolpaths are used when you want to run the same toolpath in different locations. You can transform a single toolpath or several at a time.

Toolpath Preview:

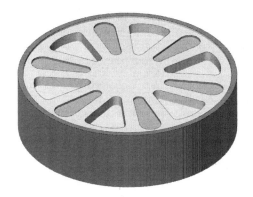

TOOLPATHS

- 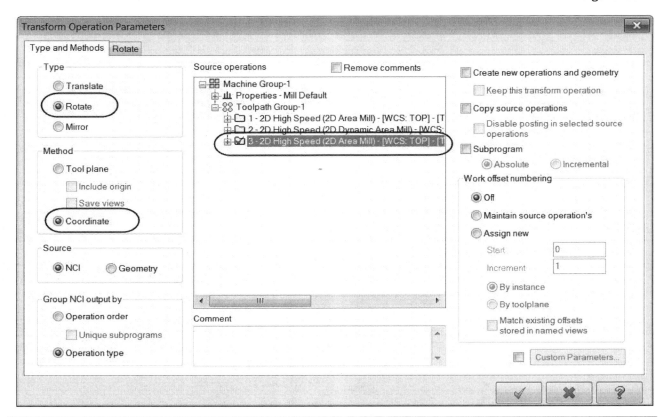 **Transform.**
- For the **Type** select **Rotate**, **Coordinate** for **Method.**
- Select **Operation 3.**
- Pick **Group NCI output by** the **Operation order** as shown in Figure: 19.0.1.

Figure: 19.0.1

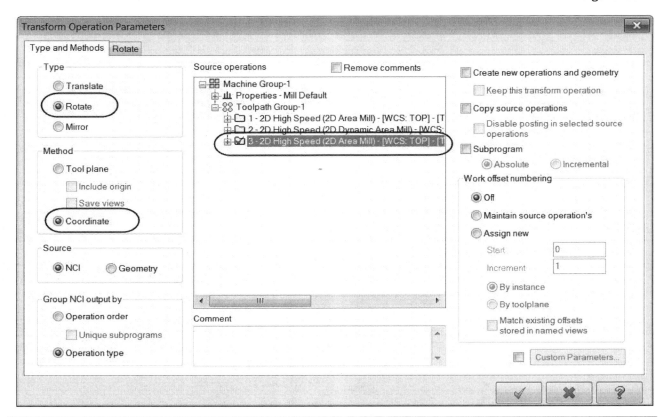

Rotate revolves the toolpath about the construction origin or a specified point. Activate the Rotate tab and you can set the rotation point and number of copies.

Coordinate creates new coordinate positions for the new toolpaths in the original tool plane.

Operation order sorts the transformed operations by the order they were selected. In our example we choose the large pocket then small pocket. It will execute them in that order (large pocket, small pocket, large pocket, small pocket, etc.).

◆ Choose the **Rotate** tab.
◆ Input the **Number of steps 5,** a **Start angle** of **0.0, and a Rotation angle** of **60.0** degrees as shown in
   Figure: 19.0.2.

Figure: 19.0.2

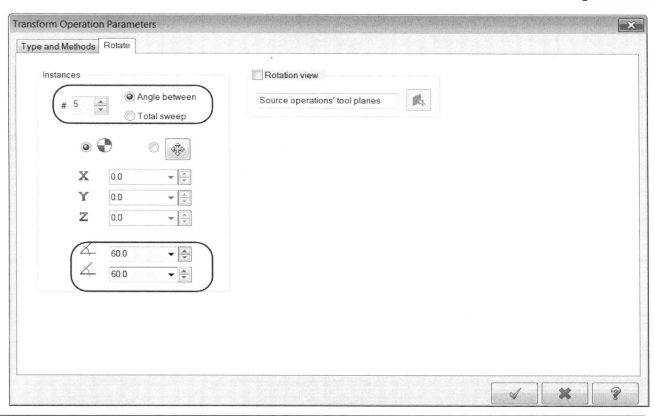

Number of steps is the number of times to rotate the toolpath.

Start angle sets the beginning angle for the rotate toolpath.

Rotation angle sets the angle of rotation for the transformed toolpath.

◆ Once complete pick the **OK** button to generate the toolpath.

◆ **Backplot** the toolpath as shown at page 152.

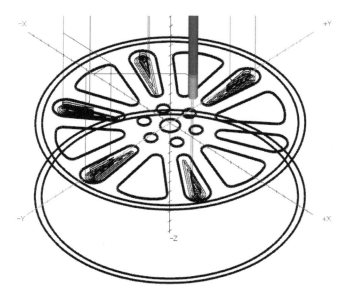

◆ Minimize **Mastercam Simulator** and select all toolpaths to **Verify** them as shown at page 155.

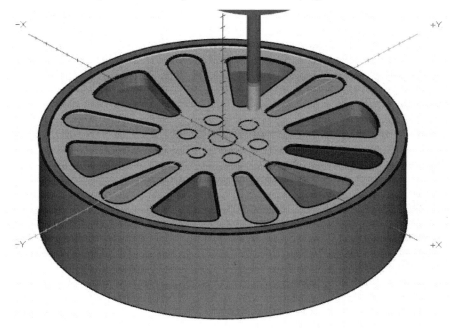

STEP 20: SPOT DRILL THE HOLES

Spot Drilling the holes allows you to start the hole. In this operation we will use the spot drill to chamfer the hole before drilling it.

Toolpath Preview:

TOOLPATHS

* 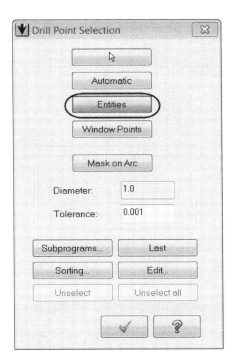 **Drill.**
* In the **Drill Point Selection** dialog box choose the option **Entities**.

◆ Select the arcs as shown in <u>Figure: 20.0.1</u>.

Figure: 20.0.1

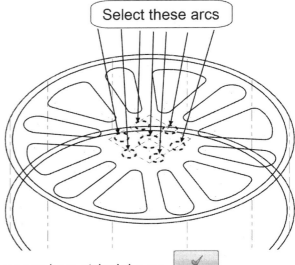

Select these arcs

◆ Select the **OK** button in the **Drill Point Selection** dialog box once you have picked the arc.
◆ In the **Toolpath Type** page, the **Drill** toolpath will be selected.

Drill   Circle Mill   Point   Helix Bore   Thread Mill

20.1 Select a 1/2" Spot Drill from the Library and set the Tool Parameters

* Select **Tool** from the Tree view list.

* Click on **Select library tool** button. `Select library tool...`
* To be able to see just the spot drill select the **Filter** button.

* Under **Tool Types** select the **None** button and then choose the **Spot drill** icon as shown in <u>Figure: 20.1.1</u>.

Figure: 20.1.1

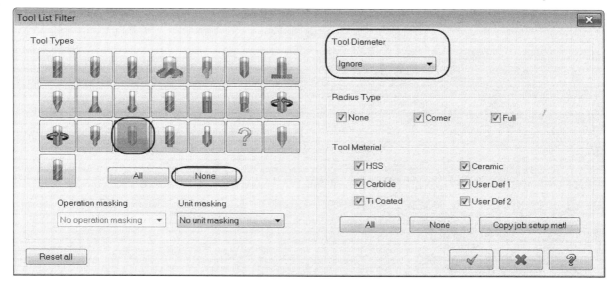

* Select **OK** button to exit the **Tool List Filter** dialog box.
* At this point you should only see **Spot Drills**.
* From that list select the **1/2" Spot Drill**.

#	Assembly Name	Tool Name	Holder Name	Dia.	Cor. rad.	Length	# Flutes	Type	Rad. Type
4	—	1/8 SPO...	—	0...	0.0	2.0	2	Sp...	None
5	—	1/4 SPO...	—	0.25	0.0	2.0	2	Sp...	None
6	—	1/2 SPO...	—	0.5	0.0	2.0	2	Sp...	None
198	—	3/4 SPO...	—	0.75	0.0	2.0	4	Sp...	None
312	—	1. SPOT...	—	1.0	0.0	2.0	4	Sp...	None
314	—	3/8 SPO...	—	0...	0.0	2.0	4	Sp...	None

* Select the tool in the **Tool Selection** page and then select the **OK** button to exit.

• Make the necessary changes to the **Tool** page as shown in Figure: 20.1.2.

Figure: 20.1.2

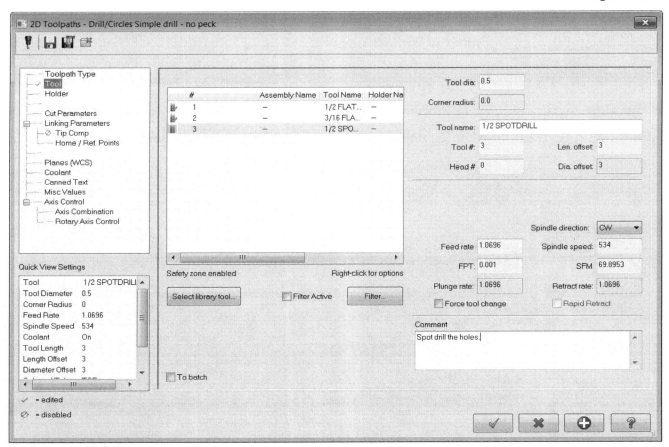

20.2 Set the Cut Parameters

♦ Select **Cut Parameters** and make the necessary changes as shown in <u>Figure: 20.2.1</u>.

Figure: 20.2.1

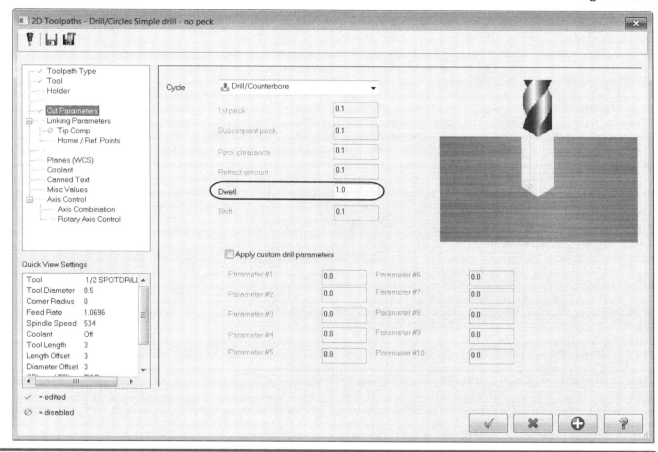

Drill/Counterbore is recommended for drilling holes with depths of less than three times the tools diameter.

Dwell sets the amount of time in seconds that the tool remains at the bottom of a drilled hole.

20.3 Set the Linking Parameters

◆ Choose **Linking Parameters**, ensure **Clearance** is enabled and set to **1.0**, the **Top of stock** is set to **Incremental** and **zero**.

◆ Set the **Depth** to **Incremental** and zero then select the **Calculator** icon.
◆ Input the following equation in the **Finish diameter** area. **0.25+0.05** and hit **Enter** to calculate the **Depth** as shown in Figure: 20.3.1.

Figure: 20.3.1

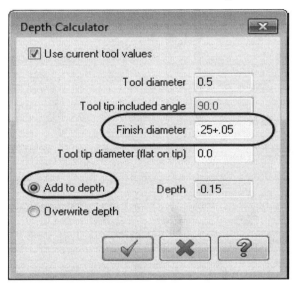

◆ Select the **OK** button to exit the **Depth Calculator**.

Mastercam.X⁸

♦ You will now see the depth we calculated for the spot drilling operation set in the **Depth** field as shown in
Figure: 20.3.2.

Figure: 20.3.2

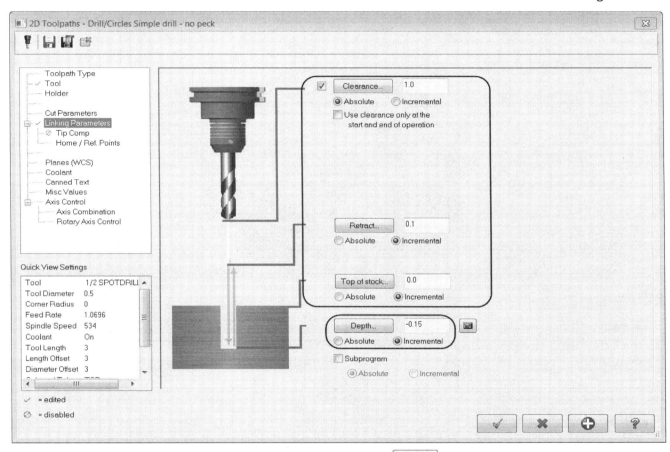

♦ Select the **OK** button to exit the **Drill/Counterbore** parameters. ✓
♦ To **Backplot** and **Verify** the toolpaths see page 152 and page 155 to review these procedures.

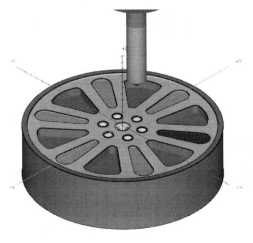

STEP 21: DRILL ALL HOLES

In this example we will drill the 1/4" holes to a specified depth.

Toolpath Preview:

TOOLPATHS

◆ 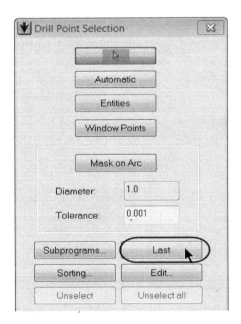 **Drill.**

◆ In the **Drill Point Selection** dialog box choose the option **Last**.

NOTE: This option will automatically select the hole for you based off the selection from the previous drill operation.

• Select the **OK** button in the **Drill Point Selection** dialog box to accept the 7 drill points.
• In the **Toolpath Type** page, the **Drill** toolpath will be selected.

Drill   Circle Mill   Point   Helix Bore   Thread Mill

21.1 Select a 1/4" Drill from the Library and set the Tool Parameters

• Select **Tool** from the **Tree view** list.

• Click on **Select library tool** button.
• To be able to see just the spot drill select the **Filter** button.

Filter Active
367 of 367 tools

• Under **Tool Types** select the **None** button and then choose the drill icon.
• Under **Tool Diameter** select **Equal** and enter **0.25** as shown in Figure: 21.1.1.

Figure: 21.1.1

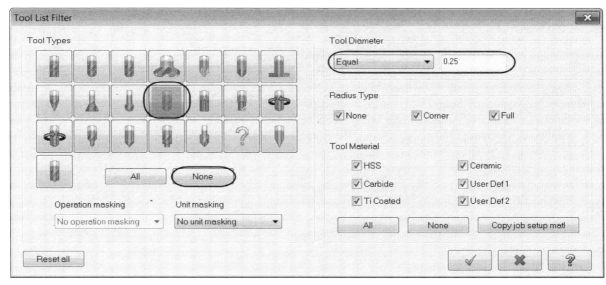

• Select **OK** button to exit the **Tool List Filter** dialog box.
• From that list select a **1/4" Drill**.

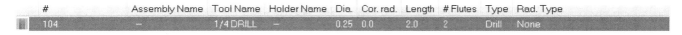

#	Assembly Name	Tool Name	Holder Name	Dia.	Cor. rad.	Length	# Flutes	Type	Rad. Type
104	--	1/4 DRILL	--	0.25	0.0	2.0	2	Drill	None

- Select the tool in the **Tool Selection** page and then choose the **OK** button to exit.
- Make the necessary changes to the **Tool** page as shown in <u>Figure: 21.1.2</u>.

Figure: 21.1.2

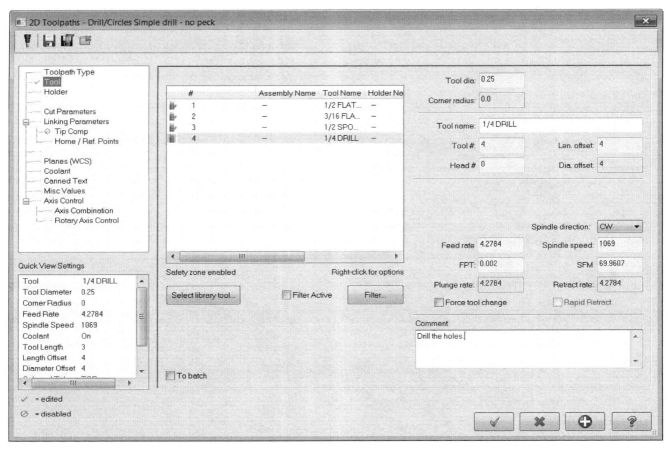

Mastercam. X

21.2 Set the Cut Parameters

◆ Select **Cut Parameters**, change the drill **Cycle** to **Chip Break** and input a **1st peck** value of **0.1** as shown in Figure: 21.2.1.

Figure: 21.2.1

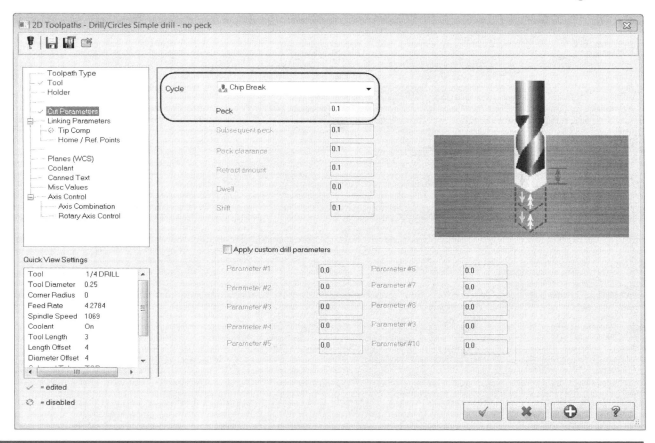

Chip Break drills holes with depths of more than three times the tool diameter. The tool retracts partially out of the drilled hole to break material chips.

1st peck sets the depth for the first peck move which plunges in and out of the material to clear and break chips.

21.3 Set the Linking Parameters

• Choose **Linking Parameters** and input a **Top of Stock** value of **0.0 Incremental** and **depth** value of **-0.5 Incremental** as shown in Figure: 21.3.1.

Figure: 21.3.1

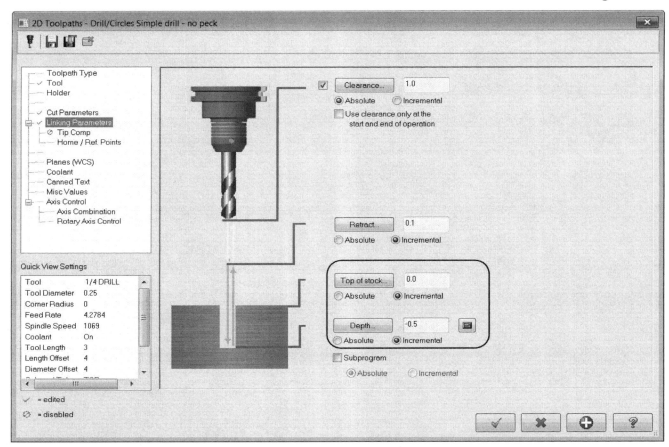

• Select the **OK** button to exit the **Drill/Counterbore** parameters.

Mastercam X⁸

- To **Backplot** and **Verify** your toolpath see page 152 and page 155 to review these procedures.

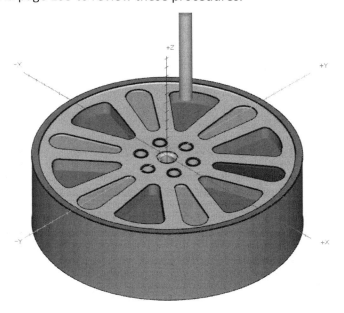

STEP 22: CIRCLE MILL THE CENTER HOLE

Circle mill toolpath is used to mill circular pockets based on a single point. Mastercam will pocket out a circular area of the diameter and to the depth that you specify. After milling the center of the circle, Mastercam calculates an entry arc before approaching the perimeter and then a similar exit arc. You can add enhancements such as multiple passes, multiple depth cuts and helical plunge moves as well fine tuning the entry and exit arcs.

Toolpath Preview:

TOOLPATHS

✦ **Circle Paths.**

✦ 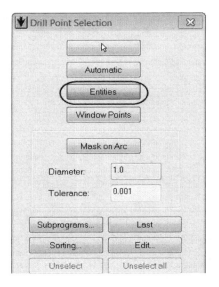 **Circle Mill.**

22.1 Select the Geometry

✦ When the **Drill Point Selection** dialog box appears choose entities.

✦ Select the arc as shown in <u>Figure: 22.1.1</u>.

Figure: 22.1.1

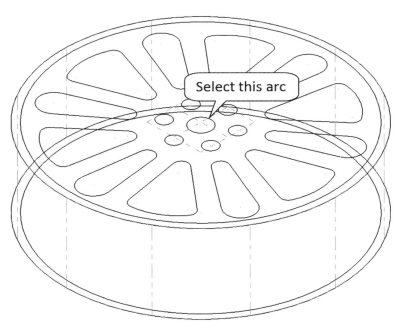

✦ Choose the **OK** button once the arc has been selected.

◆ On the **Toolpath Type** page **Circle Mill** will be picked.

Drill

Circle Mill

Point

Helix Bore

Thread Mill

22.2 Select the 3/16" Tool

◆ From the **Tree view list**, select **Tool**.
◆ Select the existing tool and change the parameters as shown in Figure: 22.2.1.

Figure: 22.2.1

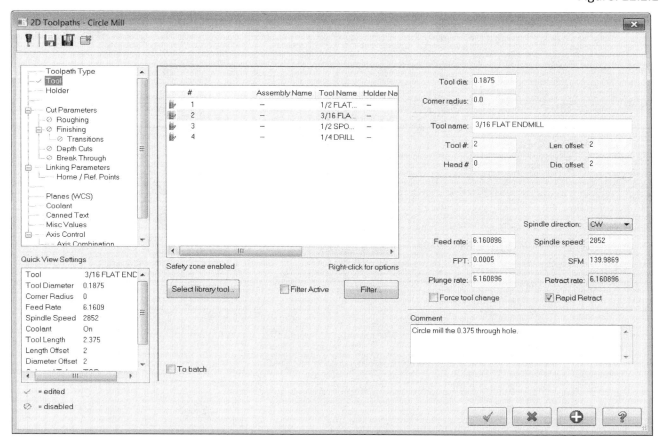

NOTE: Picking the 3/16" Flat Endmill will allow us to use the tool for this toolpath.

22.3 Set the Cut Parameters

◆ From the **Tree view list** select **Cut Parameters** and ensure the parameters appear the same as shown in
<u>Figure: 22.3.1</u>.

Figure: 22.3.1

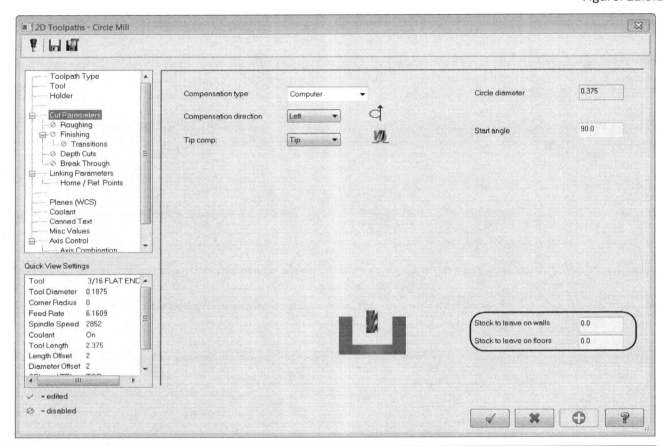

Start Angle sets the angle where the helix bore toolpath begins.

Entry/exit arc sweep sets the included angle of each entry and exit arc.

Start at center begins the toolpath at the center of the arc.

Perpendicular entry enters the thread toolpath perpendicular to the first tool move.

Overlap sets how far the tool goes past the end of the toolpath.

22.4 Set the Roughing Parameters

• Make sure the **Roughing** is disabled as shown.

22.5 Set the Finishing parameters

• From the **Tree view list**, select Finishing and enable it. Change the parameters as shown in Figure: 22.5.1.

Figure: 22.5.1

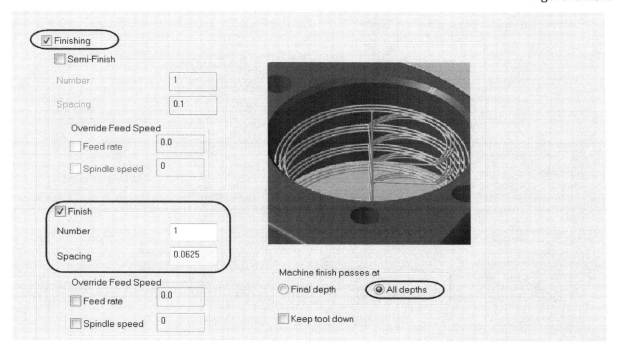

22.6 Set the Linking Parameters

◆ Select **Linking Parameters** from the **Tree view list.** Set the **Top of stock** and set the **Depth** as shown in <u>Figure: 22.6.1</u>.

Figure: 22.6.1

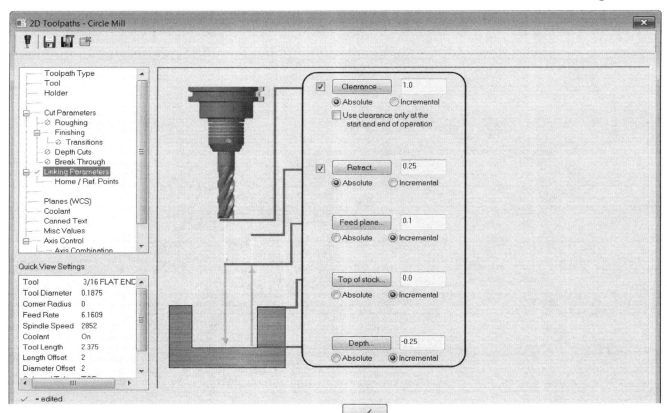

◆ Select the **OK** button to exit the **Circle Mill** parameters.

◆ To **Backplot** and **Verify** the toolpaths see page 152 and page 155 to review these procedures.

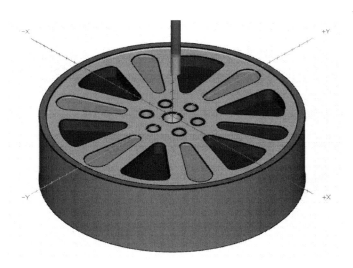

STEP 23: CHAMFER THE PART

Contour - Chamfer toolpath automatically cuts a chamfer around a contour using a chamfer mill.

Toolpath Preview:

TOOLPATHS

* ◻ **Contour.**
* Leave the default settings in the **Chaining** dialog box as shown in Figure: 23.0.1.

Figure: 23.0.1

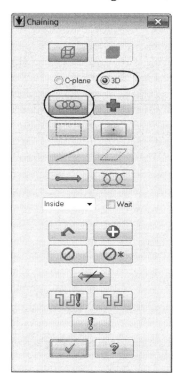

◆ Select the chains and ensure the chaining direction is the same as shown in Figure: 23.0.2.

Figure: 23.0.2

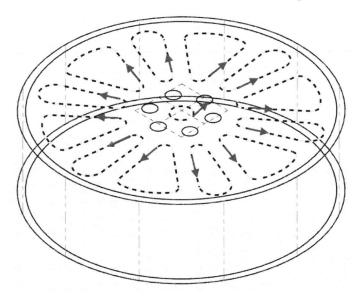

NOTE: It does not matter which contour you select first. However the first contour you select, will be the first contour cut. Make sure that all chains are selected in the same direction. Use **Reverse** button to change the direction of chain if needed.

◆ Select the **OK** button to exit the **Chaining** dialog box.

NOTE: The depth of the chamfer is based on the width and tip offset set in the Cut Parameters page. This is why we set the depth here to zero.

◆ In the **Toolpath Type** page, the **Contour** toolpath will be selected.

 Contour Pocket Facing Slot Mill

23.1 Select a 1/4" Chamfer Mill from the Library and set the Tool Parameters

◆ Select **Tool** from the **Tree view list**.

◆ Click on **Select library tool** button.
◆ To be able to see just the spot drill select the **Filter** button.

◆ Under **Tool Types** select the **None** button and then choose the **Chamfer Mill** icon as shown in Figure: 23.1.1.

Figure: 23.1.1

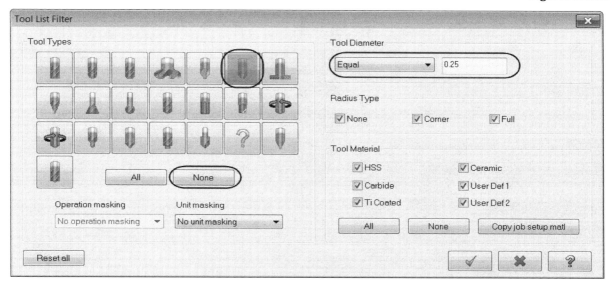

◆ Select the **OK** button to exit the **Tool List Filter** dialog box.

NOTE: You will only see a list of chamfer mills.

◆ From that list select the **1/4" Chamfer Mill**.

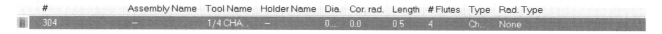

#	Assembly Name	Tool Name	Holder Name	Dia.	Cor. rad.	Length	# Flutes	Type	Rad. Type
304	–	1/4 CHA..	–	0...	0.0	0 5	4	Ch..	None

◆ Select the tool in the **Tool Selection** page and then choose the **OK** button to exit. A warning might appear stating that the **Tool Settings** were modified to conform with your current **Machine Definition/ Control Definition**.

◆ Select the **OK** buttong to continue.

◆ Make all the necessary changes as shown in <u>Figure: 23.1.2</u>.

Figure: 23.1.2

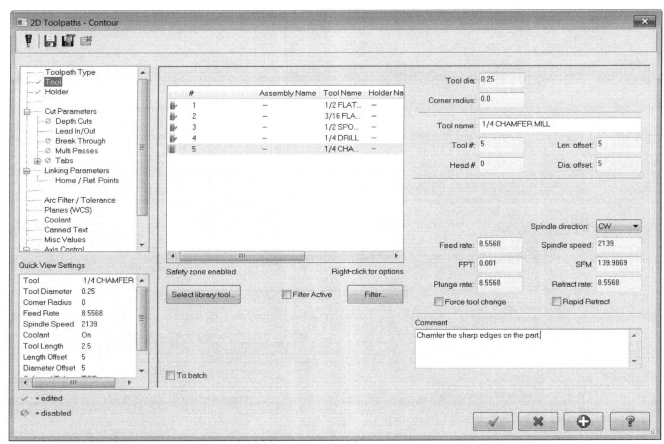

Mastercam. **X⁸**

23.2 Set the Cut Parameters

◆ Select the **Cut Parameters** page and change the **Contour type** to **2D chamfer**.
◆ Input a **Width** of **0.025** and a **Tip offset** of **0.02** as shown in Figure: 23.2.1.

Figure: 23.2.1

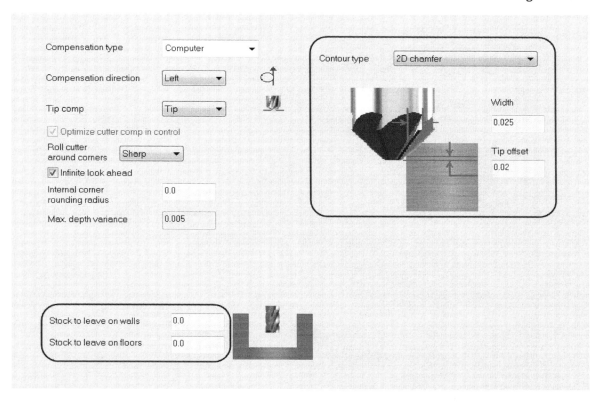

2D chamfer cuts chamfers around a contour.

Width sets the chamfer width. Mastercam measures the width from the chained geometry adjusted by the cut depths defined on the linking parameters page.

Tip offset is an amount to ensure that the tip of the tool clears the bottom of the chamfer.

23.3 Set the Lead In/Out Parameters

◆ Choose the option **Lead In/Out** and input an **Overlap** value.
◆ Make any other necessary changes as shown in Figure: 23.3.1.

Figure: 23.3.1

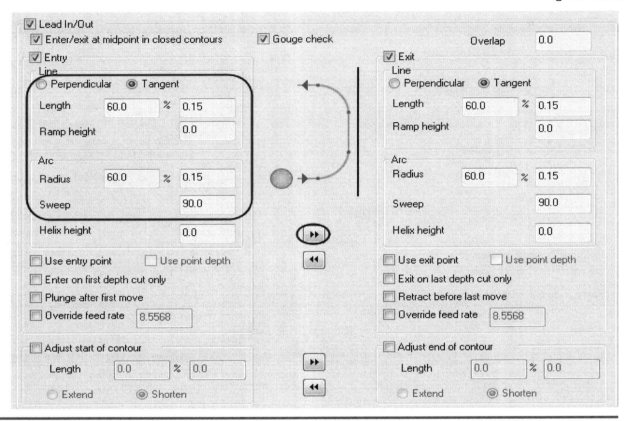

Lead In/Out allows you to can create either entry moves, exit moves, or both. **Lead in/out** move can include both lines and arcs.

Enter/Exit at midpoint in closed contours starts and ends a toolpath with closed chains at the midpoint of the first chained entity.

Gouge check entry/exit motion ensures that the entry/exit moves do not gouge the part. If the entry/exit moves cause a gouge, they are removed from the toolpath.

23.4 Set the Linking Parameters

♦ Select the **Linking Parameters** from the **Tree view list**. Set the **Top of stock** to **zero** and the **Depth** to **0.0 Incremental** as shown in <u>Figure: 23.4.1</u>.

Figure: 23.4.1

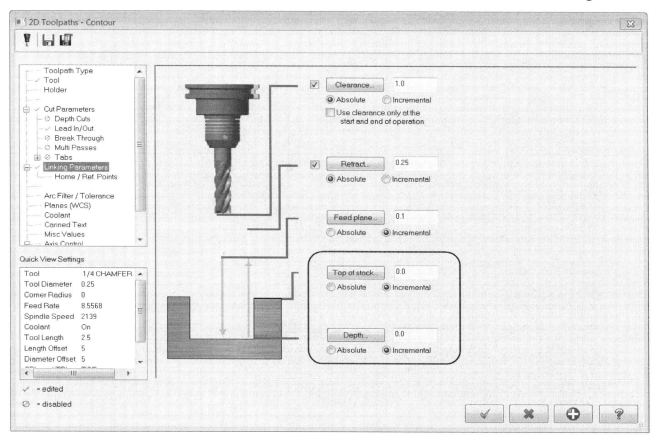

♦ Select the **OK** button to exit the toolpath parameters.

> **NOTE:** The depth of the chamfer is based on the width and tip offset set in the Cut Parameters page. This is why we set the depth here to zero.

23.5 Backplot and Verify

◆ To **Verify** the toolpath see page 155 to review the procedures.
◆ Your part will appear as shown.

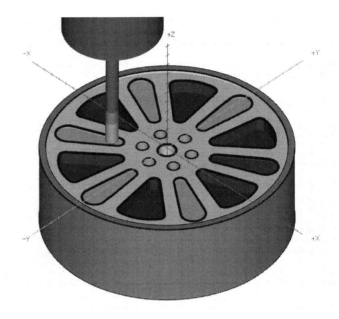

TOOLPATH CREATION - SETUP 2

SUGGESTED FIXTURE 2:

NOTE: The part is now flipped over and we will machine the part from the bottom.

SETUP SHEET 2:

TOOL LIST

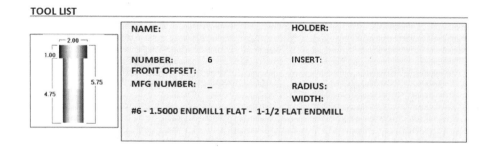

NAME:		HOLDER:
NUMBER: 6		INSERT:
FRONT OFFSET:		
MFG NUMBER: _		RADIUS:
		WIDTH:

#6 - 1.5000 ENDMILL1 FLAT - 1-1/2 FLAT ENDMILL

STEP 24: CREATING AND RENAMING TOOLPATH GROUPS

To machine the part in two different setups, we will need to have two separate programs. To be able to post process separately the operations of each setup, we will create them under different toolpath groups with different NC names.

24.1 Rename the current Toolpath Group - 1 and the NC file

◆ Click on the **Toolpath Group - 1** to highlight and then click again on it and rename it "**Setup #1.**"

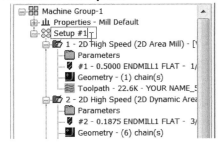

◆ Right mouse click on the toolpath group and select **Edit selected operations** and then, select **Change NC file name** as shown in Figure: 24.1.1.

Figure: 24.1.1

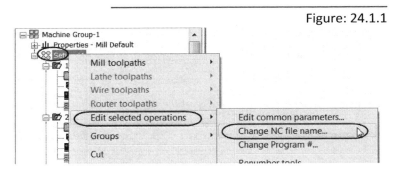

◆ Enter the new NC name: **Setup #1.**

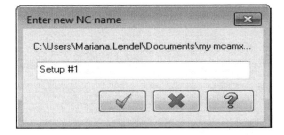

◆ Select the **OK** button to accept the new NC name.

24.2 Create a New Toolpath Group

• Right mouse click on the **Machine Group-1** and select **Groups** and then the **New Toolpath group.**

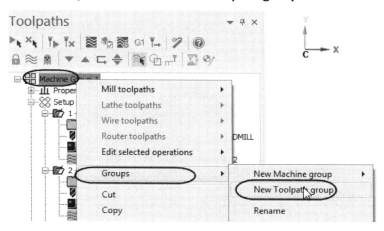

• Rename the toolpath group "**Setup #2**" as shown.

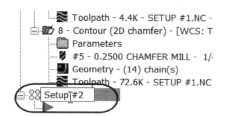

• Make sure that the **Insert arrow** is below the **Setup #2**, otherwise click on the **Move the insert arrow down an item** icon until the arrow is below the **Setup #2** group.

NOTE: The next operation is going to be generated at the insert arrow location.

STEP 25: SET THE WCS TO BOTTOM

Work coordinate system (WCS) is the active coordinate system in use by Mastercam at any given time. The WCS contains the orientation of the X, Y, Z axes plus the location of the zero point (the origin). This tells Mastercam how your part is position or orientated in the machine.

- Select **WCS** located in the **Status bar**. (WCS) Groups
- When the **WCS** menu appears select **"Plane Manager"** from it.

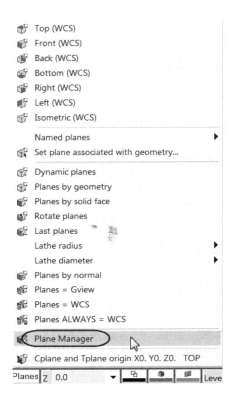

● When the **Plane Manager** dialog box appears pick **Bottom** and then **Copy** button to make a copy of the Bottom plane as shown in <u>Figure: 25.0.1</u>.

Figure: 25.0.1

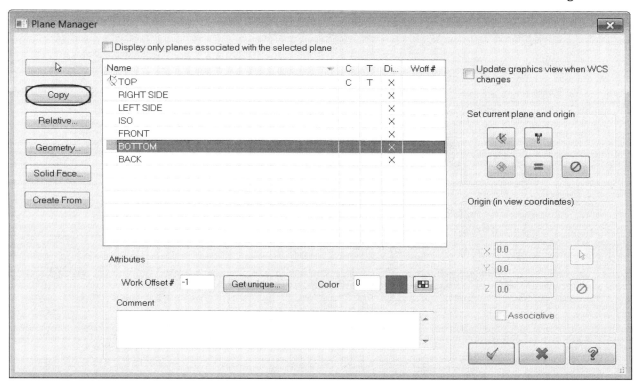

NOTE: You have to make a copy of the Bottom plane to be able to set a new origin for the plane.

♦ Set the **Work Coordinate System** (WCS), tool plane, construction plane, and their origins, to the copied Bottom plane by cliking on the equal button as shown in <u>Figure: 25.0.2</u>.

Figure: 25.0.2

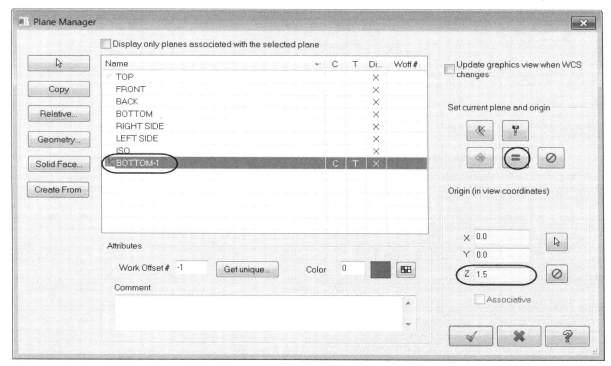

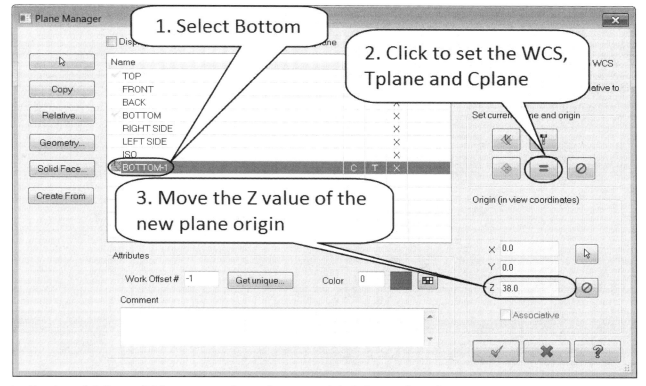

1. Select Bottom

2. Click to set the WCS, Tplane and Cplane

3. Move the Z value of the new plane origin

• Input a **Z** value of **1.5** to tell Mastercam where the new origin is located on the part.

• Select the **OK** button to exit the **Plane Manager**.

• Pick the **Isometric** graphics view to see the part in its new orientation.

• Press **F9** on your keyboard to display the coordinate axes.

> **NOTE:** The dark blue axes are the original axes and the light blue axes are the current axes.

• Your part will appear as shown up to this point.

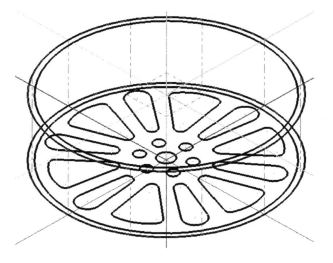

• Press **F9** to remove the axes display.

STEP 26: 2D HS DYNAMIC MILL

In this step we will utilize the 2D High Speed Dynamic Mill toolpath to remove the material in the middle of the part with the part now flipped over.

Toolpath Preview:

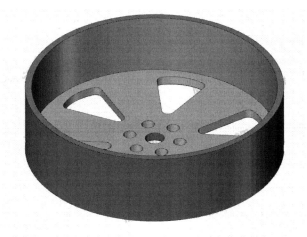

26.1 Chain Selection

TOOLPATHS

◆ **2D High speed.**

◆ 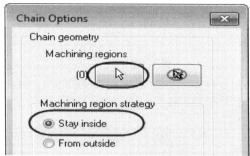 **Dynamic Mill.**

◆ From the **Chain Options** make sure that the Stay inside is enabled and then click on the **Select** button as shown.

◆ Leave the default settings in the **Chaining** dialog box and pick the first chain on the inner circle as shown in Figure: 26.1.1.

Figure: 26.1.1

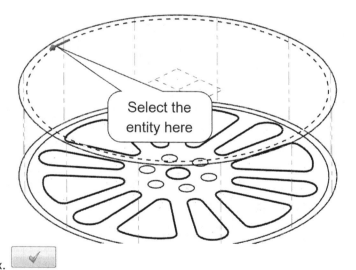

Select the entity here

◆ Select the **OK** button to exit the **Chaining** dialog box.

◆ Select the **OK** button to exit the **Chain Options** dialog box.

◆ In the **Toolpath Type** page, **Dynamic Mill** will be selected.

26.2 Select a 1 - 1/2" Flat Endmill from the Library and set the Tool parameters

* Select **Tool** from the **Tree view list**.

* Click on **Select library tool** button. Select library tool...
* Select the **Filter** button as shown.

* Select the **None** button and then under **Tool Types** choose the **Flat Endmill** icon.
* Under tool diameter pick **Greater Than** and input a value **1.0** as shown in Figure: 26.2.1.

Figure: 26.2.1

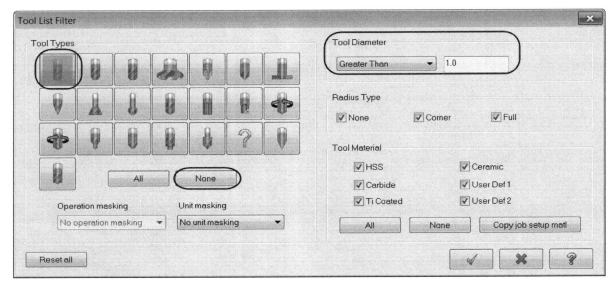

* Select the **OK** button to exit the **Tool List Filter.**
* In the **Tool Selection** dialog box you should only see **Flat Endmill's** larger than **1.0"**.

#	Assembly Name	Tool Name	Holder Name	Dia.	Cor. rad.	Length	# Flutes	Type	Rad. Type
244	–	1-1/2 FL...	–	1.5	0.0	2.5	4	En...	None
245	–	2 INCH F...	–	2.0	0.0	2.75	4	En...	None
313	–	1-3/16 FL...	–	1....	0.0	2.0	4	En...	None

* Select the **1 - 1/2" Flat Endmill** in the **Tool Selection** page.

* Select the **OK** button to exit.

• Make all the necessary changes as shown in <u>Figure: 26.2.2</u>.

Figure: 26.2.2

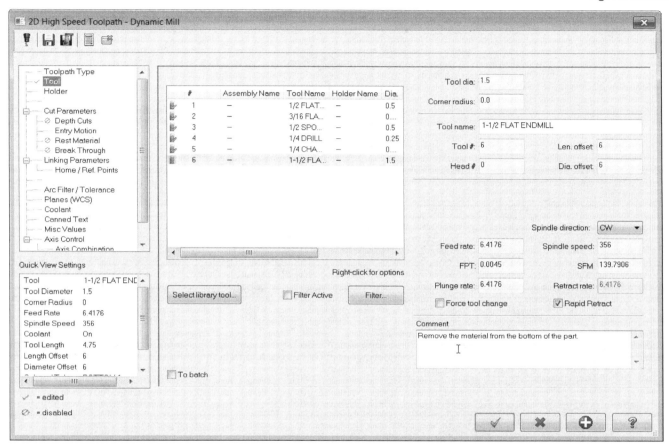

26.3 Set the Cut Parameters

♦ From the **Tree view list**, select **Cut Parameters** and make sure that the parameters are set as shown <u>Figure: 26.3.1</u>.

Figure: 26.3.1

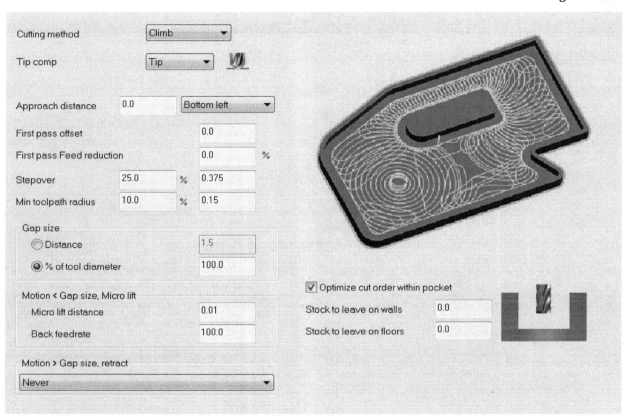

Cutting method	Climb ▼
Tip comp	Tip ▼
Approach distance	0.0 Bottom left ▼
First pass offset	0.0
First pass Feed reduction	0.0 %
Stepover	25.0 % 0.375
Min toolpath radius	10.0 % 0.15

Gap size
- ○ Distance   1.5
- ◉ % of tool diameter   100.0

Motion < Gap size, Micro lift
- Micro lift distance   0.01
- Back feedrate   100.0

Motion > Gap size, retract
- Never ▼

☑ Optimize cut order within pocket

Stock to leave on walls   0.0

Stock to leave on floors   0.0

NOTE: For more information on these settings see page 350.

26.4 Set the Depth Cuts Parameters

◆ From the **Tree view list**, disable the **Depth Cuts** if needed as shown.

☐ Depth cuts

26.5 Set the Entry Motion

◆ Set the **Entry method** to **Helix only**.
◆ Set the **Helix radius** to **0.75** and the rest of the parameters as shown in <u>Figure: 26.5.1</u>.
◆ Enable **Entry feeds / speeds** and set a **Ramp feed rate** of **10.0** Inches per minute, a **Ramp spindle speed** of **800** RPM and **Dwell before cut spindle speed** of **3.0** seconds as shown in <u>Figure: 26.5.1</u>.

Figure: 26.5.1

Entry method	
Helix only ▼	

Chain geometry

(0)   [▷]   [⊗]

Helix radius	0.75
Trochoidal loop radius	0.0
Additional slot width	0.0
☑ Output 3D arc moves	☐ Center helix on point

Z clearance	0.125
⊙ Plunge angle	2.0
○ Entry pitch	0.0

☑ Entry feeds / speeds	
Ramp feed rate	10.0
Ramp spindle speed	3500
Dwell before cut spindle speed	3.0

NOTE: For more information on these settings see page 351.

26.6 Set the Linking Parameters

♦ Select **Linking Parameters** and input the **Depth** of **-1.25** as shown in <u>Figure: 26.6.1</u>.

Figure: 26.6.1

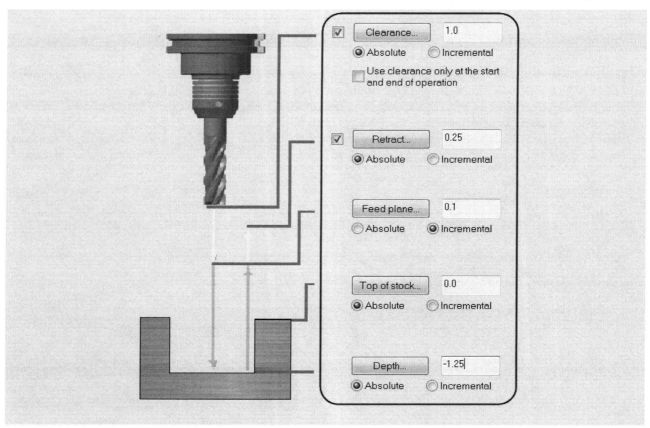

♦ Once complete pick the **OK** button to generate the toolpath.

◆ To **Backplot** and **Verify** your toolpath see page 152 and page 155 to review these procedures.

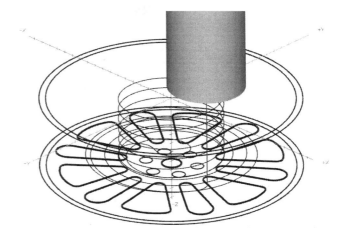

◆ Once complete the part will appear as shown.

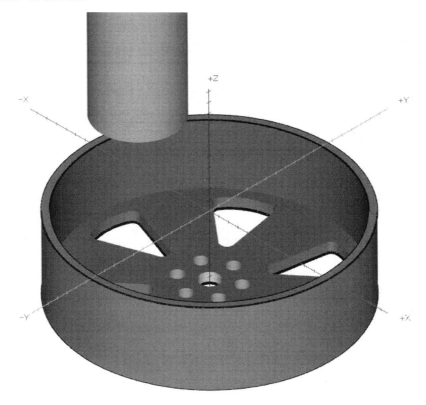

◆ To exit Mastercam Simulator click on the **Close** icon.

STEP 27: RENAME THE NC FILE

The **2D High Speed dynamic mill** operation in Setup #2 kept the NC name from Setup #1. We need to rename this operation so it will create 2 separate programs.

* Select only operation #9.
* Right click on Operation #9, choose the option **Edit selected operations** and then pick **Change NC file name**.

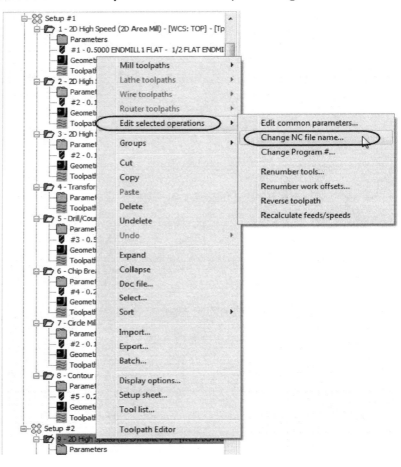

* When the **Enter new NC name** dialog box appears select **"Setup #2"**.

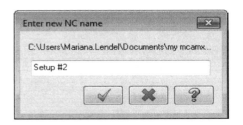

- Select the **OK** button to apply the changed **NC name** to operation **#9**.
- The result you should see **Setup #2.NC** in the last item of text for operation **#8**.

Toolpath - 72.6K - SETUP #1.NC
Setup #2
9 - 2D High Speed (2D Dynamic Area
Parameters
#6 - 1.5000 ENDMILL1 FLAT - 1-
Geometry - (1) chain(s)
Toolpath - 84.6K - SETUP #2.NC

STEP 28: POST THE FILE

- Ensure all operations are selected, if they are not use the button **Select all operations** in the **Toolpaths Manager.**

- Select the **Post selected operations** button from the **Toolpaths Manager.** G1
- In the **Post processing** window make the necessary changes as shown in Figure: 28.0.1.

Figure: 28.0.1

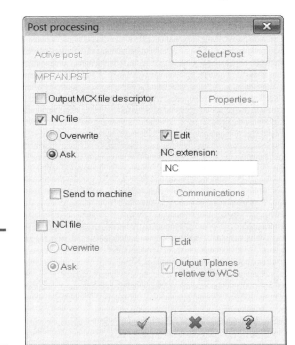

NC File enabled allows you to keep the NC file and to assign the same name as the MCX file.

Edit enabled allows you to automatically launch the default editor.

- Select the **OK** button to continue.
- Save Setup #1 NC file.

♦ Save Setup #2 NC file.
♦ A window with Mastercam Code Expert will be launched and the NC program will appear as shown in <u>Figure: 28.0.2</u>.

Figure: 28.0.2

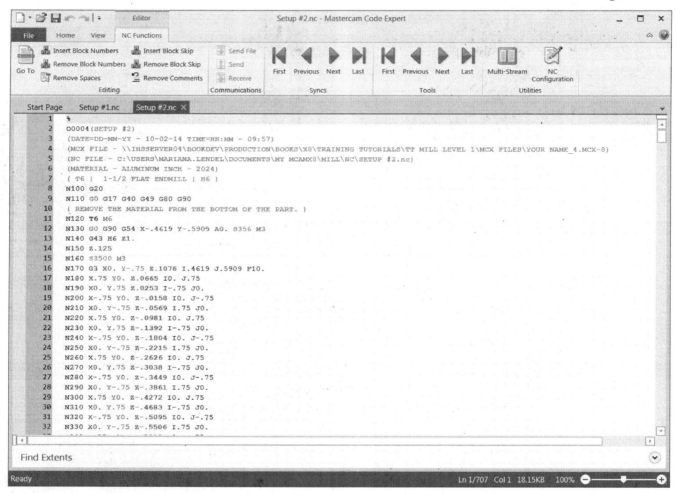

♦ Select the **"X"** box at the upper right corner to exit the editor.

STEP 29: SAVE THE UPDATED MCX FILE

REVIEW EXERCISE -STUDENT PRACTICE

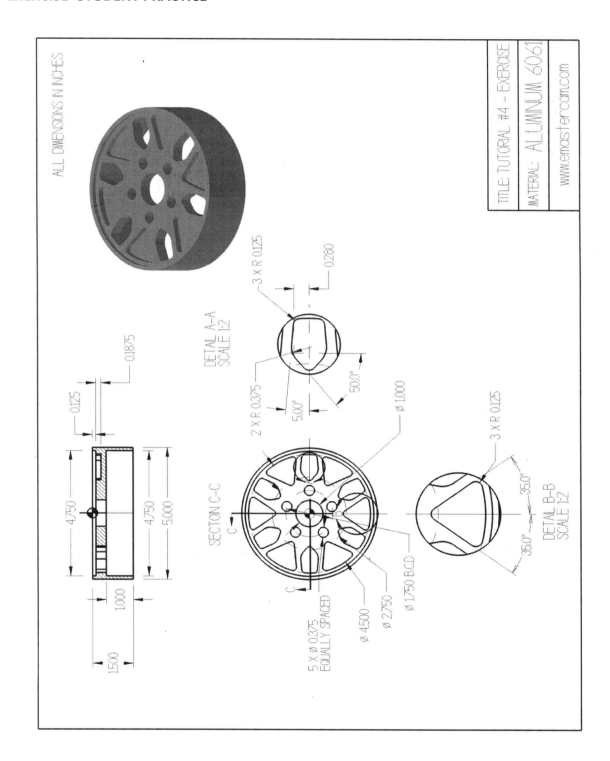

ALL DIMENSIONS IN INCHES

TITLE: TUTORIAL #4 – EXERCISE

MATERIAL: ALUMINUM 6061

www.emastercam.com

DETAIL A-A
SCALE 1:2

3 X R 0.125

0.280

2 X R 0.375

5.00°

50.0°

Ø 1.000

0.1875

0.125

4.750

4.750
5.000

1.000

1.500

SECTION C-C

C

C

5 X Ø 0.375
EQUALLY SPACED

Ø 4.500

Ø 2.750

Ø 1.750 B.C.D

3 X R 0.125

35.0°

35.0°

35.0°

DETAIL B-B
SCALE 1:2

CREATE THE GEOMETRY FOR TUTORIAL #4 EXERCISE

Use these commands to create the geometry:

◆ Create Circle Center Point.
◆ Create Tangent Lines.
◆ Xform Mirror.
◆ Create Arc Tangent.
◆ Create Arc Polar.
◆ Trim/Break/Extend.
◆ Create Fillets.
◆ Delete Entities.
◆ Xform Rotate.
◆ Xform Translate.

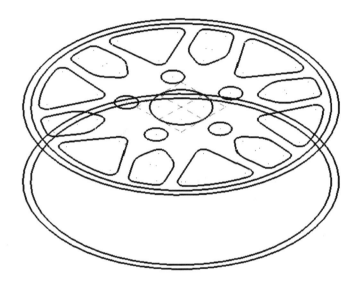

Mastercam X⁸

CREATE THE TOOLPATHS FOR TUTORIAL #4 EXERCISE

Create the Toolpaths for Tutorial #4 Exercise as per the instructions below.

Set the machine properties including the stock setup.

Remove the material in the center of the part.
- Use a **1" Flat Endmill**.
- Disable **Depth Cuts**.
- Set the **Entry Motion**.
- Set the **Depth** according to the drawing.

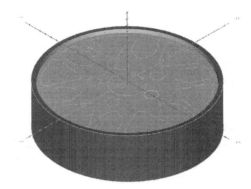

Area Mill one of the large pockets.
- Select Pocket and take note of the angle which the pocket is set at.
- Use a **1/4" Flat Endmill**.
- Disable **Depth Cuts**.
- Set the **Transitions** to **Entry helix**.
- Set the **Top of Stock** and **Depth** according to the drawing.

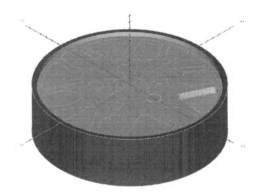

Dynamic Mill one of the small pockets.
- Select the chain and and enable Stay inside.
- Use a **1/4" Flat Endmill**.
- Enable and set **Depth Cuts**.
- Set the **Entry Motion** to **Helix only**.
- Set the **Top of Stock** and **Depth** according to the drawing.

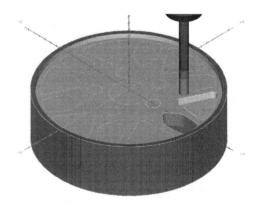

Transform Toolpaths.
- Choose **Rotate** and select **Operation #2** and **#3**.
- Select **Coordinate** and **Operation order**.
- Enable **Copy** source operations.
- Ensure disable posting in selected source operations is enabled.
- Select the **Rotate** tab.
- Input the number of steps **# = 5**.
- **Start angle** = **60.0**.
- **Rotation angle** = **60.0**.

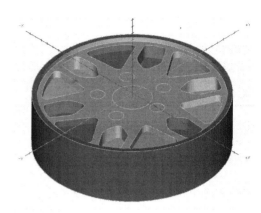

Spot Drill the holes.
- Use a **1/2" Spot Drill**.
- Set the **Cycle** and **Dwell**.
- Set the **Top of Stock** and **Depth** using the depth calculator.

Drill the holes.
- Use a **3/8"Drill**.
- Set the **Cycle** to **Peck** and input your increments.
- Set the **Top of Stock** and **Depth** using the depth calculator.

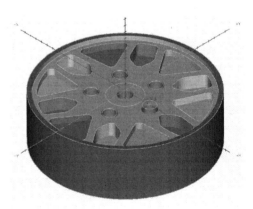

Mastercam. X

Circle Mill the Center Hole.
- Use the **1/4" Flat Endmill.**
- Enable **Roughing**.
- Enable **Depth Cuts** and set **Max rough step** to **0.25"**.
- Enable **Multi Passes** and set **1 Finish** at a **Spacing** of **0.02"**.
- Set the depth to the appropriate depth.

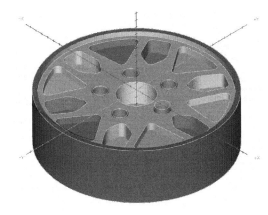

Flip the part over Setup #2.

Set WCS to Bottom and input correct depth.
- Use **Dynamic Mill** and enable **Stay inside** to remove the material starting from the center.
- Use the **1" Flat Endmill**.
- Disable **Depth cuts**.
- Set the **Entry Motion**.
- Set the **Depth** according to the drawing.

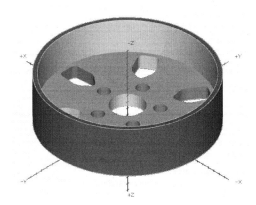

- Your part should appear as shown once complete.

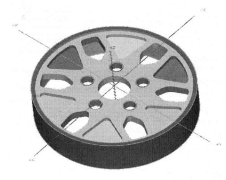

NOTES:

Mastercam. X⁸

TUTORIAL #4 QUIZ

◆ What does Circle Mill toolpath do?

◆ What does a "Dwell before cut spindle speed" do?

◆ What does a transform toolpath operation do?

TUTORIAL #5

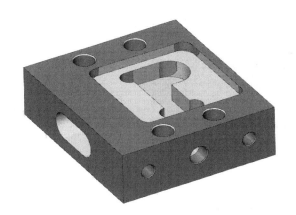

OVERVIEW OF STEPS TAKEN TO CREATE THE FINAL PART:

Import the 2D CAD Model and prepare it to generate Toolpaths from:
* The student will open the Solidworks file in Mastercam.

Create the necessary Toolpaths to machine the part:
* The student will set up the stock size to be used and the clamping method used. Three setups will be used to machine the part from the top and then from the bottom.
* A 2D High Speed Area Mill toolpath will be created to remove the material inside of the step.
* Two 2D High Speed Area Mill toolpaths will be created to remove the material inside the pockets.
* Drill toolpaths will be created to machine the three holes in the front view.
* A Slot Mill toolpath will be created to remove the material inside of the slot from the left side view.

Backplot and Verify the file:
* The Backplot will be used to simulate a step by step process of the tool's movements.
* The Verify will be used to watch a tool machine the part out of a solid model.

Post Process the file to generate the G-code:
* The Student will then post process the file to obtain an NC file containing the necessary code for the machine.

 This tutorial takes approximately two hours to complete.

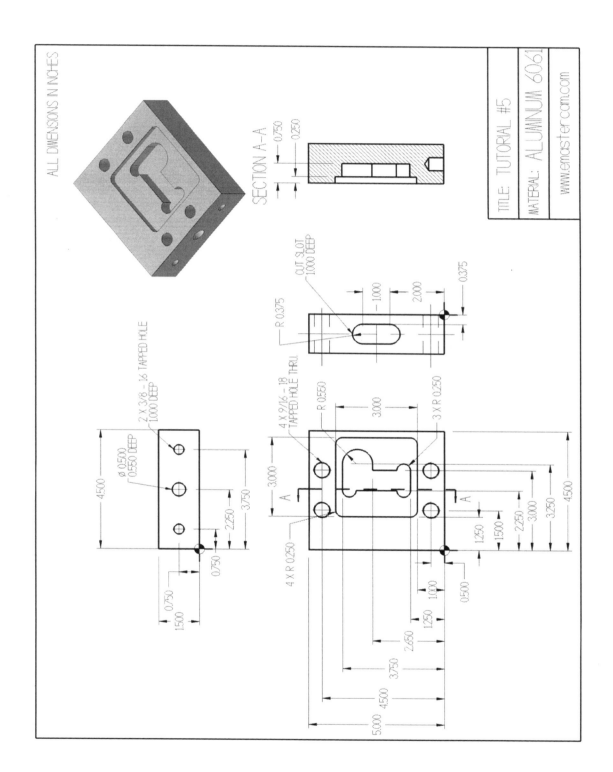

GEOMETRY CREATION

STEP 1: SETTING UP THE GRAPHIC USER INTERFACE

Please refer to the **Getting Started** section to set up the graphics user interface.

STEP 2: IMPORTING THE SOLIDWORKS FILE GEOMETRY

Mastercam lets you read (import) a variety of CAD file types into the Mastercam database. You can also write (export) Mastercam files to a variety of different file formats.

To import a SolidWorks file in Mastercam you have to use the Open function and then select from the File of type list the SolidWorks files.

Download the files from www.emastercam.com/files.

Save the file at a preferred location.

FILE

♦  **Open.**

♦ In the file name extension click on the drop down arrow as shown.

Mastercam. X⁸

• From the File of type list, select Solisworks Files (*.sldprt;*sldasm) as shown.

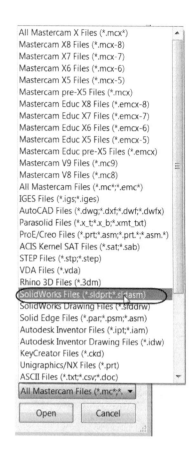

• Find and select **TUTORIAL #5.sldprt.**
• Click on the **Options** button.

• Leave the **Solids** enabled to import the file as a solid and enable **Edge** curves for Mastercam to automatically create curves at the edges of the solid. To better see the curves, enable also **Use System Color for imported Solids** as shown.

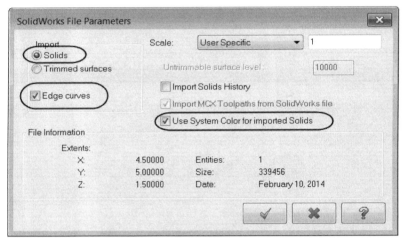

• Select the **OK** button to exit the **SolidWorks File Parameters** dialog box.
• Open the file.

• Select the **Isometric** graphic view.

• Select the **Fit** icon to fit the geometry to the screen.
• The geometry should look as shown.

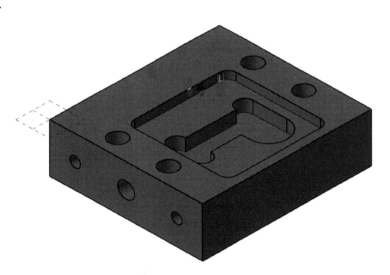

STEP 3: SAVE THE FILE

FILE

• **Save As.**
• File name: "**Your Name_5**".

TOOLPATH CREATION - SETUP 1

SUGGESTED FIXTURE:

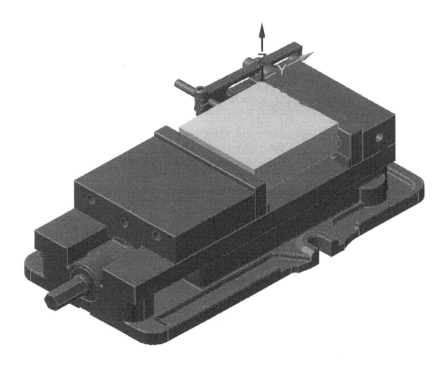

NOTE: In order to machine this part we will have 3 setups and output 3 NC files. To view the second setup see page 480 and to view the third setup see page 519.

SETUP SHEET:

TOOL LIST

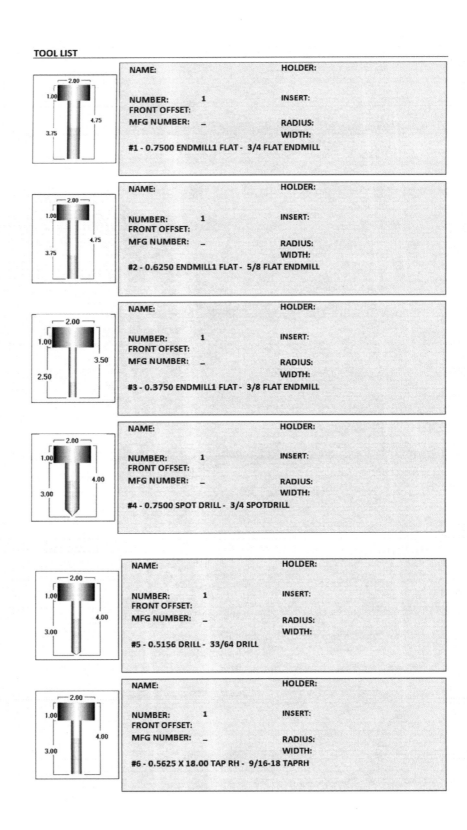

Mastercam. X⁸

STEP 4: SELECT THE MACHINE AND SET UP THE STOCK

In Mastercam, you select a **Machine Definition** before creating any toolpaths. The **Machine Definition** is a model of your machines capabilities and features. It acts like a template for setting up your machine. The machine definition ties together three main components. The schematic model of your machines components, the control definition that models your control capabilities, and the post processor that will generate the required machine code (G-code). For a Mill Level 1 exercise (2D toolpaths) we need just a basic machine definition.

NOTE: For the purpose of this tutorial, we will be using the Default milling machine.

* To display the **Toolpaths Manager** press **Alt + O**.

* Use the **Fit** icon to fit the drawing to the screen.

MACHINE TYPE
* **Mill.**
* **Default.**

* Select the plus sign in front of **Properties** in the **Toolpaths Manager** to expand the **Toolpaths Group Properties.**

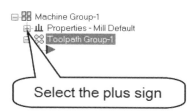

* Select **Tool Settings** to set the tool parameters.

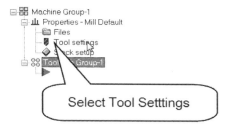

◆ Change the parameters to match the Figure: 4.0.1.

Figure: 4.0.1

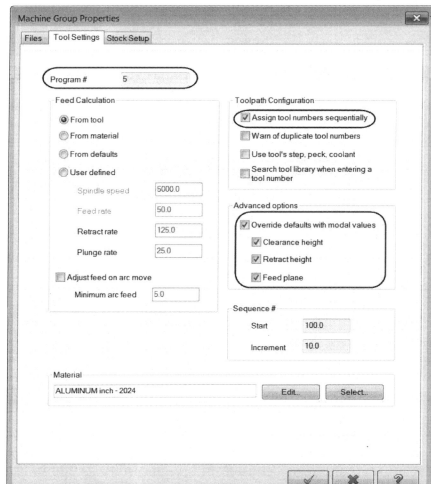

Program # is used to enter a number if your machine tool requires a number for a program name.

Assign tool numbers sequentially allows you to overwrite the tool number from the library with the next available tool number. (First operation tool number 1; Second operation tool number 2, etc.)

Warn of duplicate tool numbers allows you to get a warning if you enter two tools with the same number.

Override defaults with modal values enables the system to keep the values that you enter.

Feed Calculation set **From tool** uses feed rate, plunge rate, retract rate and spindle speed from the tool definition.

◆ Select the **Stock Setup** tab to define the stock.
◆ Pick the **Rectangular** shape option.

♦ Pick the **All Entities** button to define the stock size as shown in <u>Figure: 4.0.2</u>.

Figure: 4.0.2

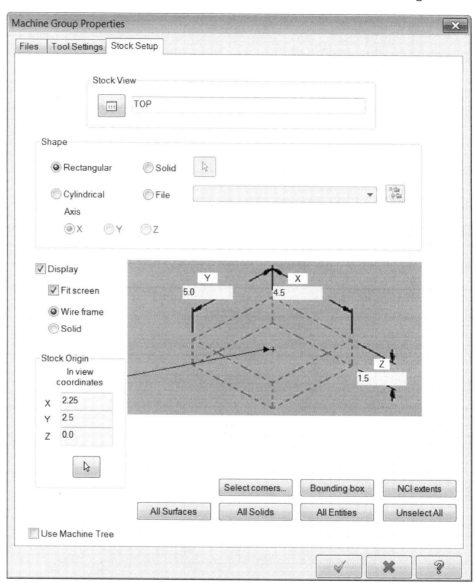

The **Stock Origin** values adjust the positioning of the stock, ensuring that you have equal amount of extra stock around the finished part.

Display options allow you to set the stock as **Wireframe** and to fit the stock to the screen. (Fit Screen)

NOTE: The **stock** model that you create can be displayed with the part geometry when viewing the file or the toolpaths, during backplot, or while verifying toolpaths. In the graphics, the plus shows you where the stock origin is. The default position is the middle of the stock.

♦ Select the **OK** button to exit **Machine Group Properties**.

• The stock model will appear as shown.

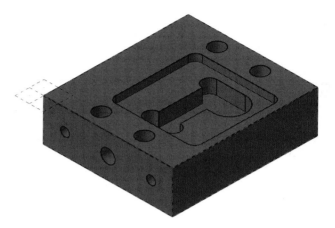

> **NOTE:** You may not be able to see the stock very clearly due to the fact that the stock is the same size as the part. The stock is not geometry and can not be selected.
> There will not be a facing toolpath because the stock is already to size.

STEP 5: 2D HIGH SPEED AREA MILL

2D High Speed Area Mill allows you to machine pockets, material that other toolpaths left behind, and standing bosses or cores. The toolpath depends on the **Machining strategy** that you choose in the **Chain Options**. If the strategy choosed is **From outside**, the toolpaths starts at the outmost chain and works its way in taking on the final shape of the part as it approaches the final pass. You can also machine pockets in which case the strategy selected is **Start inside** which keeps the tool inside the machining regions helical entries and tangent stepovers create efficient motion for your machine. Cut parameters let you control smoothing to create the best toolpath, avoiding sharp corners or direction changes.

Toolpath Preview:

5.1 Chain Selection

TOOLPATHS
- **2D High Speed.**

- **Area.**

- When the new NC name dialog box appears select the **OK** button to accept the name.

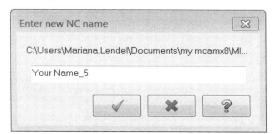

- From the **Chain Options**, click on the **Select** button.

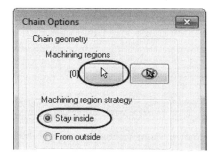

* When the chaining dialog box appears select **C-plane** as shown.
* Leave the chaining method set to **Chain** as shown in <u>Figure: 5.1.1</u>.

Figure: 5.1.1

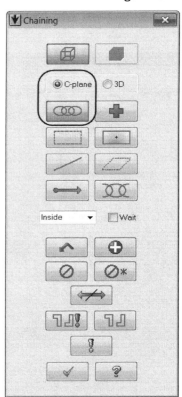

Cplane chains only the entities that are parallel to the current construction plane and at the same Z depth as the first entity you chain.

* Select the bottom of the pocket as shown in <u>Figure: 5.1.2</u>.

Figure: 5.1.2

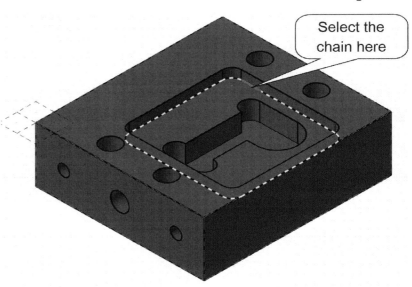

Select the chain here

• Select the **OK** button to exit the **Chaining** dialog box.

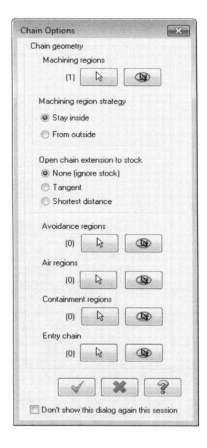

• Select the **OK** button to exit the **Chain Options**.
• In the **Toolpath Type** page, make sure that **Area Mill** is selected.

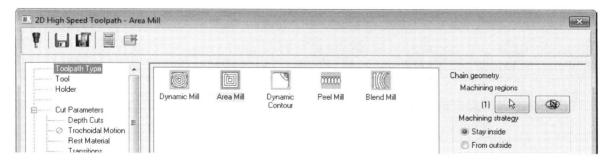

5.2 Select a 3/4" Flat endmill from the library and set the Tool parameters

◆ Select **Tool** from the **Tree view list**.

◆ Click on **Select library tool** button.
◆ Select the **Filter** button as shown.

◆ Select the **None** button and then under **Tool Types** choose the **Flat Endmill** icon.
◆ Under tool diameter pick **Equal** and input a value of **0.75** as shown in <u>Figure: 5.2.1</u>.

Figure: 5.2.1

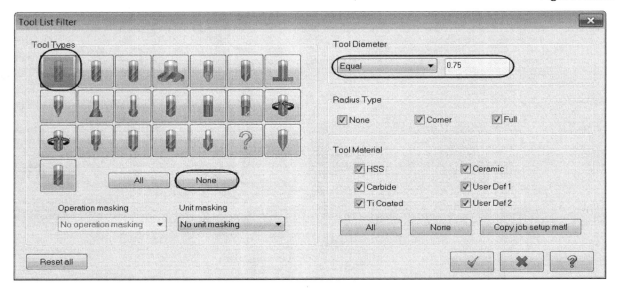

◆ Select the **OK** button to exit the **Tool List Filter.**
◆ In the **Tool Selection** dialog box you should only see a **3/4" Flat Endmill**.

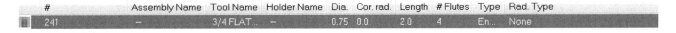

#	Assembly Name	Tool Name	Holder Name	Dia.	Cor. rad.	Length	# Flutes	Type	Rad. Type
241	–	3/4 FLAT...	–	0.75	0.0	2.0	4	En...	None

◆ Select the **3/4" Flat Endmill** in the **Tool Selection** page and then select the **OK** button to exit.

◆ Make all the necessary changes as shown in <u>Figure: 5.2.2</u>.

Figure: 5.2.2

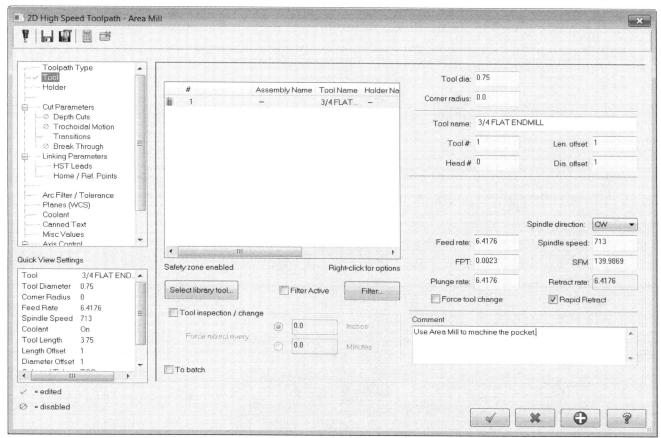

5.3 Set the Cut Parameters

- From the **Tree view list**, select **Cut Parameters**.
- Enable **Corner rounding** and ensure the settings appear as shown in Figure: 5.3.1.

Figure: 5.3.1

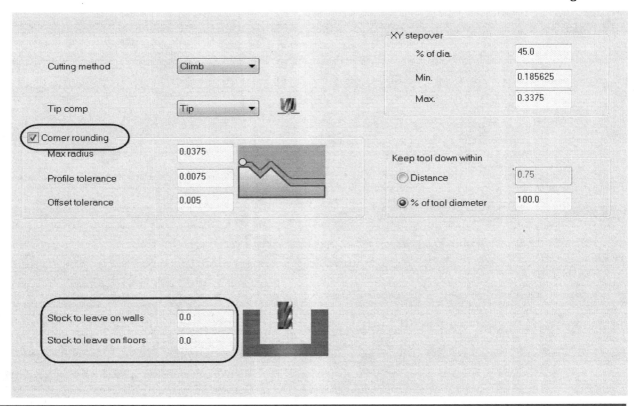

Corner rounding replaces sharp corners with arcs for faster and smoother transitions in tool direction. For more information on the parameters select the **Help** button [?] and then the **Field definitions** tab.

Max radius inputs the radius of the largest arc that you will allow Mastercam to insert to replace a corner. Larger arcs will result in a smoother toolpath but with a greater deviatation from the part corner.

Profile tolerance represents the maximum distance that the outermost profile of a toolpath with corner rounding can deviate from the original toolpath.

Mastercam. X⁸

5.4 Set the Depth Cuts Parameters

◆ From the **Tree view list**, select the **Depth Cuts Parameters** and make sure it is disabled as shown in
Figure: 5.4.1.

Figure: 5.4.1

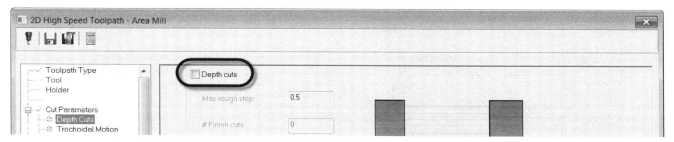

5.5 Set the Transitions

◆ Enable **Entry helix**, set the **Entry helix** to **0.500** and ensure the parameters are the same as shown in
Figure: 5.5.1.

Figure: 5.5.1

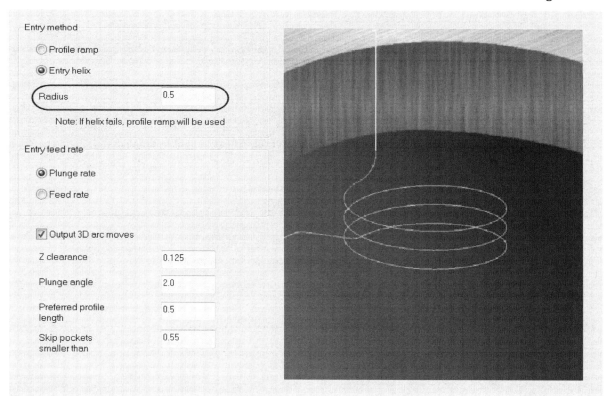

5.6 Set the Linking Parameters

◆ Select **Linking Parameters,** enable **Clearance** and input a value of **1.0**.
◆ You will notice the depth has been input based on the geometry we selected as shown in Figure: 5.6.1.

Figure: 5.6.1

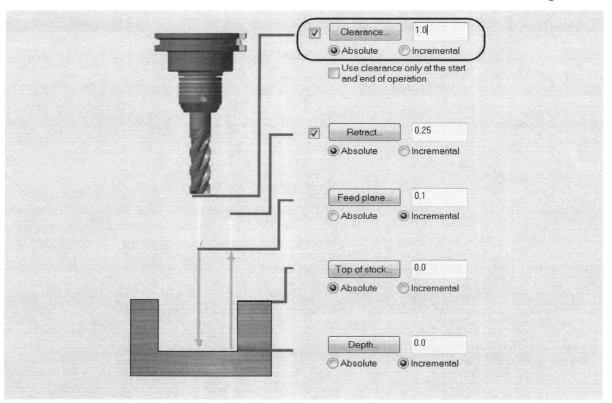

> **NOTE:** The **Depth** set to **Incremental** and **zero** is relative to the location of the chained geometry which was selected at the bottom of the pocket.

◆ Once complete pick the **OK** button to generate the toolpath.

STEP 6: BACKPLOT THE TOOLPATHS

Backplotting shows the path the tools take to cut the part. This display lets you spot errors in the program before you machine the part. As you backplot toolpaths, Mastercam displays additional information such as the X, Y, and Z coordinates, the path length, the minimum and maximum coordinates and the cycle time. It also shows any collisions between the workpiece and the tool.

◆ Make sure that the toolpaths are selected (signified by the green check mark on the folder icon). If the operation is not selected choose the **Select all operations** icon.

◆ Select the **Backplot selected operations** button.

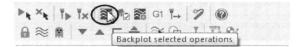

NOTE: Mastercam launches a new window that allows you to check the part using **Backplot** or **Verify**. For more information on how to set and use **Backplot** and **Verify** please check Tutorial 2 page 152.

◆ In the Visibility area make sure that the Workpiece is enabled as shown.
◆ Select the **Play** button in the **VCR** bar to run **Backplot**.

* After Backplot is completed the toolpath should look as shown.

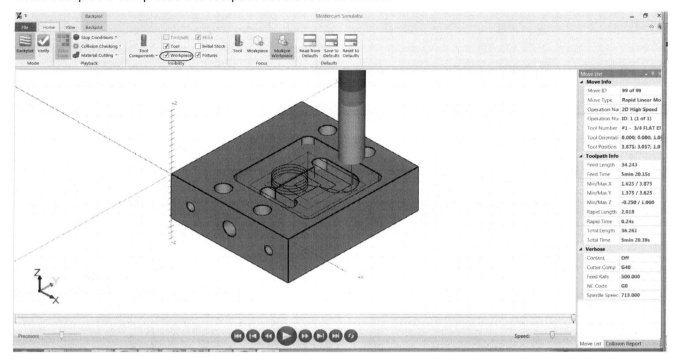

STEP 7: SIMULATE THE TOOLPATH IN VERIFY

Verify Mode shows the path the tools take to cut the part with material removal. This display lets you spot errors in the program before you machine the part. As you verify toolpaths, Mastercam displays additional information such as the X, Y, and Z coordinates, the path length, the minimum and maximum coordinates and the cycle time. It also shows any collisions between the workpiece and the tool.

* From **Mastercam Backplot Home** tab, switch to **Verify** and disable **Workpiece** in the **Visibility** and **Focus** as shown in <u>Figure: 7.0.1</u>.

Figure: 7.0.1

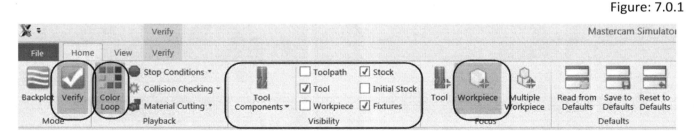

* Select the **Play** button in the **VCR** bar to run **Verify**.

• The part will appear as shown.

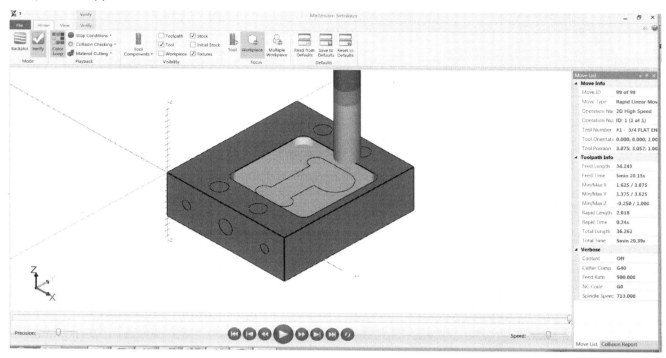

• To go back to Mastercam window, minimize Mastercam Simulator window as shown.

STEP 8: 2D HIGH SPEED AREA MILL

In this step you will learn how to copy a toolpath and reselect geometry. The main advantage of copying a toolpath is the parameters for the 1st toolpath remain intact for the second toolpath.

Toolpath Preview:

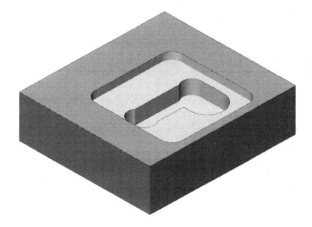

* To remove the toolpath display, from the Toolpaths Manager, click on the **Toggle display on selected operations** or press **Alt + T**.

8.1 Copy the Previous Toolpath

* Select operation #1.

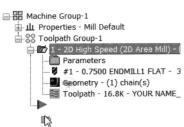

* Right click and hold the right mouse button down and drag the operation to a point below it as shown.

* Release the right mouse button and select the option **Copy After.**

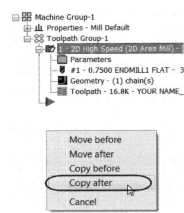

* Select the **Move insert arrow down one item** button to move the insert arrow down.

Mill Level 1 Training Tutorial

- The **Insert Arrow** should appear at the bottom of the list as shown in Figure: 8.1.1.

Figure: 8.1.1

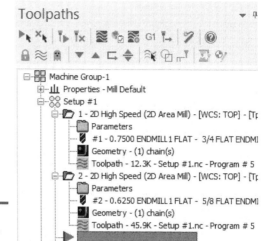

Insert Arrow controls where the new operation will be inserted.

8.2 Re-Chain the Geometry

- In Operation #2 pick the **Geometry** as shown.

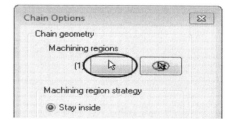

- Click on the **Select** button as shown.

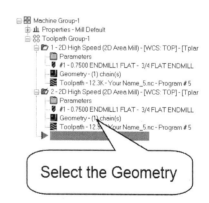

- When the **Chain Manager** appears select **Chain 1**.

* Right click and pick the option **Rechain all** as shown.

* When the **Chaining** dialog box appears select **C-plane.**

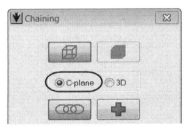

* Select the bottom of the pocket as shown in Figure: 8.2.1.

Figure: 8.2.1

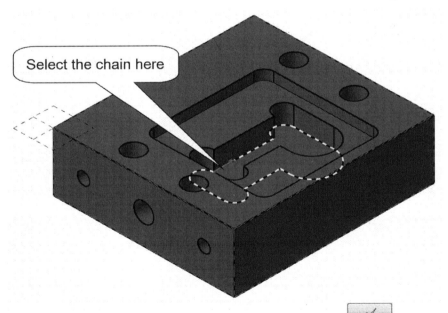

Select the chain here

* Once the geometry has been selected choose the **OK** button to exit the **Chaining** dialog box.

* Pick the **OK** button to exit the **Chain Manager** box.

* Pick the **OK** button to exit the **Chain Options** box.

8.3 Select a 5/8" Flat Endmill from the Library and set the Tool Parameters

♦ Choose **Parameters** under Operation #2.

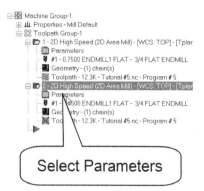

Select Parameters

♦ Select **Tool** from the **Tree view list**.

♦ Click on the **Select library tool** button.

♦ Select the **Filter** button.

Filter...
☐ Filter Active

♦ Select the **None** button and then under **Tool Types** choose the **Flat Endmill** icon.
♦ Under tool diameter pick **Equal** and input a value of **0.625** as shown in Figure: 8.3.1.

Figure: 8.3.1

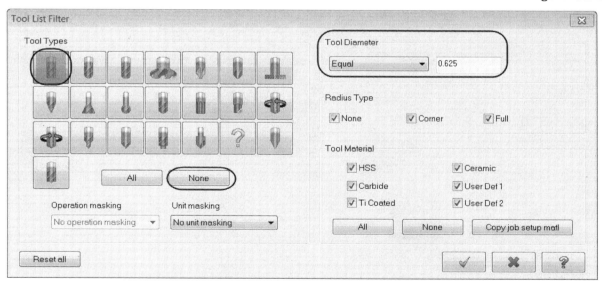

♦ Select the **OK** button to exit the **Tool List Filter.**

* In the **Tool Selection** dialog box you should only see a **5/8" Flat Endmill**.

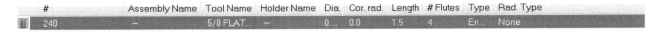

#	Assembly Name	Tool Name	Holder Name	Dia.	Cor. rad.	Length	# Flutes	Type	Rad. Type
240	–	5/8 FLAT...	–	0....	0.0	1.5	4	En..	None

* Select the **5/8" Flat Endmill** in the **Tool Selection** page and then select the **OK** button to exit.
* Make all the necessary changes as shown in Figure: 8.3.2.

Figure: 8.3.2

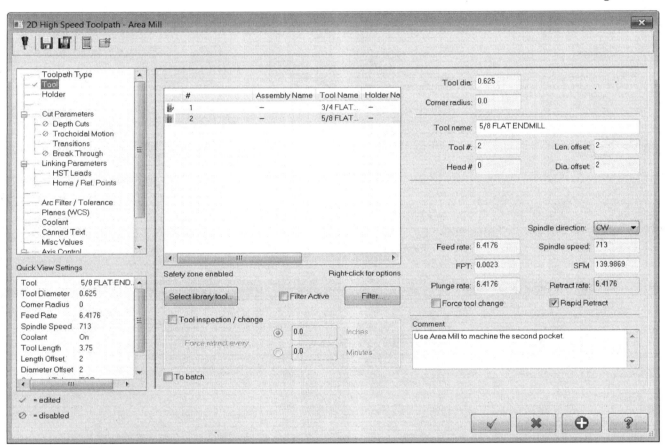

NOTE: Since this toolpath has been copied all the parameters remain the same. Therefore the only parameters shown are the ones we will be changing.

8.4 Set the Depth Cuts parameters

◆ From the **Tree view list**, select the **Depth Cuts** and enable **Depth Cuts**.
◆ Input a **Max rough step** of **0.25** as shown in <u>Figure: 8.4.1</u>.

Figure: 8.4.1

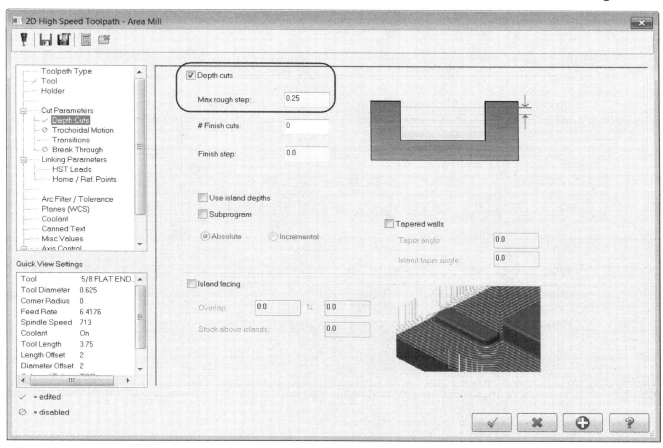

8.5 Set the Transitions

- Enable **Profile ramp** and enter a **Preferred Profile length** of **0.75** as shown in Figure: 8.5.1.

Figure: 8.5.1

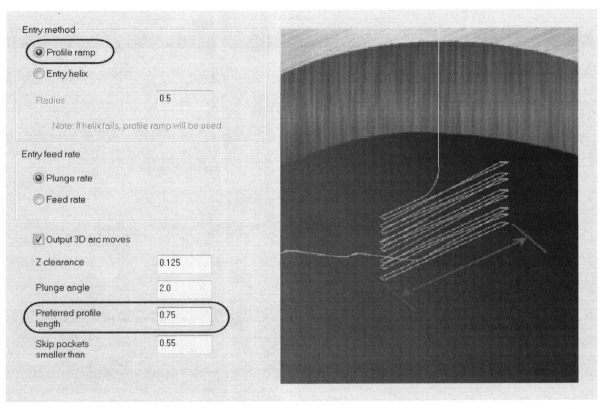

Profile Ramp creates a ramp motion to descend the tool.

Preferred profile length enters a minimum size for the profile in order for a ramp to be created.

Mill Level 1 Training Tutorial

8.6 Set the Linking Parameters

- Select **Linking Parameters** from the **Tree view list**.
- Set the **Top of Stock** and the **Depth** to **Absolute**.
- Select the **Top of Stock** button (this will return you to the graphics screen).

- Pick the line endpoint as shown in Figure: 8.6.1.

Figure: 8.6.1

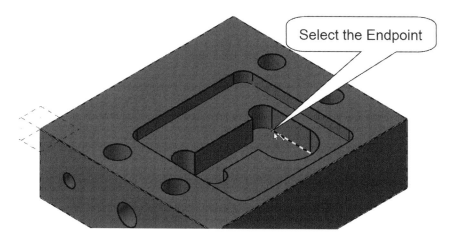

- Choose the **Depth** button (this will return you to the graphics screen).
- Pick the line endpoint as shown in Figure: 8.6.2.

Figure: 8.6.2

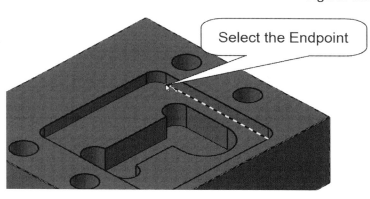

♦ **Top of Stock will be** set to **-0.25** and the **Depth** set to **-0.75** as shown in Figure: 8.6.3.

Figure: 8.6.3

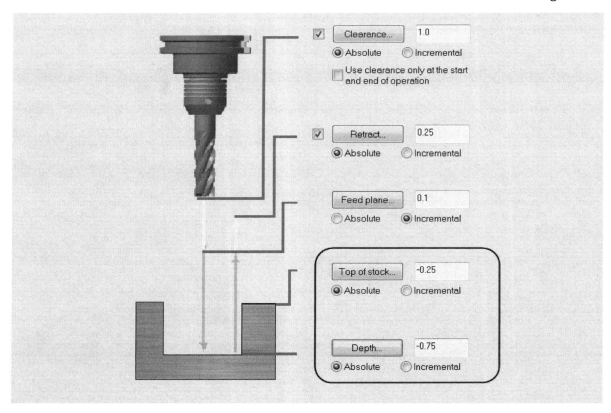

♦ Select the **OK** button to generate the **Area Mill** toolpath.
♦ Choose to **Regenerate all dirty operations**.

8.7 Backplot the toolpath

♦ Once the operation has been regenerated **Backplot** the toolpath. See page 437 to review these procedures.

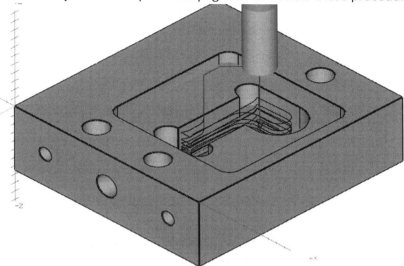

♦ To go back to Mastercam window, minimize Mastercam Simulator window as shown.

8.8 Verify the toolpaths

♦ To verify all toolpaths, from the Toolpaths Manager, choose the **Select all operations** icon.
♦ See page 438 to review these procedures.

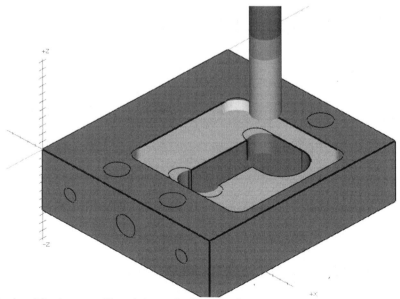

♦ To go back to Mastercam window, minimize Mastercam Simulator window as shown.

STEP 9: AREA MILL T0 REMACHINE THE REMAINING MATERIAL

High Speed Area Mill toolpath with Rest Material options enabled targets material left behind by the previous toolpaths.

Toolpath Preview:

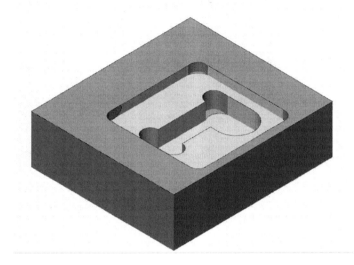

9.1 Copy the previous Toolpaths

• Pick the **Select all operations** button.

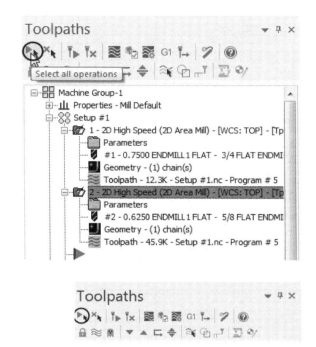

NOTE: Both toolpaths should be selected as shown.

● Right click and hold the right mouse button down and drag the operation to a point below it as shown in Figure: 9.1.1.

Figure: 9.1.1

```
Machine Group-1
   Properties - Mill Default
   Toolpath Group-1
      1 - 2D High Speed (2D Area Mill) - [WC
         Parameters
         #1 - 0.7500 ENDMILL1 FLAT - 3/4 F
         Geometry - (1) chain(s)
         Toolpath - 16.8K - YOUR NAME_6.N
      2 - 2D High Speed (2D Area Mill) - [WC
         Parameters
         #2 - 0.6250 ENDMILL1 FLAT - 5/8 F
         Geometry - (1) chain(s)
         Toolpath - 55.1K - YOUR NAME_6.N
```

● Release the right mouse button and select the option **Copy After** as shown in Figure: 9.1.2.

Figure: 9.1.2

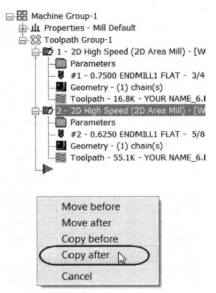

◆ Pick the button twice to move the insert arrow down as shown.

◆ Choose **Parameters** under operation #3.

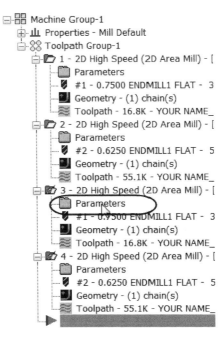

9.2 Select a 3/8" Flat Endmill from the Library and set the Tool parameters

◆ Select **Tool** from the **Tree view list**.

◆ Click on the **Select library tool** button.
◆ Select the **Filter** button.

◆ Select the **None** button and then under **Tool Types** choose the **Flat Endmill** Icon.

* Under tool diameter pick **Equal** and input a value of **0.375** as shown in <u>Figure: 9.2.1</u>.

Figure: 9.2.1

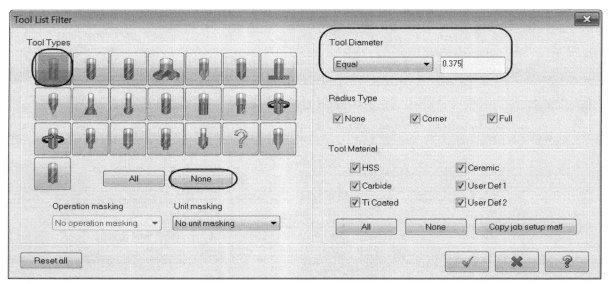

* Select the **OK** button to exit the **Tool List Filter.**
* In the **Tool Selection** dialog box you should only see a **3/8" Flat Endmill**.

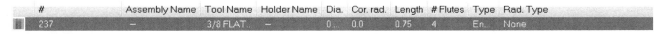

#	Assembly Name	Tool Name	Holder Name	Dia.	Cor. rad.	Length	# Flutes	Type	Rad. Type
237	—	3/8 FLAT..	—	0..	0.0	0.75	4	En..	None

* Select the **3/8" Flat Endmill** in the **Tool Selection** page and then select the **OK** button to exit.

◆ Make the necessary changes as shown in <u>Figure: 9.2.2</u>.

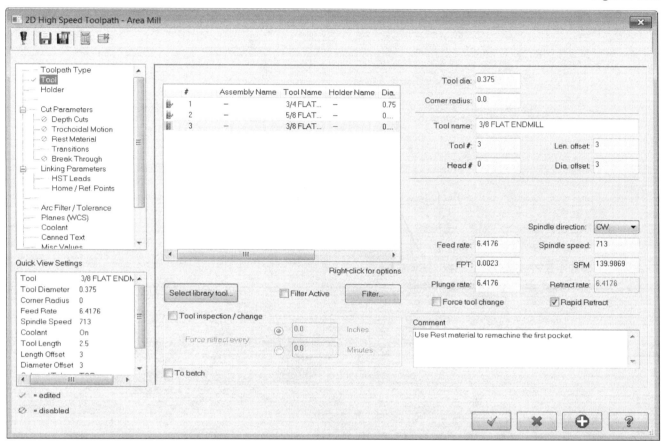

9.3 Set the Rest Material

• Enable Rest Material and set the parameters the same as shown in Figure: 9.3.1.

Figure: 9.3.1

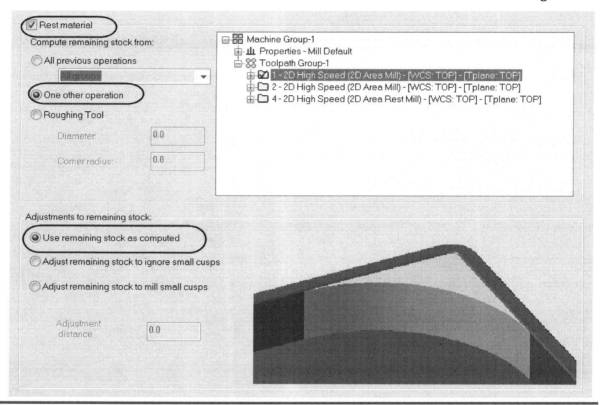

Rest material page allows you to set how Mastercam calculates the remaining stock.

One other operation calculates the remaining stock from one source operation.

• Choose the **OK** button to generate the toolpath.

NOTE: Since this toolpath has been copied all the parameters remain the same. Therefore we do not have to view all the parameters.

9.4 Repeat the same steps for operation #4

- Make sure that in Rest material page you enable the second operation.
- Regenerate the dirty operations.

9.5 Backplot and Verify the toolpaths

- To **Backplot** both toolpaths see page 437.
- To select both operations, hold down the **Ctrl** key.
- The toolpaths should look as shown.

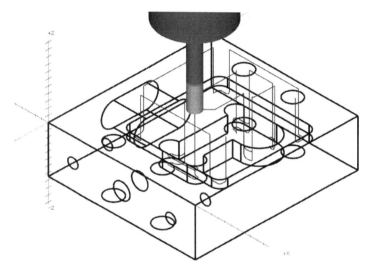

- To go back to Mastercam window, minimize Mastercam Simulator window as shown.

- To **Verify** make sure that all toolpaths are selected by choosing the **Select all operations** icon.
- See page 438 for more information.

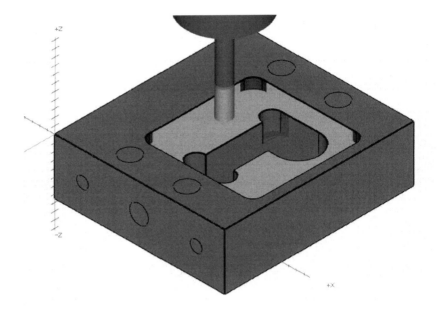

- To go back to Mastercam window, minimize Mastercam Simulator window as shown.

STEP 10: SPOT DRILL THE HOLE

Spot Drilling the holes allows you to start the hole. In this operation we will use the spot drill to chamfer the hole before drilling it.

Toolpath Preview:

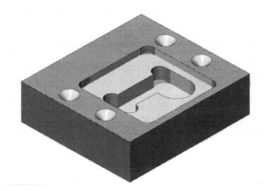

TOOLPATHS

- 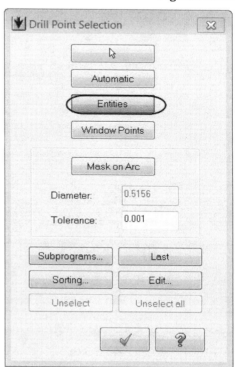 **Drill.**
- In the **Drill Point Selection** dialog box choose the option **Entities** as shown in Figure: 10.0.1.

Figure: 10.0.1

* Select the circles as shown in <u>Figure: 10.0.2</u>.

Figure: 10.0.2

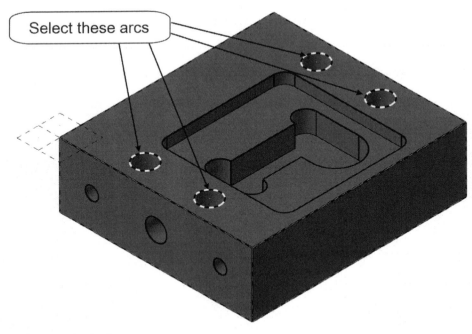

Select these arcs

* Hit **Enter** once the entities have been selected.

* Select the **OK** button in the **Drill Point Selection** dialog box once you have picked the arc.
* In the **Toolpath Type** page, the **Drill** toolpath will be selected.

Drill   Circle Mill   Point   Helix Bore   Thread Mill

10.1 Select a 3/4"Spot Drill from the Library and set the Tool Parameters

* Select **Tool** from the **Tree view list**.

* Click on the **Select library tool** button. [Select library tool...]
* To be able to see just the spot drill select the **Filter** button.

[Filter...]
☐ Filter Active
367 of 367 tools

◆ Under **Tool Types** select the **None** button and then choose the **Spot drill** icon.
◆ Ensure the **Diameter** is set to **0.75** as shown in <u>Figure: 10.1.1</u>.

Figure: 10.1.1

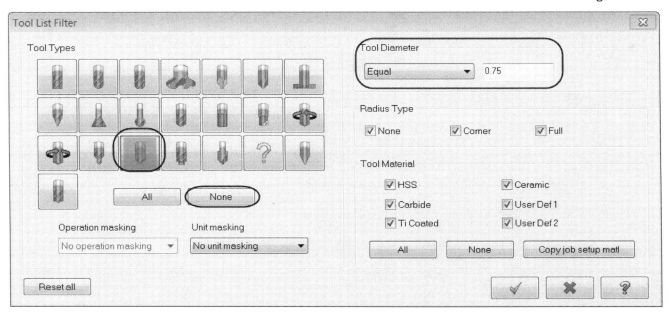

◆ Select the **OK** button to exit the **Tool List Filter** dialog box.
◆ Select the **3/4" Spot Drill**.

#	Assembly Name	Tool Name	Holder Name	Dia.	Cor. rad.	Length	# Flutes	Type	Rad. Type
198	—	3/4 SPO...	—	0.75	0.0	2.0	4	Sp...	None

◆ Select the tool in the **Tool Selection** page and then select the **OK** button to exit.

• Make the necessary changes to the **Tool** page as shown in <u>Figure: 10.1.2</u>.

Figure: 10.1.2

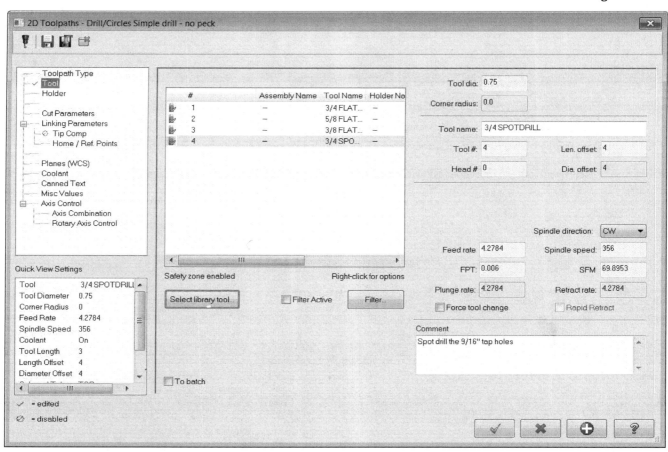

10.2 Set the Cut Parameters

◆ Select **Cut Parameters** and make the necessary changes as shown in Figure: 10.2.1.

Figure: 10.2.1

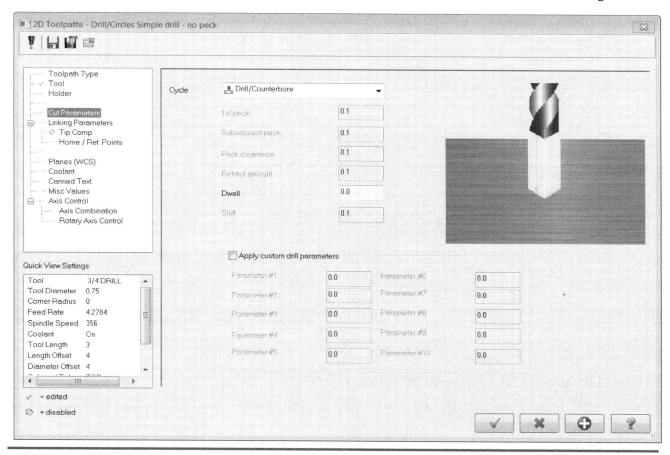

Drill/Counterbore is recommended for drilling holes with depths of less than three times the tools diameter.

Dwell sets the amount of time in seconds that the tool remains at the bottom of a drilled hole.

10.3 Set the Linking Parameters

* Choose **Linking Parameters**, ensure clearance is enabled and set the **Top of stock** and the **Depth** to **Absolute** and **0**.

* To input the depth select the **Calculator** icon.
* Input the following equation in the **Finish diameter** area: **9/16 + 0.05** (diameter of the finish hole + 2 X the chamfer size) as shown in <u>Figure: 10.3.1</u> and hit **Enter** to calculate the **Depth.**

Figure: 10.3.1

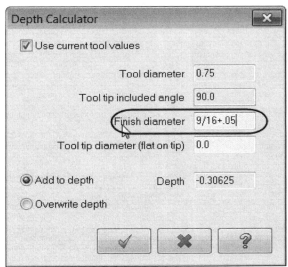

* Select the **OK** button to exit the **Depth Calculator**.

• You will now see the depth we calculated for the spot drilling operation set in the **Depth** field as shown in Figure: 10.3.2.
• This will chamfer the hole for the tapping operation.

Figure: 10.3.2

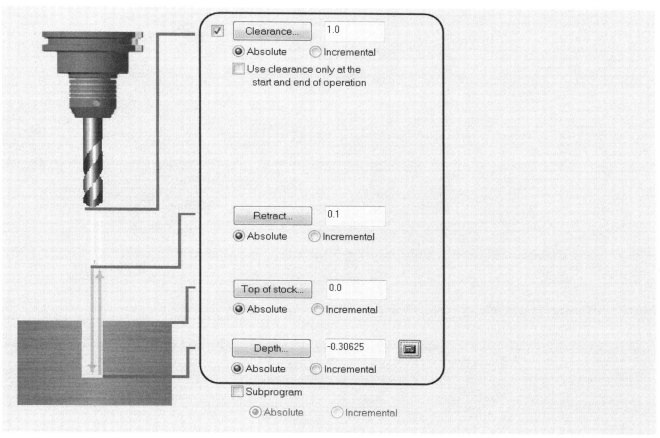

• Select the **OK** button to exit the **Drill/Counterbore** parameters.

10.4 Backplot and Verify the toolpaths

◆ To **Backplot** and **Verify** your toolpaths see page 437 and page 438.

◆ To verify all toolpaths, from the Toolpaths Manager, choose the **Select all operations** icon.
◆ The part should look as shown.

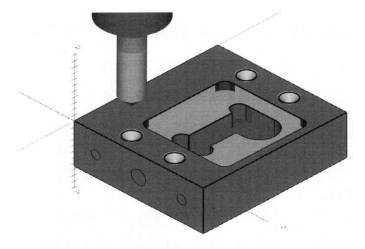

STEP 11: DRILL THE HOLES

In this example we will drill the holes through the part.

Toolpath Preview:

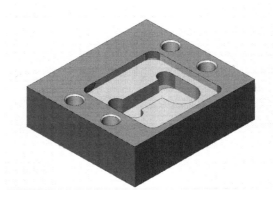

TOOLPATHS

◆ Drill.

• In the **Drill Point Selection** dialog box choose the option **Last**.

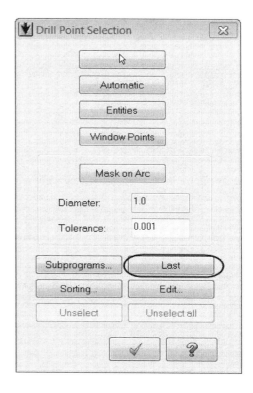

NOTE: This option will automatically select the hole for you based off the selection from the previous drill operation.

• Select the **OK** button in the **Drill Point Selection** dialog box to accept the 4 drill points.
• In the **Toolpath Type** page, the **Drill** toolpath will be selected.

Drill   Circle Mill   Point   Helix Bore   Thread Mill

11.1 Select a 33/64" Drill from the Library and set the Tool Parameters

• Select **Tool** from the **Tree view list**.

• Click on the **Select library tool** button.
• To be able to see just the spot drill select the **Filter** button.

Filter Active
367 of 367 tools

- Under **Tool Types** select the **None** button and then choose the **Drill** icon as shown in Figure: 11.1.1.
- Under **Tool Diameter** select **Equal** and enter the value **33/64** as shown in Figure: 11.1.1.

Figure: 11.1.1

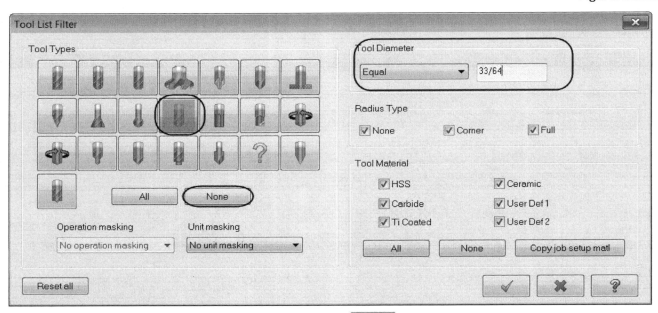

- Select the **OK** button to exit the **Tool List Filter** dialog box.
- At this point you should see only a **33/64"** drill.
- From that list select the **33/64" Drill** as shown in Figure: 11.1.2.

Figure: 11.1.2

#	Assembly Name	Tool Name	Holder Name	Dia.	Cor. rad.	Length	# Flutes	Type	Rad. Type
142	–	33/64 D...	–	0...	0.0	2.0	2	Drill	None

- Select the tool in the **Tool Selection** page and then choose the **OK** button to exit.

♦ Make the necessary changes to the **Tool** page as shown in <u>Figure: 11.1.3</u>.

Figure: 11.1.3

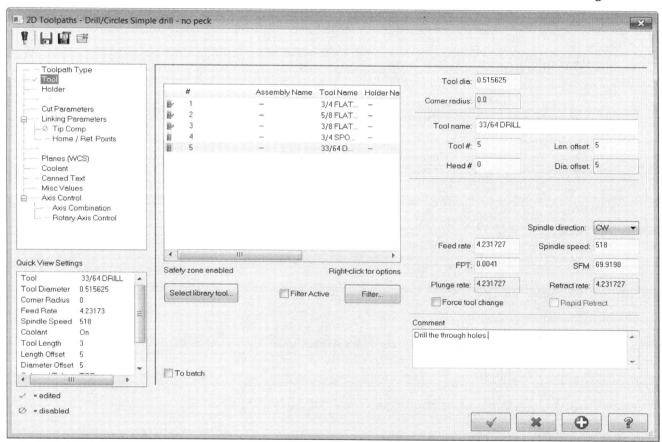

11.2 Set the Cut Parameters

♦ Select **Cut Parameters**, change the drill **Cycle** to **Peck Drill** and input a **1st peck** value of **0.25** as shown in <u>Figure: 11.2.1</u>.

Figure: 11.2.1

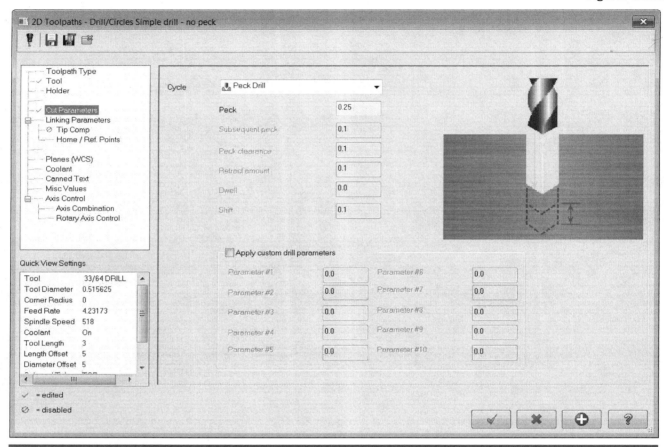

Peck Drill is recommended for drilling holes with depths of more than three times the tool diameter. The drill retracts fully out of the drilled hole to remove material.

Peck sets the depth for the peck move.

11.3 Set the Linking Parameters

◆ Choose **Linking Parameters** and input a **depth** value of **-1.5** as shown in <u>Figure: 11.3.1</u>.

Figure: 11.3.1

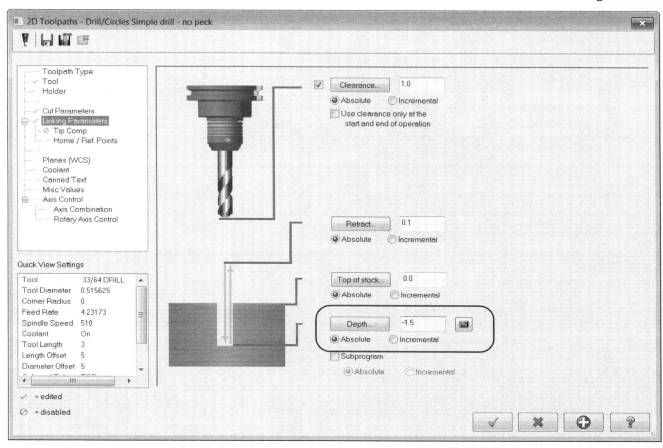

11.4 Set the Tip Comp Parameters

• Pick **Tip Comp** and enable this option. Input a **Breakthrough amount** of **0.1** as shown in Figure: 11.4.1.

Figure: 11.4.1

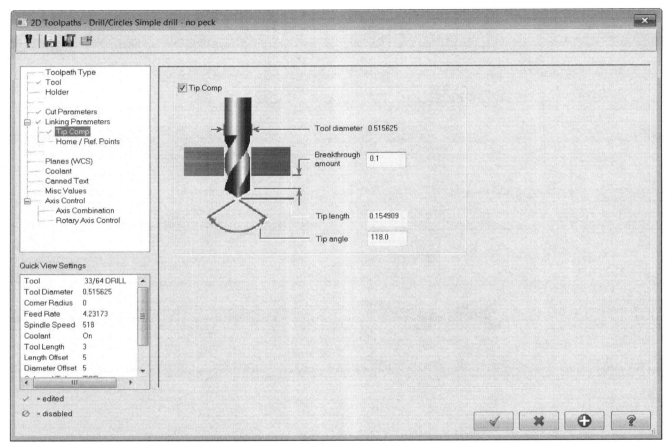

• Select the **OK** button to exit the **Drill/Counterbore** parameters.

11.5 Backplot and Verify

◆ To **Backplot** and **Verify** the toolpaths see page 437 and page 438.

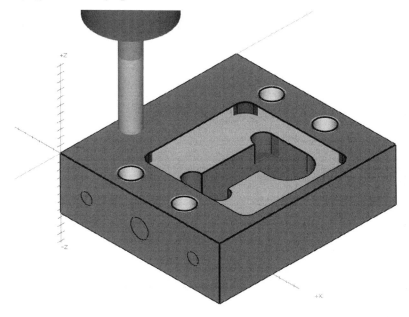

STEP 12: TAP THE HOLES

Tap cycle taps right or left internal threaded holes.

Toolpath Preview:

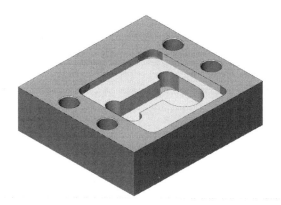

TOOLPATHS

◆  **Drill.**

• In the **Drill Point Selection** dialog box choose the option **Last**.

NOTE: This option will automatically select the hole for you based off the selection from the previous drill operation.

• Select the **OK** button in the **Drill Point Selection** dialog box to accept the 4 drill points.
• In the **Toolpath Type** page, the **Drill** toolpath will be selected.

Drill   Circle Mill   Point   Helix Bore   Thread Mill

12.1 Select a 9/16 - 18 RH Tap from the Library and set the Tool Parameters

• Select **Tool** from the **Tree view** list.

• Click on the **Select library tool** button. ⌊Select library tool...⌋
• To be able to see just the spot drill select the **Filter** button.

```
Filter...
☐ Filter Active
367 of 367 tools
```

• Under **Tool Types** select the **None** button and then choose the **Tap RH** icon. Under **Tool Diameter** select **Equal** and enter the value **9/16** as shown in Figure: 12.1.1.

Figure: 12.1.1

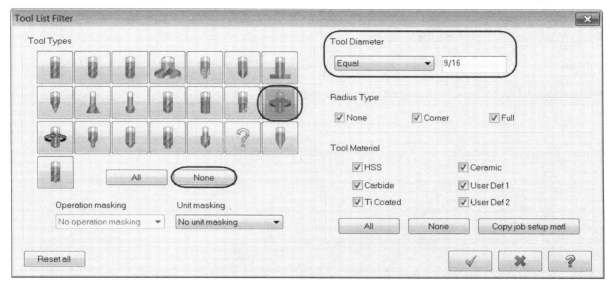

• Select **OK** button to exit the **Tool List Filter** dialog box.
• At this point you should see a list full of taps.
• From that list, select the **9/16 - 18 Tap RH** as shown.

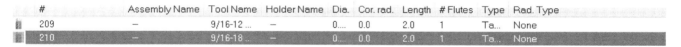

#	Assembly Name	Tool Name	Holder Name	Dia.	Cor. rad.	Length	# Flutes	Type	Rad. Type
209	—	9/16-12 ...	—	0....	0.0	2.0	1	Ta...	None
210	—	9/16-18 ...	—	0...	0.0	2.0	1	Ta...	None

• Select the tool in the **Tool Selection** page and then choose the **OK** button to exit.

♦ Make the necessary changes in the **Tool** page as shown in <u>Figure: 12.1.2</u>.

Figure: 12.1.2

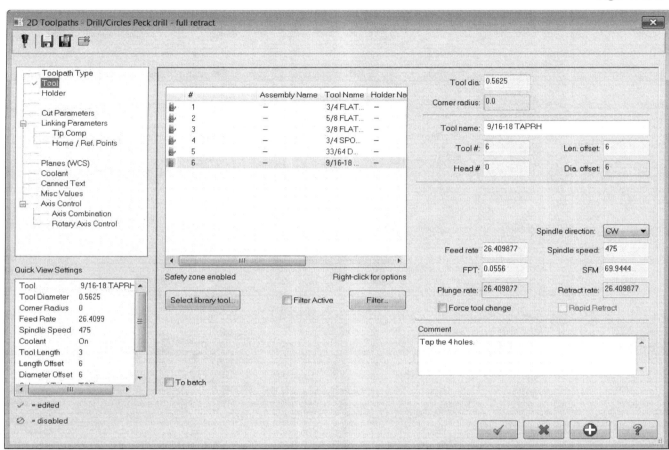

12.2 Set the Cut Parameters

◆ Select **Cut Parameters**, change the drill **Cycle** to **Tap** as shown in Figure: 12.2.1.

Figure: 12.2.1

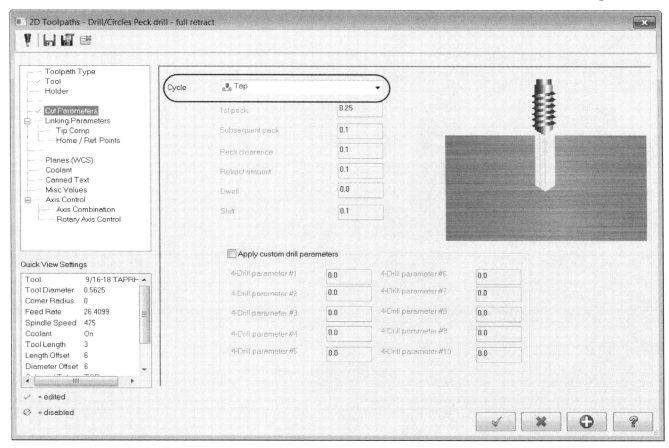

12.3 Set the Linking Parameters

◆ Choose **Linking Parameters** and input a **Depth** value of **-1.5** as shown in Figure: 12.3.1.

Figure: 12.3.1

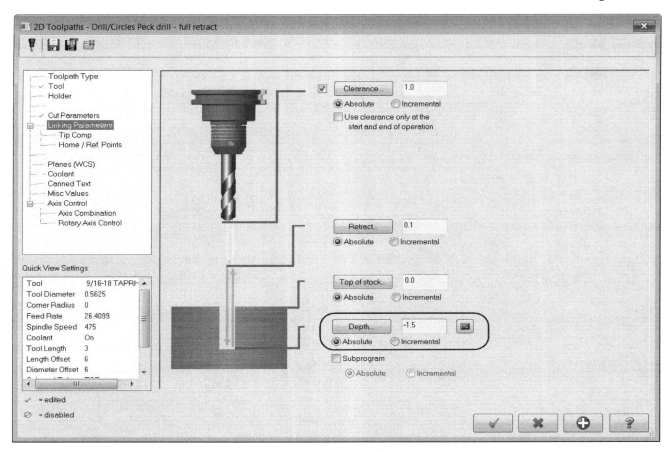

12.4 Set the Tip Comp Parameters

◆ Pick **Tip Comp** and enable this option.
◆ Input a **Break through amount** of **0.1** as shown in <u>Figure: 12.4.1</u>.

Figure: 12.4.1

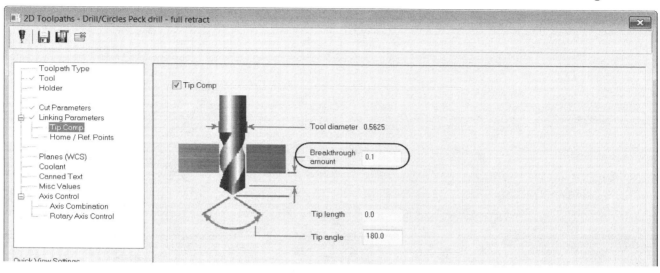

◆ Select the **OK** button to exit the **Drill/Counterbore** parameters.
◆ To **Backplot** and **Verify** the toolpaths see page 437 and page 438.

◆ To make sure that all toolpaths are selected, choose the **Select all operations** icon.

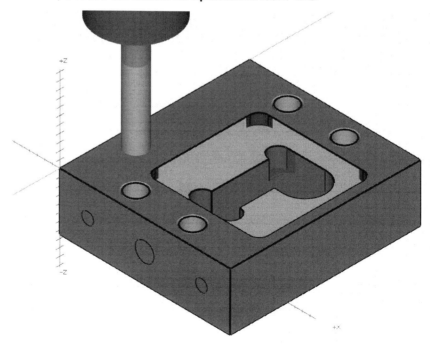

TOOLPATH CREATION - SETUP 2

SUGGESTED FIXTURE:

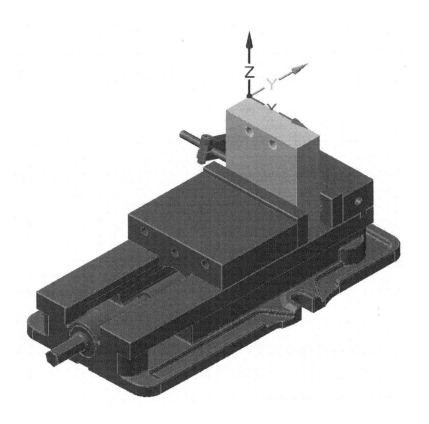

NOTE: The part is now flipped over and we will machine the part from the **Front**.

SETUP SHEET:

TOOL LIST

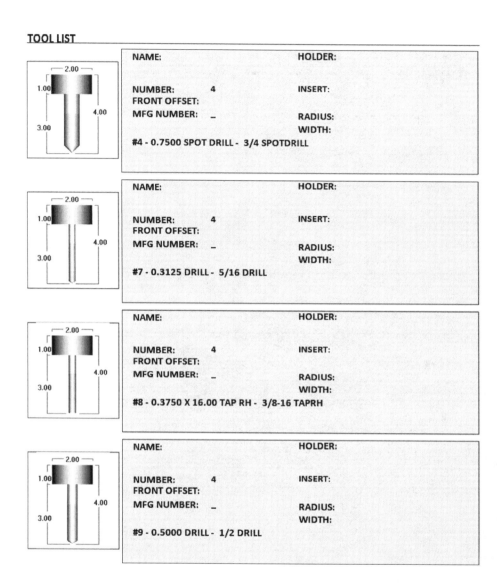

NAME:	HOLDER:
NUMBER: 4	INSERT:
FRONT OFFSET:	
MFG NUMBER: _	RADIUS:
	WIDTH:

#4 - 0.7500 SPOT DRILL - 3/4 SPOTDRILL

NAME:	HOLDER:
NUMBER: 4	INSERT:
FRONT OFFSET:	
MFG NUMBER: _	RADIUS:
	WIDTH:

#7 - 0.3125 DRILL - 5/16 DRILL

NAME:	HOLDER:
NUMBER: 4	INSERT:
FRONT OFFSET:	
MFG NUMBER: _	RADIUS:
	WIDTH:

#8 - 0.3750 X 16.00 TAP RH - 3/8-16 TAPRH

NAME:	HOLDER:
NUMBER: 4	INSERT:
FRONT OFFSET:	
MFG NUMBER: _	RADIUS:
	WIDTH:

#9 - 0.5000 DRILL - 1/2 DRILL

STEP 13: CREATING AND RENAMING TOOLPATH GROUPS

To machine the part in different setups, we will need to have separate programs. To be able to post the operations separate of each setup, we will create them under different toolpath groups with different NC names.

13.1 Rename the Current Toolpath Group - 1 and NC File

* Click on the Toolpath Group - 1 to highlight it and then click again to rename it "Setup #1."

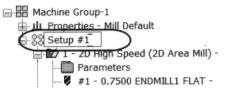

* Right mouse click on the toolpath group and select **Edit selected operations** and then, select **Change NC file name.**

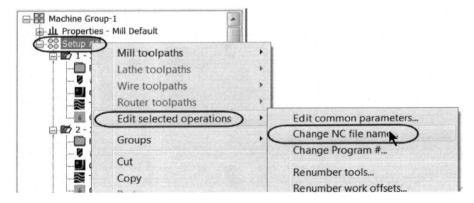

*Mastercam.X*⁸

• Enter the new NC name: **"Setup #1."**

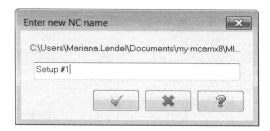

• Select the **OK** button to accept the new **NC name**.

13.2 Create a new Toolpath Group.

• Right mouse click on the **Machine Group 1.**
• From the list, select **Groups** and then **New Toolpath group** as shown.

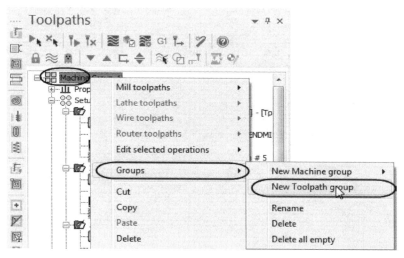

• Double click on the new **Toolpath Group 1** and rename it **"Setup #2 - Front."**

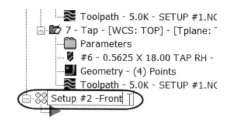

STEP 14: SET WCS TO FRONT

Work coordinate system (WCS) is the active coordinate system in use by Mastercam at any given time. The WCS contains the orientation of the X-Y-Z axes plus the location of the zero point (the origin). This tells Mastercam how your part is positioned or orientated in the machine.

- Select **WCS** located in the status bar.
- When the **WCS** menu appears select **Plane Manager** from it.

*Mastercam. X*⁸

- When the **Plane Manager** dialog box appears pick **Front.**
- Set the **Work Coordinate System (WCS)**, **Tool plane**, **Construction plane** to the **Front,** by selecting the equal icon as shown in Figure: 14.0.1.
- The **Origin** will remain the same as the one for the top plane as shown in Figure: 14.0.1.

Figure: 14.0.1

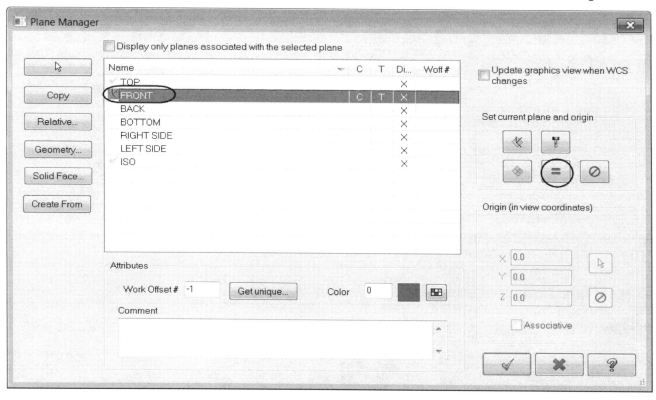

- Select the **OK** button to exit the **Plane Manager.**

- Pick the **Isometric** graphics view to see the part in its new orientation.
- Press **F9** on your keyboard to view the coordinate axes.

NOTE: The color of the coordinate axes remains the same because it is the same origin.

- Select the **Fit** icon.

◆ Your part should look as shown.

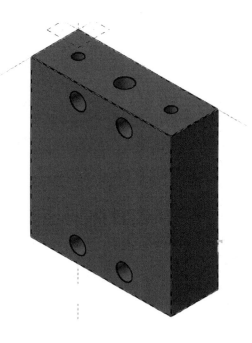

◆ Press **F9** again to remove the axes display.

STEP 15: SPOT DRILL ALL 3 HOLES

Toolpath Preview:

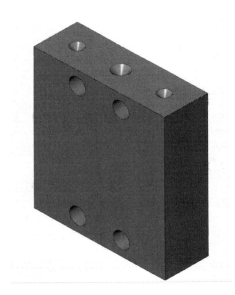

TOOLPATHS

◆ 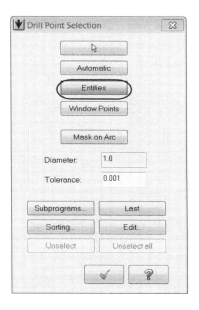 **Drill.**

◆ In the **Drill Point Selection** dialog box choose the option **Entities** as shown.

◆ Select the 3 circles as shown in <u>Figure: 15.0.1</u>, then press **Enter**.

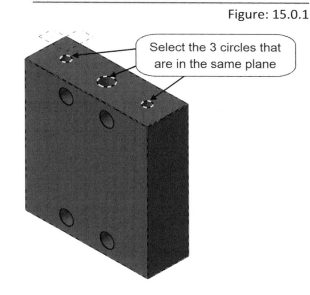

Figure: 15.0.1

Select the 3 circles that are in the same plane

◆ Press **Enter** to finish the selection.

◆ Select the **OK** button in the **Drill Point Selection** dialog box once you have picked the arcs.

- In the **Toolpath Type** page, the **Drill** toolpath will be selected.

Drill   Circle Mill   Point   Helix Bore   Thread Mill

- Select the **3/4" Spot Drill** from the list.
- Make the necessary changes to the **Tool** page as shown in Figure: 15.0.2.

Figure: 15.0.2

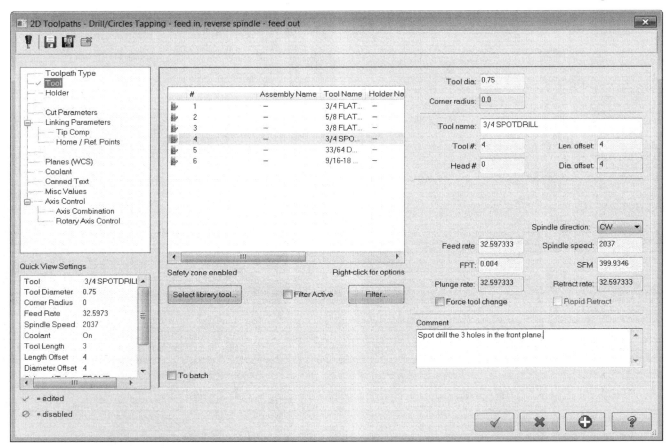

15.1 Set the Cut Parameters

◆ Select **Cut Parameters** and change the **Cycle** to **Drill/Counterbore** as shown in <u>Figure: 15.1.1</u>.

Figure: 15.1.1

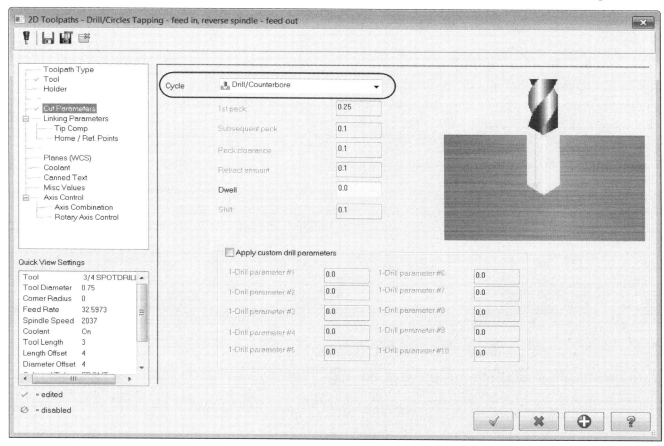

15.2 Set the Linking Parameters

- Choose **Linking Parameters**, ensure clearance is enabled and the **Top of stock** and **Depth** is set to **Absolute** and **0**.

- To input the **Depth** select the **Calculator** icon.
- Input the following equation in the **Finish diameter** area: **3/8+0.04** and hit **Enter** to calculate the **Depth** as shown in Figure: 15.2.1.

Figure: 15.2.1

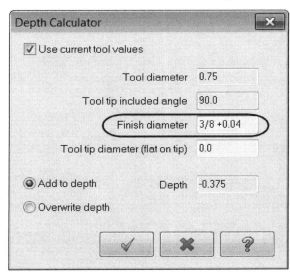

- Select the **OK** button to exit the **Depth Calculator**.

• You will now see the depth we calculated for the spot drilling operation set in the **Depth** field as shown in Figure: 15.2.2. This will chamfer the holes for the tapping operation.

Figure: 15.2.2

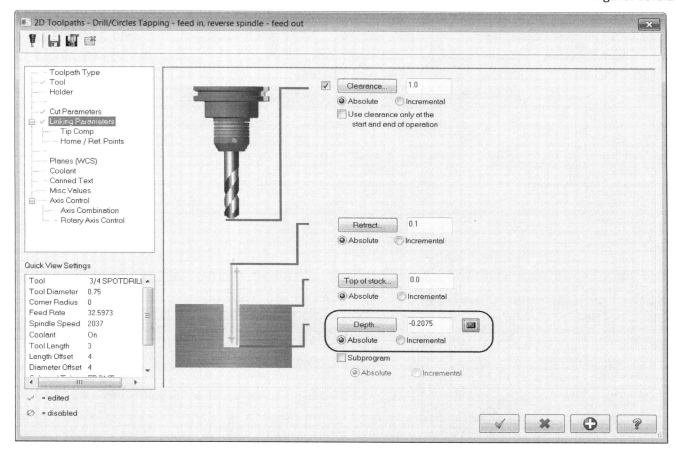

15.3 Set the Tip Comp

• Select **Tip Comp** and disable this option. If left enabled the holes would be drilled much deeper as shown in Figure: 15.3.1.

Figure: 15.3.1

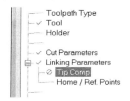

• Select the **OK** button to exit the **Drill/Counterbore** parameters and generate the toolpath.

> **NOTE:** All 3 holes are spot drilled to the same depth. The 0.5" diameter hole has to be drilled to a deeper depth.

15.4 Adjust the Depth of the Spot Drill

• Left click on **Geometry** in **Operation #8**.
• When the **Drill Point Manager** appears, select the point which represents the **0.5" diameter hole**.
• Then right click on it and pick the option to **Change at point** as shown in Figure: 15.4.1.

Figure: 15.4.1

*Mastercam. X*⁸

• When the **Drill change at point** dialog box appears enable **Depth** and change the depth to **-0.27** as shown in <u>Figure: 15.4.2</u>.

Figure: 15.4.2

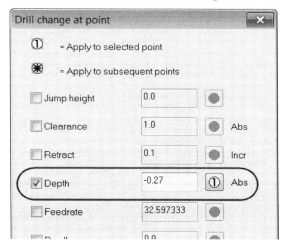

Drill Change At Point allows you to make point-specific changes to a drill toolpath.

Depth changes the hole depth at the selected point. The coordinate you enter here will be output as either an absolute or incremental value, depending on the original settings for the operation.

• Select the **OK** button to apply the changes and exit the dialog box.

• Choose the **OK** button to exit the **Drill Point Manager**.

• Pick the button **Regenerate all dirty operations**.

Toolpaths

15.5 Backplot and Verify the toolpaths

• To **Backplot** and **Verify** your toolpaths see page 437 and page 438.

• To make sure that all toolpaths are selected, choose the **Select all operations** icon.

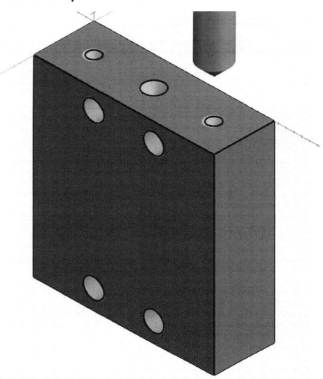

• When backplotting the toolpath, if you want to check the depth of the holes you can check the values in the **Move List** as shown in <u>Figure: 15.5.1</u>.

Figure: 15.5.1

NOTE: The depth value is the Y value 0.208 as the **Move Info** does not reflect the tool plane change. The Tool Orientation has the -1.000 which should be multiply with the 0.208 for a correct direction.

While backplotting the toolpath, in the **Move Info** section you will be able to see the coordinates of where the tool is located.

The **Toolpath Info** found under the **Move info** tab are related to cycle time and the distance the tool travels. The cycle time is based on your rapid rates and feed rates.

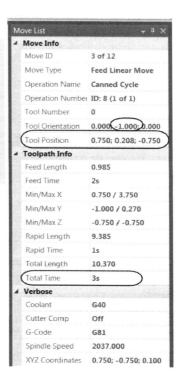

STEP 16: DRILL THE TWO 3/8" TAPPED HOLES

In this example we will drill the holes to a specific depth.

Toolpath Preview:

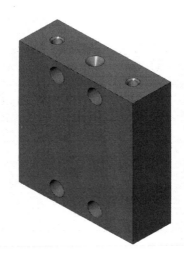

TOOLPATHS

♦ **Drill.**

♦ In the **Drill Point Selection** dialog box choose the option **Entities**.

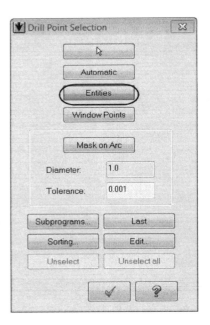

NOTE: This option will let you select the arcs we wish to drill.

◆ Pick the arcs as shown in <u>Figure: 16.0.1</u>.

Figure: 16.0.1

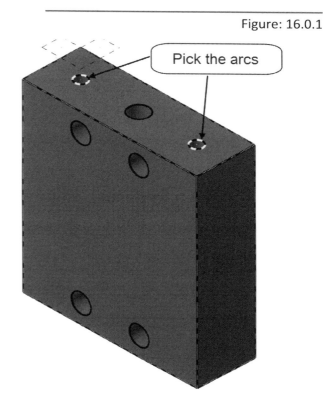

Pick the arcs

◆ Press **Enter** to finish the selection.

◆ Select the **OK** button in the **Drill Point Selection** dialog box to accept the 2 drill points.

◆ In the **Toolpath Type** page, the **Drill** toolpath will be selected.

Drill   Circle Mill   Point   Helix Bore   Thread Mill

16.1 Select a 5/16" Drill from the Library and set the Tool Parameters

◆ Select **Tool** from the **Tree view list**.

◆ Click on the **Select library tool** button.

◆ To be able to see just the **5/16" Drill** select the **Filter** button.

- Under **Tool Types** select the **None** button and then choose the **Drill** icon.
- Under **Tool Diameter** select **Equal** and enter the value **5/16** as shown in <u>Figure: 16.1.1</u>.

Figure: 16.1.1

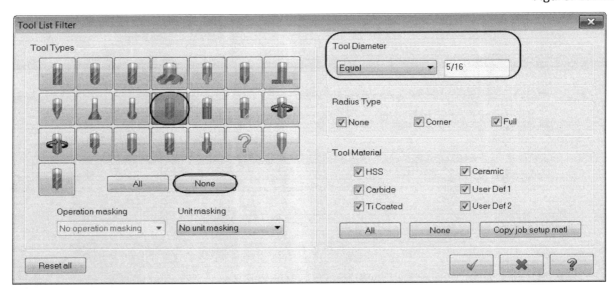

- Select the **OK** button to exit the **Tool List Filter** dialog box.
- At this point you should see only a **5/16" Drill**.
- Select the **5/16" Drill**.

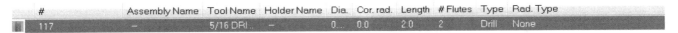

#	Assembly Name	Tool Name	Holder Name	Dia.	Cor. rad.	Length	# Flutes	Type	Rad. Type
117	—	5/16 DRI..	—	0...	0.0	2.0	2	Drill	None

- Select the tool in the **Tool Selection** page and then choose the **OK** button to exit.

◆ Make the necessary changes to the **Tool** page as shown in Figure: 16.1.2.

Figure: 16.1.2

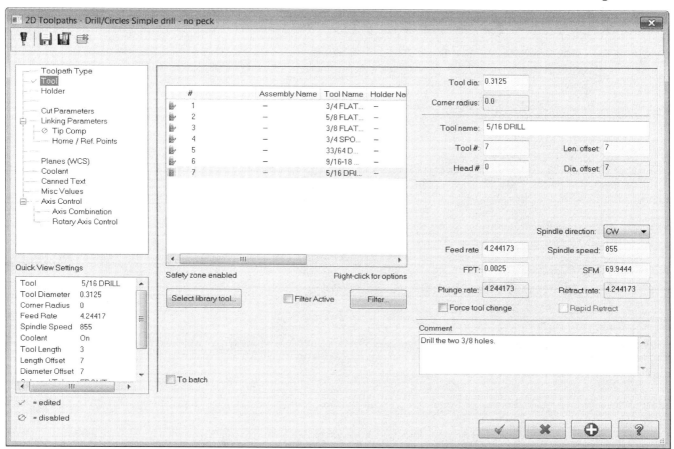

16.2 Set the Cut Parameters

◆ Select **Cut Parameters**, change the drill **Cycle** to **Peck Drill** and input a **1st peck** value of **0.25** as shown in Figure: 16.2.1.

Figure: 16.2.1

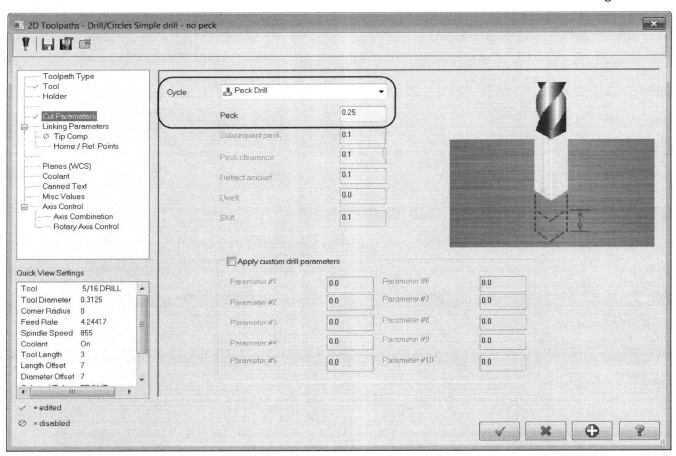

NOTE: For more information regarding the settings found on this page, see page 470.

16.3 Set the Linking Parameters

◆ Choose **Linking Parameters** and input a **Depth** value of **-1.25** as shown in <u>Figure: 16.3.1</u>.

Figure: 16.3.1

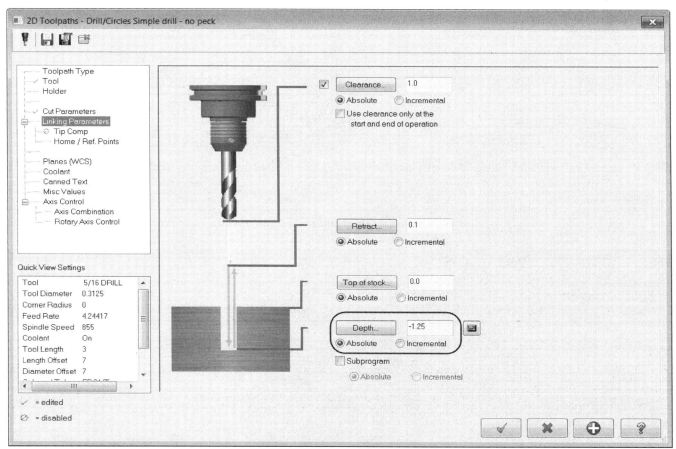

◆ Pick **Tip Comp** and ensure this option is disabled.

◆ Select the **OK** button to exit the **Drill** parameters.

16.4 Backplot and Verify

- To **Backplot** and **Verify** the toolpaths see page 437 and page 438.
- Use the mouse wheel to rotate the part as shown.

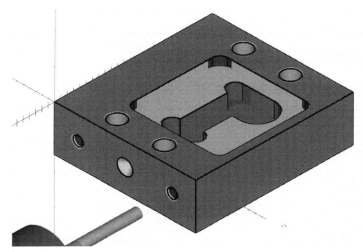

STEP 17: TAP THE TWO HOLES

Toolpath Preview:

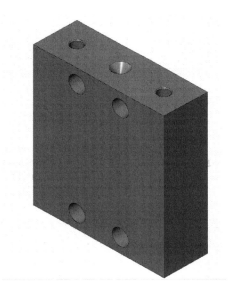

*Mastercam. X*⁸

TOOLPATHS

- **Drill.**
- In the **Drill Point Selection** dialog box choose the option **Last**.

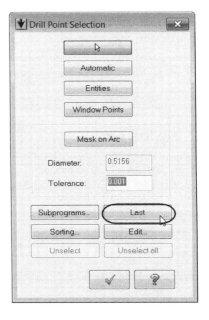

NOTE: This option will automatically select the holes for you based on the selection from the previous drill operation.

- Select the **OK** button in the **Drill Point Selection** dialog box to accept the **2 drill points**.
- In the **Toolpath Type** page, the **Drill** toolpath will be selected.

Drill   Circle Mill   Point   Helix Bore   Thread Mill

17.1 Select a 3/8 - 16 RH Tap from the Library and set the Tool Parameters

- Select **Tool** from the **Tree view list**.

- Click on the **Select library tool** button. Select library tool...
- To be able to see just the spot drill select the **Filter** button.

Filter Active
367 of 367 tools

◆ Under **Tool Types** select the **None** button and then choose the **Tap RH** Icon. Under **Tool Diameter** make sure the the **Equal** option is selected and enter the diameter **3/8** as shown in Figure: 17.1.1.

Figure: 17.1.1

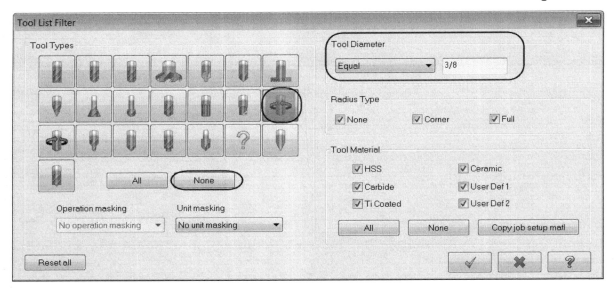

◆ Select **OK** button to exit the **Tool List Filter** dialog box.
◆ From the list select the **3/8 - 16 Tap RH** as shown in Figure: 17.1.2.

Figure: 17.1.2

#	Assembly Name	Tool Name	Holder Name	Dia.	Cor. rad.	Length	Type	Ra...
223	--	3/8-24 TAPRH	--	0....	0.0	2.0	Ta...	No...
224	--	3/8-16 TAPRH	--	0....	0.0	2.0	Ta...	No...

◆ Select the tool in the **Tool Selection** page and then choose the **OK** button to exit.

◆ Make the necessary changes to the **Tool** page as shown in Figure: 17.1.3.

Figure: 17.1.3

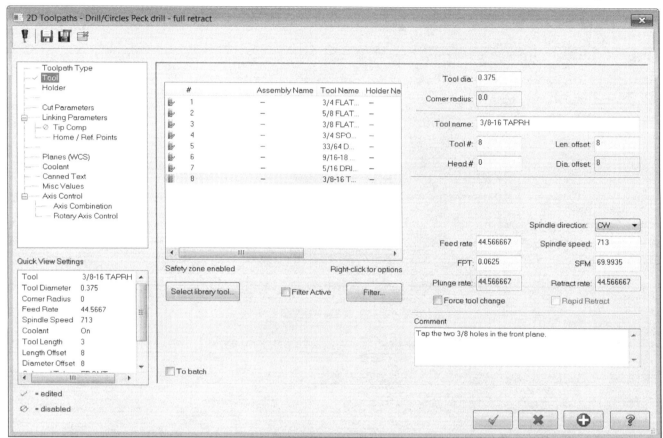

17.2 Set the Cut Parameters

◆ Select **Cut Parameters**, change the drill **Cycle** to **Tap** as shown in Figure: 17.2.1.

Figure: 17.2.1

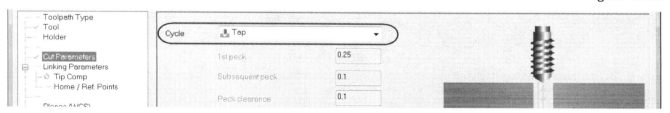

17.3 Set the Linking Parameters

◆ Choose **Linking Parameters** and input a **Depth** of **-1.0** as shown in <u>Figure: 17.3.1</u>.

Figure: 17.3.1

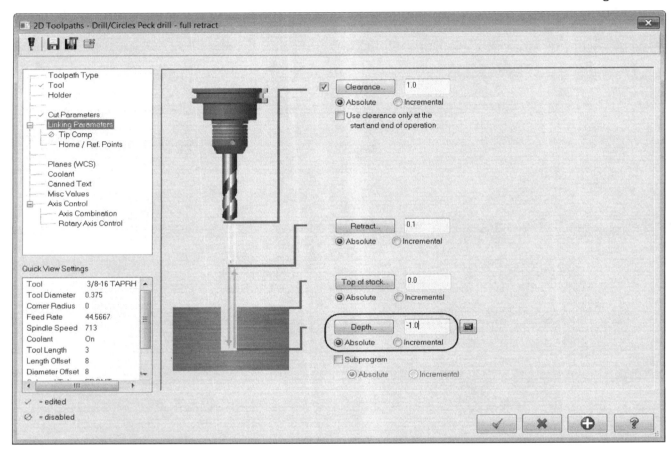

◆ Pick **Tip Comp** and ensure this option is disabled. The **Depth** set in the **Linking Parameters** page is as deep as we would like the tap to go.

◆ Select the **OK** button to exit the **Tap** parameters.

17.4 Backplot and Verify

♦ To **Backplot** and **Verify** the toolpaths see page 437 and page 438.

♦ To make sure that all toolpaths are selected, choose the **Select all operations** icon.

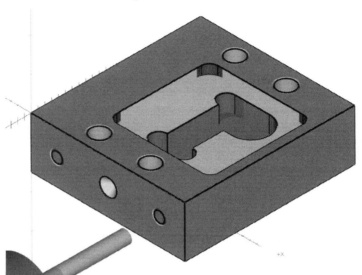

STEP 18: DRILL THE 1/2" HOLE

You will drill the hole to a specific depth.

Toolpath Preview:

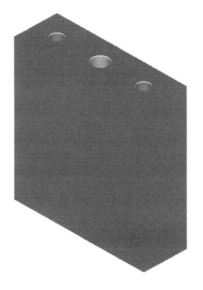

TOOLPATHS

- **Drill.**
- In the **Drill Point Selection** dialog box choose the option **Entities** as shown in Figure: 18.0.1.

Figure: 18.0.1

- This option will let you select the arcs we wish to drill. Pick the arc as shown in Figure: 18.0.2.

Figure: 18.0.2

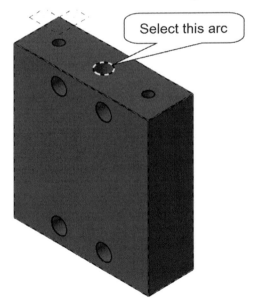

Select this arc

- Press **Enter**.

- Select the **OK** button in the **Drill Point Selection** dialog box to accept the 1 drill point.

◆ In the **Toolpath Type** page, the **Drill** toolpath will be selected.

 Drill   Circle Mill   Point   Helix Bore   Thread Mill

18.1 Select a 1/2" Drill from the Library and set the Tool Parameters

◆ Select **Tool** from the **Tree view list**.

◆ Click on **Select library tool** button. Select library tool...
◆ To be able to see just the **1/2" Drill** select the **Filter** button.

◆ Under **Tool Types** select the **None** button and then choose the **drill** Icon. Under **Tool Diameter** select **Equal** and enter the value **0.5** as shown in Figure: 18.1.1.

Figure: 18.1.1

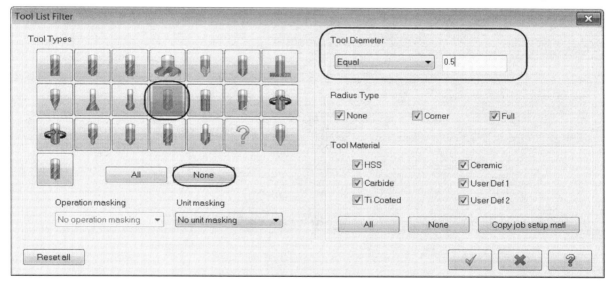

◆ Select the **OK** button to exit the **Tool List Filter** dialog box.
◆ Select the **1/2 Drill**.

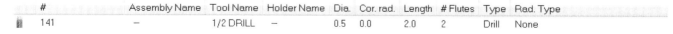

#	Assembly Name	Tool Name	Holder Name	Dia.	Cor. rad.	Length	# Flutes	Type	Rad. Type
141	–	1/2 DRILL	–	0.5	0.0	2.0	2	Drill	None

◆ Select the tool in the **Tool Selection** page and then choose the **OK** button to exit.

◆ Make the necessary changes to the **Tool** page as shown in Figure: 18.1.2.

Figure: 18.1.2

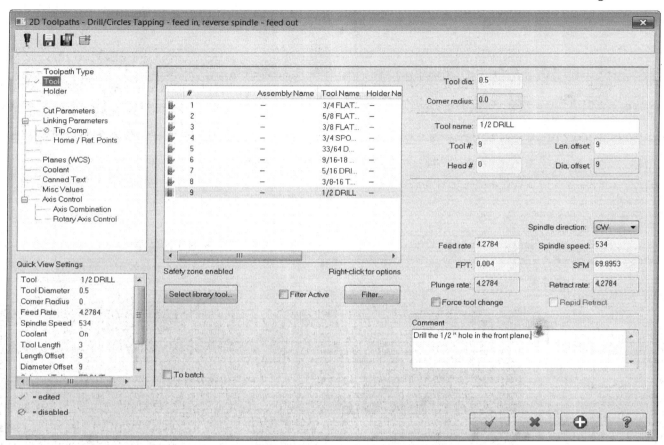

18.2 Set the Cut Parameters

◆ Select **Cut Parameters**, change the drill **Cycle** to **Chip Break** and input a **Peck** of **0.25** as shown in Figure: 18.2.1.

Figure: 18.2.1

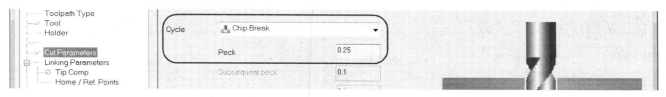

Chip Break retracts partially out of the drilled hole to break the material chips.

18.3 Set the Linking Parameters

◆ Choose **Linking Parameters** and input a **Depth** value of **-0.55** as shown in Figure: 18.3.1.

Figure: 18.3.1

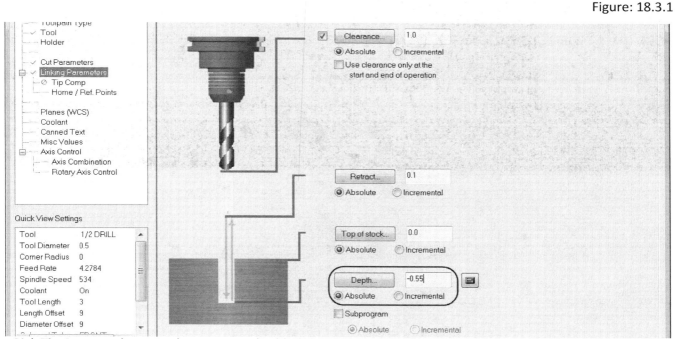

◆ Pick **Tip Comp** and ensure this option is disabled.

◆ Select the **OK** button to exit the **Drill/Counterbore** parameters.

18.4 Backplot and Verify

• To **Backplot** and **Verify** the toolpaths see page 437 and page 438.

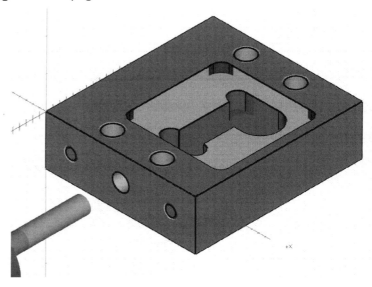

STEP 19: COUNTERBORE THE 1/2" HOLE

Counterbore hole in this example you will drill the holes to a specific depth using a 1/2 Flat endmill to give us a flat bottom hole.

Toolpath Preview:

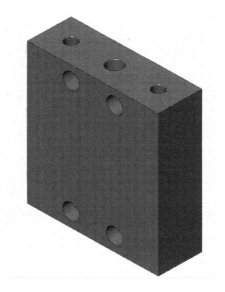

TOOLPATHS

•  **Drill.**

- In the **Drill Point Selection** dialog box choose the option **Last** as shown in Figure: 19.0.1.

Figure: 19.0.1

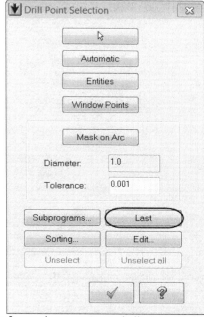

- This option will automatically select the hole for you based off the selection from the previous drill operation.

- Select the **OK** button in the **Drill Point Selection** dialog box to accept the drill point.
- In the **Toolpath Type** page, the **Drill** toolpath will be selected.

Drill   Circle Mill   Point   Helix Bore   Thread Mill

19.1 Select a 1/2" Flat Endmill from the Library and set the Tool Parameters

- Select **Tool** from the **Tree view list**.

- Click on **Select library tool** button. Select library tool...
- To be able to see just the **flat endmill** select the **Filter** button.

Filter...
☐ Filter Active
367 of 367 tools

Filter...
☐ Filter Active
651 of 651 tools

* Under **Tool Types** select the **None** button and then choose the **Flat Endmill** icon. Under **Tool Diameter** select **Equal** and enter the value **0.5** as shown in Figure: 19.1.1.

Figure: 19.1.1

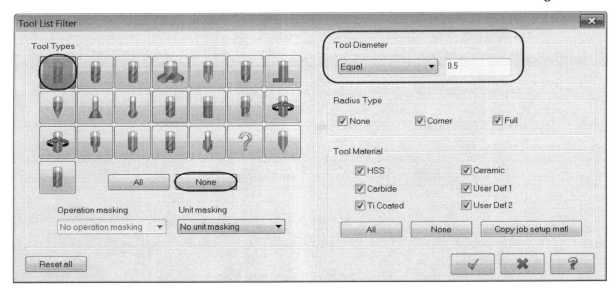

* Select the **OK** button to exit the **Tool List Filter** dialog box.
* Select the **1/2" Flat Endmill** as shown in Figure: 19.1.2.

Figure: 19.1.2

#	Assembly Name	Tool Name	Holder Name	Dia.	Cor. rad.	Length	Type	Ra...
290	--	1/2 FLAT ENDMILL	--	0.5	0.0	1.0	En...	No...

* Select the tool in the **Tool Selection** page and then choose the **OK** button to exit.

◆ Make the necessary changes to the **Tool** page as shown in Figure: 19.1.3.

Figure: 19.1.3

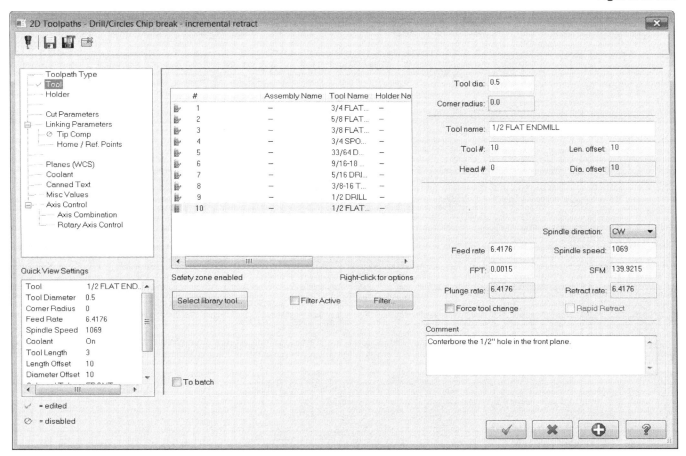

19.2 Set the Cut Parameters

♦ Select **Cut Parameters**, change the drill **Cycle** to **Drill/Counterbore** and input a **Dwell** of **1.0** second as shown in Figure: 19.2.1.

Figure: 19.2.1

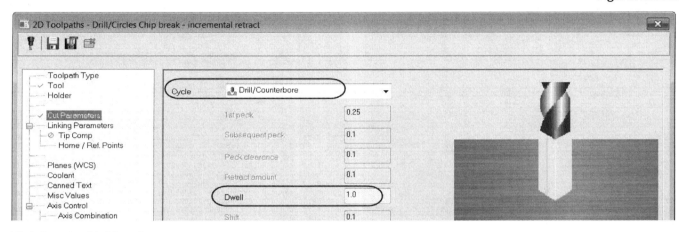

19.3 Set the Linking Parameters

♦ Choose **Linking Parameters** and input a **Depth** value of **-0.55** as shown in Figure: 19.3.1.

Figure: 19.3.1

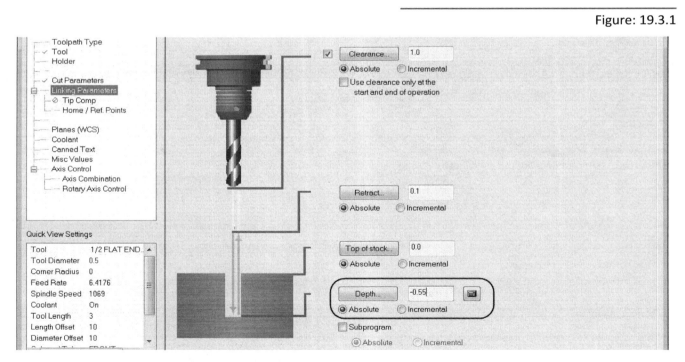

♦ Pick **Tip Comp** and ensure this option is disabled.

♦ Select the **OK** button to exit the **Drill/Counterbore** parameters and generate the toolpath.

19.4 Backplot and Verify

- To **Backplot** and **Verify** the toolpaths see page 437 and page 438.

- To make sure that all toolpaths are selected, choose the **Select all operations** icon.
- The part should look as shown.

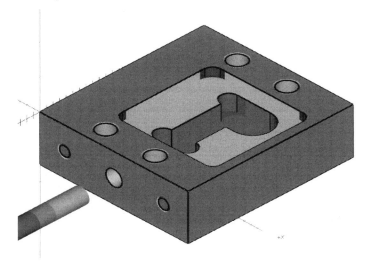

STEP 20: RENAME NC FILE

The Drilling and Tapping operations in "Setup #2 - Front" kept the NC name from Setup #1. We need to rename this operation so it will create a separate program for this setup.

- Select "Setup #2 - Front" (make sure all the operations in setup #2 are selected).
- Right click on the group , choose the option **Edit selected operations** and then pick **Change NC file name**.

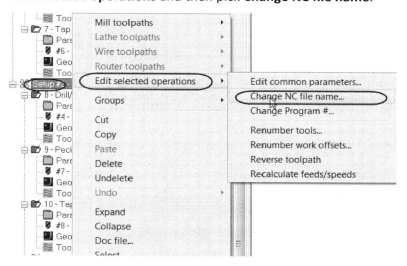

◆ When the **Enter new NC name** dialog box appears enter **"Setup #2 - Front"**.

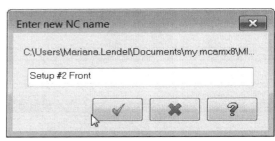

◆ Select the **OK** button to apply the changed NC name to all the operations in the second setup.

◆ The result you should see is **Setup #2 - Front.NC** in any of the operations in the second setup.

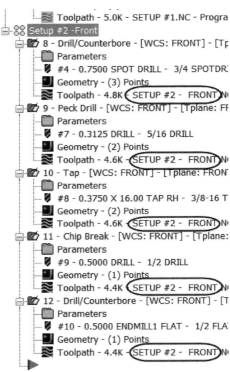

TOOLPATH CREATION - SETUP 3

SUGGESTED FIXTURE:

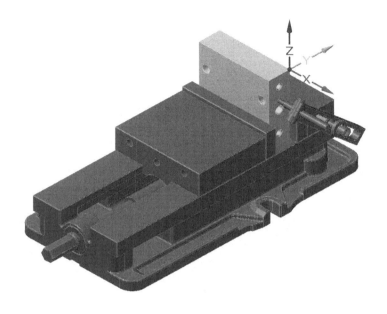

> **NOTE:** The part is now flipped and we will machine the part from the left side.

SETUP SHEET:

TOOL LIST

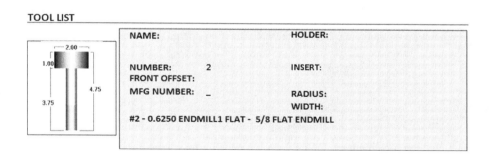

NAME:		HOLDER:
NUMBER:	2	INSERT:
FRONT OFFSET:		
MFG NUMBER:	_	RADIUS:
		WIDTH:

#2 - 0.6250 ENDMILL1 FLAT - 5/8 FLAT ENDMILL

STEP 21: CREATING AND RENAMING TOOLPATH GROUPS

To machine the part in different setups, we will need to have separate programs. To be able to post the operations separate of each setup, we will create them under different toolpath groups with different NC names.

21.1 Create Toolpath Group #3 (Setup #3 - Left)

+ Right mouse click on the **"Machine Group-1**.
+ Select **Groups** and then **New Toolpath Group** as shown in <u>Figure: 21.1.1</u>.

Figure: 21.1.1

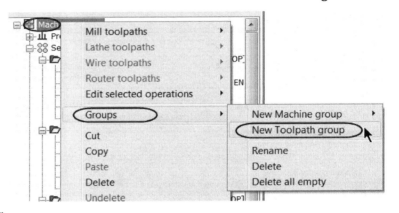

+ Rename the toolpath group **"Setup #3 - Left."**

Figure: 21.1.2

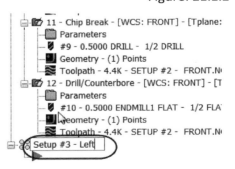

+ Ensure the arrow is below **"Setup #3 - Left."**

STEP 22: SET THE WCS TO LEFT

Work coordinate system (WCS) is the active coordinate system in use by Mastercam at any given time. The WCS contains the orientation of the X-Y-Z axes plus the location of the zero point (the origin). This tells Mastercam how your part is positioned or orientated in the machine.

♦ Select **WCS** located in the status bar. ──── ▾ WCS Groups

♦ When the **WCS** menu appears select **Plane Manager** from it.

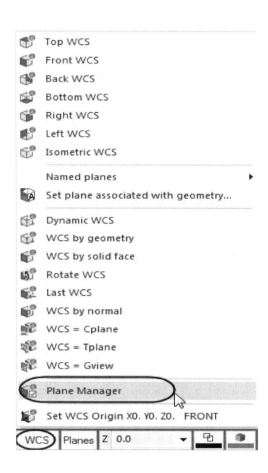

♦ When the **Plane Manager** dialog box appears pick **Left** and then choose to set the **Work Coordinate System (WCS), Tool plane, Construction plane**, and their origins, to the selected view as shown in Figure: 22.0.1.

Figure: 22.0.1

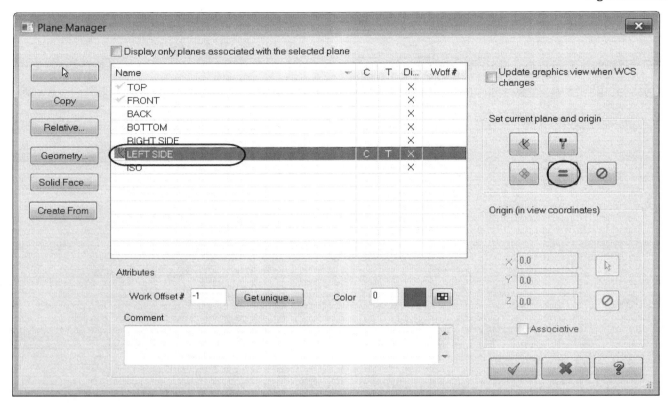

♦ Select the **OK** button to exit the **Plane Manager**.

♦ Pick the **Isometric** graphics view to see the part in its new orientation.

♦ Select the **Fit** icon.

♦ Press **F9** on your keyboard to view the coordinate axes.

NOTE: The color of the coordinate axes remains the same because it is the same origin.

◆ Your part will appear as shown up to this point.

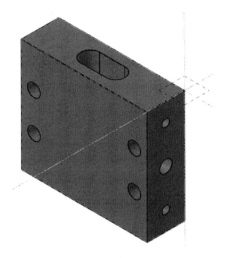

◆ Press **F9** to remove the axes display.

STEP 23: MACHINE THE SLOT

Slot Mill efficiently machines obround slots. This toolpath automatically calculates plunge, entry and exit points appropriate for slots.

Toolpath Preview:

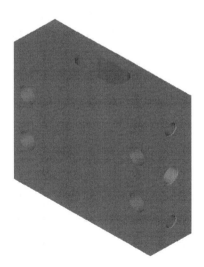

TOOLPATHS
+ **Circle Paths.**

+ **Slot Mill.**

+ When the **Chaining** dialog box appears make sure that the **C-plane** is enabled as shown.

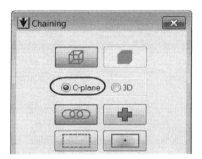

+ Select the slot as shown in <u>Figure: 23.0.1</u>.

Figure: 23.0.1

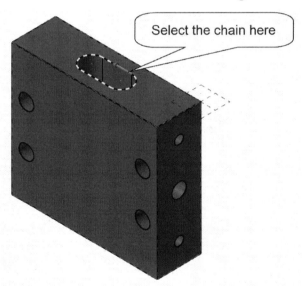

Select the chain here

+ Select the **OK** button in the chaining dialog box to continue.
+ In the **Toolpath Type** page, the **Slot Mill** toolpath will be selected as shown in <u>Figure: 23.0.2</u>.

Figure: 23.0.2

Contour   Pocket   Facing   Slot Mill

23.1 Select the 5/8" Flat Endmill from the Tool List

* Select **Tool** from the **Tree view list**.
* Pick the **5/8" Flat Endmill** tool from the list.
* Make the necessary changes to the **Tool** page as shown in Figure: 23.1.1.

Figure: 23.1.1

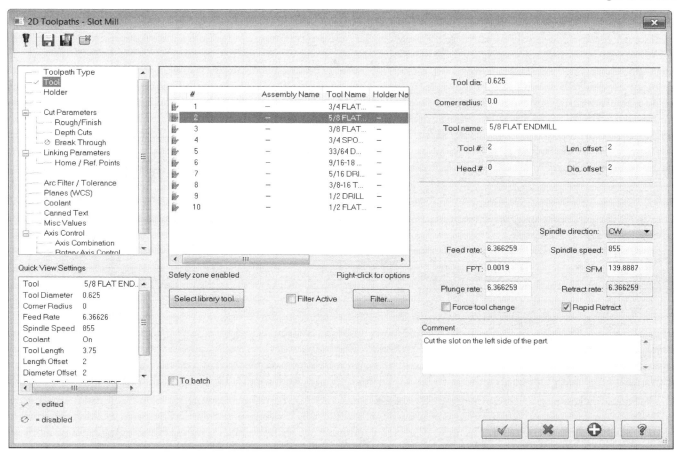

23.2 Set the Cut Parameters

◆ Select **Cut Parameters**, and add an overlap of **0.02 as shown in** <u>Figure: 23.2.1</u>.

Figure: 23.2.1

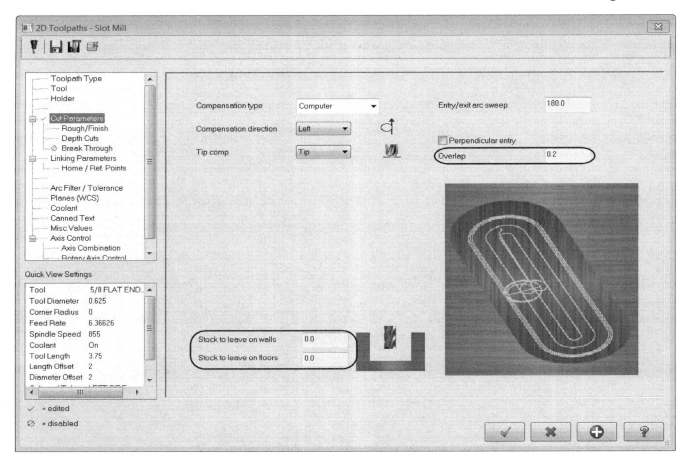

Entry/exit arc sweep sets the included angle of each entry and exit arc. If this value is set to less than 180 degrees a line will be created.

Overlap sets how far the tool goes past the end of the toolpath before exiting for a cleaner finish.

23.3 Set the Rough/Finish Parameters

◆ Choose **Rough/Finish Parameters** and ensure your settings appear as shown in Figure: 23.3.1.

Figure: 23.3.1

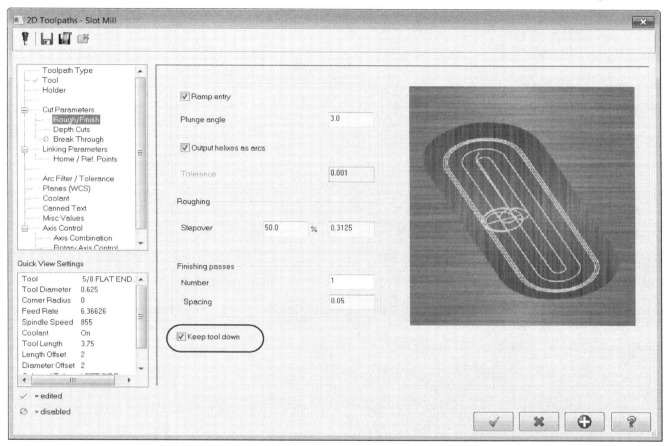

23.4 Set the Depth Cut Parameters

• Select **Depth Cuts**, input a **Max rough step** of **0.2** as shown in <u>Figure: 23.4.1</u>.
• Enter a **# of Finish Cuts** value of **1** and a **Finish step** of **0.05**.

NOTE: These settings instruct Mastercam to rough the slot leaving 0.05" and then create one lighter cut removing 0.1" of material for a finish pass.

Figure: 23.4.1

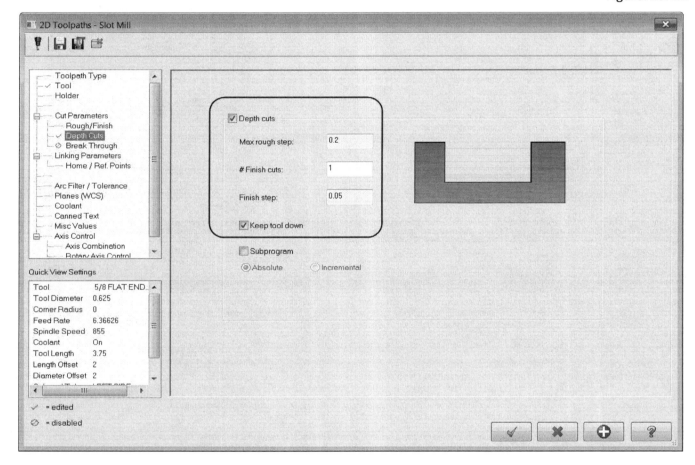

23.5 Set the Linking Parameters

◆ Select **Linking Parameters**, enable **Clearance** and set it to **1.0** and input a **Depth** of **-1.0** as shown in
Figure: 23.5.1.

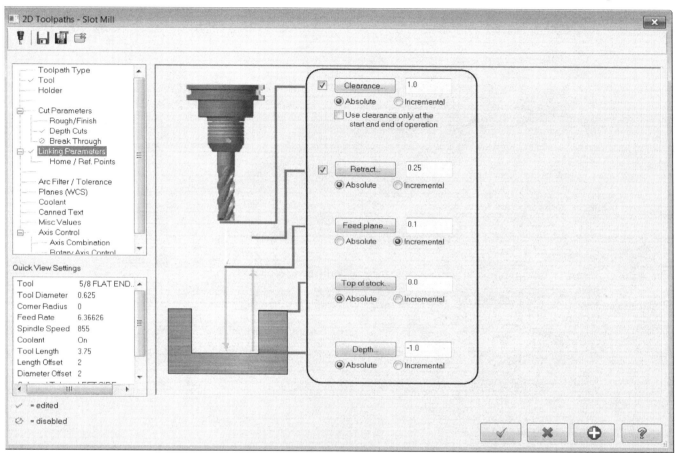

◆ Select the **OK** button to exit the **Slot Mill** parameters and generate the toolpath.

23.6 Backplot and Verify

- To **Backplot** and **Verify** the toolpaths see page 437 and page 438.
- Ensure all operations are selected, if they are not use the **Select all operations** icon from the **Toolpaths**

  Manager.
- To rotate the part, pick a point in the center of the part with the mouse wheel and slowly move the cursor in the graphics window.

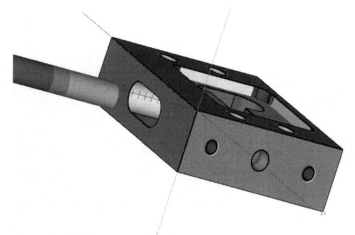

- Release the mouse wheel when the part is in the desired positon.

- To exit Mastercam Simulator click on the **Close** icon.

STEP 24: RENAME THE NC FILE

The Slot milling operation in "Setup #3 - Left" kept the NC name from Setup #2 _Front. We need to rename this operation so it will create a separate program for this setup.

• Select **"Setup #3 - Left"**, right click on the group (make sure all the operations in setup #3 are selected), choose the option **Edit selected operations** and then pick **Change NC file name** as shown in Figure: 24.0.1.

Figure: 24.0.1

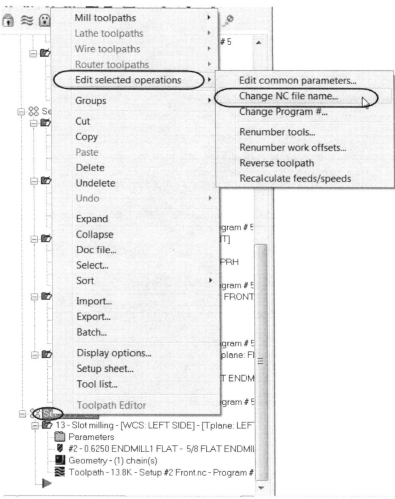

• When the **Enter new NC name** dialog box appears enter **"Setup #3 - Left"**.

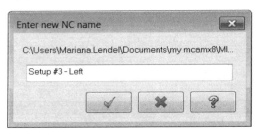

• Select the **OK** button to apply the changed **NC name** to all the operations in the second setup. ✓
• The result you should see is **Setup #3 - Left.NC** in the last operation in the third setup as shown in
<u>Figure: 24.0.2</u>.

Figure: 24.0.2

```
             Toolpath   4.4K   SETUP #2 - FRONT.N
 ⊟ 8⅜ Setup #3 - Left
    ⊟🗂 13 - Slot milling - [WCS: LEFT SIDE] - [Tpla
         📁 Parameters
         🔧 #2 - 0.6250 ENDMILL1 FLAT -  5/8 FLAT
         🔷 Geometry - (1) chain(s)
         ≋ Toolpath - 14.8K  SETUP #3 -  LEFT.NC
    ▶
```

STEP 25: POST THE FILE

◆ Ensure all operations are selected, if they are not use the button **Select all operations** from the **Toolpaths Manager.**

◆ Select the **Post selected operations** button from the **Toolpaths Manager.** G1

◆ In the **Post processing** window make the necessary changes as shown in Figure: 25.0.1.

Figure: 25.0.1

NC File enabled allows you to keep the NC file and to assign the same name as the MCX file.

Edit enabled allows you to automatically launch the default editor.

◆ Select the **OK** button to continue.
◆ Save your file and name it Setup #1.NC.
◆ Save your file and name it Setup #2 - Front.NC.
◆ Save your file and name it Setup #3 - Left.NC.

♦ A window with Mastercam Code Expert will be launched and the NC program will appear as shown in <u>Figure: 25.0.2</u>.

Figure: 25.0.2

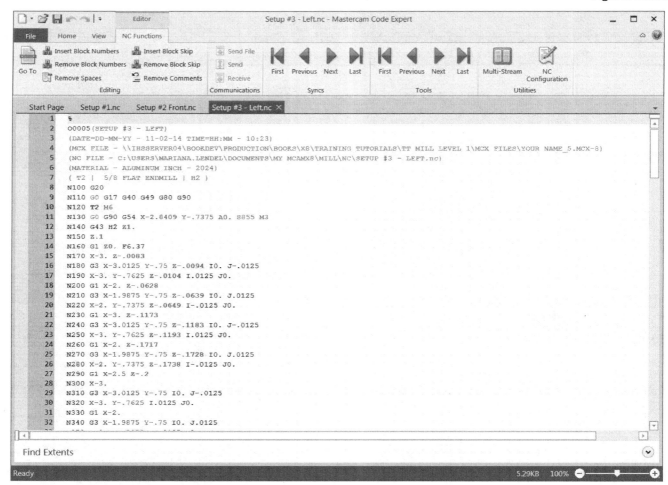

♦ Select the **"X"** box at the upper right corner to exit the editor.

STEP 26: SAVE THE UPDATED MCX FILE

REVIEW EXERCISE -STUDENT PRACTICE

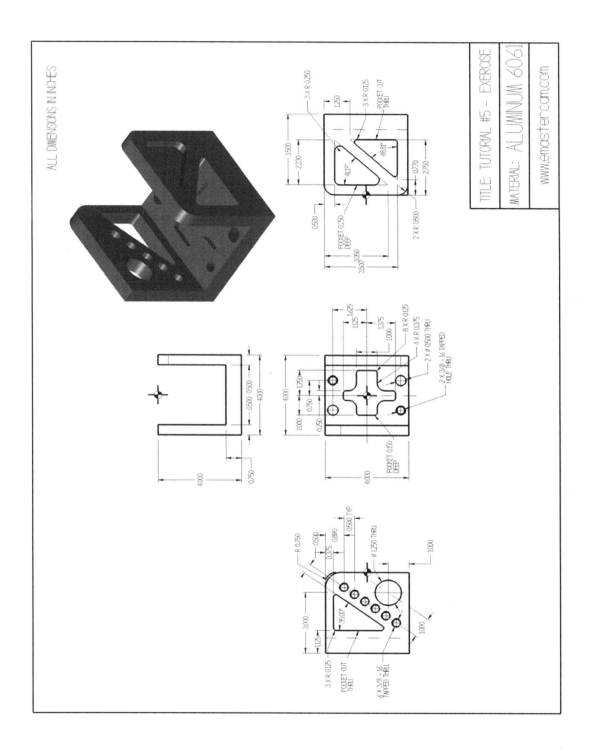

ALL DIMENSIONS IN INCHES

TITLE: TUTORIAL #5 – EXERCISE

MATERIAL: ALUMINUM 6061

www.emastercam.com

IMPORT THE GEOMETRY FOR TUTORIAL #5 EXERCISE

Download the file from emastercam.com.

◆ Save the file to a known location.

Use File Open.

◆ Set the extension to SolidWorks (*.sldprt, *.sldasm).
◆ Select Tutorial #5 Exercise.SLDPRT.
◆ In **Options** enable **Solids**, **Edge curves** and **Use System Color for imported Solids.**
◆ Open the file.
◆ The geometry should look as shown.

Use Xform Translate 3D to rotate the part for machining.

◆ Make a Window around the entire part.
◆ **Xform.**
◆ **Translate 3D.**
◆ Set the parameters to make the **Back** view **Top** view as shown.

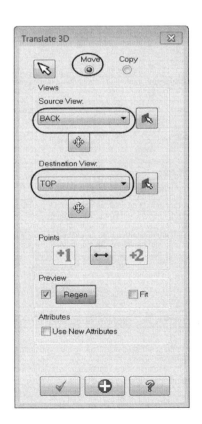

◆ Clear color and the part should look as shown.

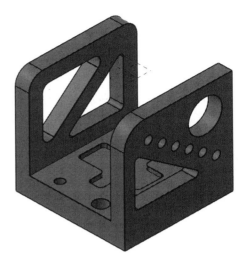

Save the file.
◆ Save the file as Your Name_5 Exercise.

CREATE THE TOOLPATHS FOR TUTORIAL #5 EXERCISE

Create the Toolpaths for the Tutorial #5 Exercise as per the instructions below.

Select the Mill Default.
Set the machine properties including the stock setup.
♦ The stock will appear as shown.

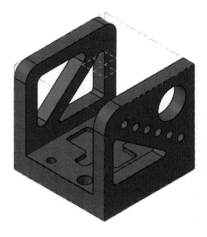

Remove the material in the center of the part using 2D HS Dynamic Mill.
♦ As machining regions select the bottom rectangle (enable C-plane).
♦ Enable **From outside**.

♦ As **Avoidance regions** switch in the **Chaining** dialog to **Solids** selection and enable only the face button as shown.

- Select the top faces as shown.

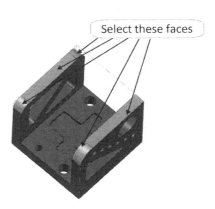

Select these faces

- Use a **1" Flat Endmill**.
- Ensure the **Machining direction** is set to **Climb**.
- **Approach distance =1.0.**
- **Stepover = 25%.**
- **Min toolpath radius = 10%.**
- **Gap size % of tool diameter = 100.**
- **Stock to leave on walls = 0.05.**
- **Depth Cuts** set the **Max rough step = 1.0.**
- Choose an **Entry method Helix**.
- No **Break Through**.
- Set the depth according to the drawing.

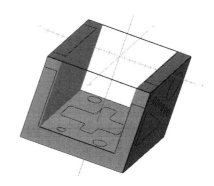

Use Contour toolpath to finish the vertical faces.
- Go back to **Wireframe** mode in the **Chaining** dialog box and use **Single** chain as shown.

- Select the two lines in the clock wise direction.
- Use a **3/4" Flat Endmill**.
- Set the **Compensation direction** to **Right**.
- **Depth cuts** set to **Max rough step** of **0.375**.
- **Lead In/Out** disable **Entry** and **Exit** and enable **Adjust start/end of contour** setting the **Length** to **Extend** 100%.
- Set the Linking parameters according to the drawing.

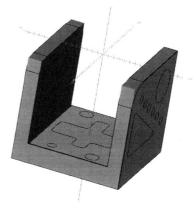

Machine the Pocket.
* Use a **1/4" Flat Endmill** edit the tool cutting length to 4".

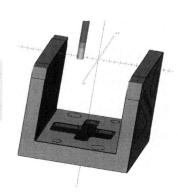

> **NOTE:** To edit the tool, in the **Tool** page, right mouse click on the tool then change the **Cutting length** to 4, the **Shoulder length** to 4.25 and the **Overall length** to 4.5.

* Ensure the **Machining direction** is set to **Climb**.
* Select a desired cutting method.
* Choose an **Entry method**.
* Set the **Finish** parameters.
* Enable **Lead In/Out**.
* Disable **Depth Cuts**, and **Break Through**.
* Set the **Top of stock** and the **Depth** according to the drawing.

Spot Drill the holes.
* Use a **3/4" Spot Drill** edit the tool **Cutting length** to 4".
* Set the **Drill cycle** to **Drill/Counterbore**.
* Set the top of stock according to the material.
* Set the depth to leave a **0.05" Chamfer** on all the holes.

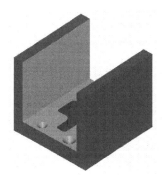

Drill the 1/2" Holes.
* Use a **1/2" Drill**.
* Set the **Drill cycle** to **Drill/Counterbore**.
* Set the top of stock according to the material.
* Set the depth and include tip comp.

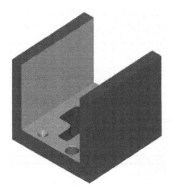

Drill the 3/8Tapped Holes.
- Use a **5/16" Drill**.
- Set the **Drill cycle** to **Drill/Counterbore**.
- Set the top of stock according to the material.
- Set the depth and include tip comp.

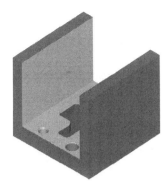

Tap the 3/8 - 16 Holes.
- Use a **3/8 - 16 NC Tap RH**.
- Set the **Drill Cycle** to **Tap**.
- Set the top of stock according to the material.
- Set the depth and include tip comp.

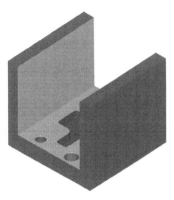

Set the WCS to Right and input an Origin Z value of 2.0".
Create a new Toolpath Group and rename the NC File name for the last toolpath group.
- **Pocket** the two triangles to the depths shown on the drawing.
- Use a **1/4" Flat Endmill**.

- Create a **Contour** toolpath around the two fillets.
- Use the **1/4" Flat Endmill**.
- Set the depth according to the drawing.

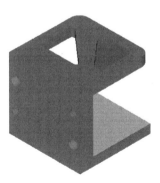

Set the WCS to Left and input an Origin Z value of 2.0".
Create a new Toolpath Group and rename the NC File name for the last toolpath group.

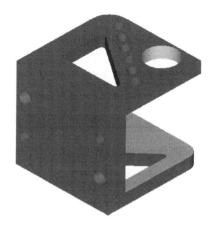

◆ Pocket the triangle to the depths shown on the drawing.
◆ Use a **1/4" Flat Endmill**.

◆ **Drill** the 6 Holes.
◆ Use the **5/16" Drill**.

◆ **Tap** the 6 Holes.
◆ Use the **3/8 - 16 Tap**.

◆ **Circle Mill** the Ø1.25" Hole.
◆ Use a **1/2" Flat Endmill**.
◆ Enable **Roughing**.
◆ Enable **Finishing** and set the **Finish Passes** to **2** with a spacing of **0.02"**.
◆ Set the depth according to the drawing.

◆ Create a **Contour** operation to remove the material around the fillet.
◆ Use a **1/2" Flat Endmill**.

Once complete your part will appear as shown.

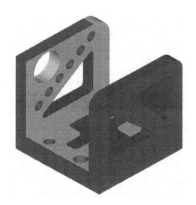

NOTES:

TUTORIAL #5 QUIZ

♦ What settings do you need to use to remachine a pocket using High Speed Area Mill Toolpath?

♦ What is the use of WCS in Mastercam?

♦ After creating a new toolpath group why do you rename the NC file?

TUTORIAL #6

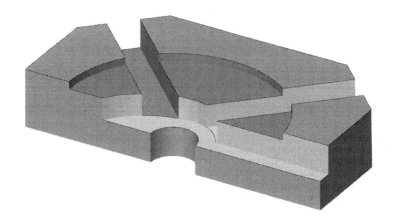

OVERVIEW OF STEPS TAKEN TO CREATE THE FINAL PART:

From Drawing to CAD Model:
- The student should examine the drawing on the following page to understand what part is being created in the tutorial.
- From the drawing we can decide how to go about creating the geometry in Mastercam.

Create the 2D CAD Model used to generate Toolpaths from:
- The student will create the Top 2D geometry needed to create the toolpaths.
- Geometry creation commands such as create rectangle, circle center point, line polar and line parallel will be used.
- The student will also learn how to clean up the geometry using the trimming functions.

Create the necessary Toolpaths to machine the part:
- The student will set up the stock size to be used and the clamping method used.
- A 2D High Speed Dynamic Mill toolpath will be created to remove the material outside of the step.
- A 2D High Speed Mill toolpath will be created to machine the step.
- A 2D High Speed Blend Mill toolpath will be created to machine the semi arc shape pocket.
- Two 2D High Speed Peel Mill toolpaths will be created to machine the two slots.

Backplot and Verify the file:
- The Backplot will be used to simulate a step by step process of the tool's movements.
- The Verify will be used to watch a tool machine the part out of a solid model.

Post Process the file to generate the G-code:
- The Student will then post process the file to obtain an NC file containing the necessary code for the machine.

 This tutorial takes approximately two hours to complete.

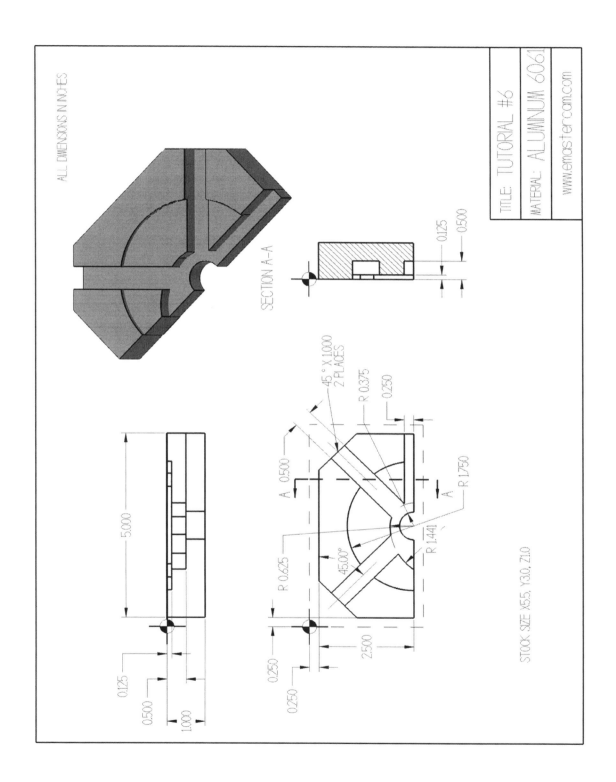

GEOMETRY CREATION

STEP 1: SETTING UP THE GRAPHIC USER INTERFACE

Please refer to the **Getting Started** section to set up the graphics user interface.

STEP 2: CREATE RECTANGLES

In this step we will create rectangles using the rectangular command. The rectangle we create will be based off the origin.

Step Preview:

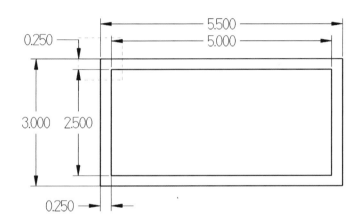

2.1 Create the 5.5" by 3.0" rectangle

CREATE

♦ ☐ **Rectangle.**

♦ [Select position of first corner]: Select the **Origin** as shown in Figure: 2.1.1.

Figure: 2.1.1

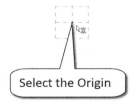

Select the Origin

♦ Make sure that when selecting the origin, the visual cue of the cursor changes as shown.

Mastercam X⁸

- [Select position of second corner]: Pick a point to right of the origin and below it as shown in Figure: 2.1.2.

Figure: 2.1.2

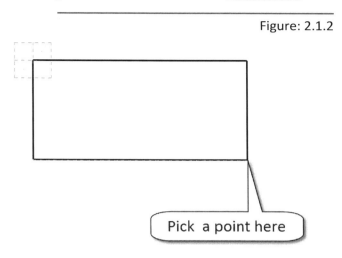

Pick a point here

NOTE: You can make this rectangle as small or as large as you want. The entities are still live therefore we can modify the values to get the size we want.

- Enter a **Width** 🔲 of **5.5** and a **Height** 🔲 of **-3.0** as shown in Figure: 2.1.3.

Figure: 2.1.3

- Choose the **Apply** button to continue. ⊕

NOTE: During the geometry creation of this tutorial, if you make a mistake you can undo the last step using the

Undo icon. 🔾 You can undo as many steps as needed. If you delete or undo a step by mistake, just use the

Redo icon. 🔾 To delete unwanted geometry, select it first and then press **Delete** from the keyboard.

- Use the **Fit** icon to fit the drawing to the screen. 🔳

2.2 Create the 5.0" by 2.5" rectangle

- [Select position of first corner]: Pick the **Fast Point** icon. ⁺⚡
- Enter the coordinate values of **0.25, -0.25.**
- Hit **Enter** on your keyboard to set the first position of the corner.
- Enter a **Width** 🔲 of **5.0** and a **Height** 🔲 of **-2.5**.
- Choose the **OK** button to exit the command. ☑

STEP 3: CREATE CIRCLES AND ARC TANGENT

Create Circle Center Point lets you create circles knowing the center point and the radius or the diameter.
Create Arc Tangent 1 Entity lets you create an arc knowing the radius, the arc that is tangent too and the tangency point.

Step Preview:

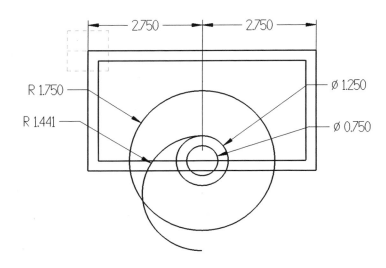

3.1 Create the Circles using Circle Center Point command

CREATE
* **Arc.**

* ⊕ **Circle Center Point.**

* Enter a **Radius** 🔘 value of **0.375** and pick the line **Midpoint** as shown in Figure: 3.1.1.

Figure: 3.1.1

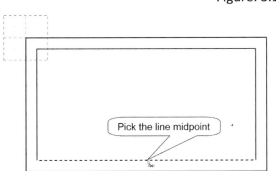

Pick the line midpoint

* Make sure that when selecting the origin, the visual cue of the cursor changes as shown.

* Select the **Apply** button to continue. ⊕

◆ Enter a **Radius** value of **0.625** and pick the same line midpoint.

◆ Select the **Apply** button to continue.

◆ Enter a **Radius** value of **1.75** and pick the same line midpoint.

◆ Choose the **OK** button to exit the command.

◆ Select the **Fit** screen icon.

◆ The geometry should look as shown.

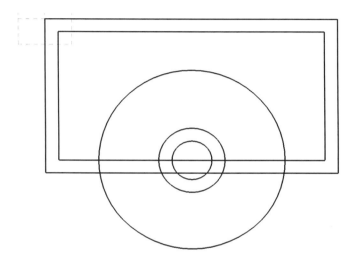

3.2 Create the Arc tangent to an entity

CREATE

◆ **Arc.**

◆ **Arc Tangent.**

◆ From the **Ribbon Bar** select the **Tangent 1 Entity** as shown.

◆ Enter a **Radius** value of **1.441**.

◆ [Select the entity that the arc is to be tangent to]: Select the arc as shown in Figure: 3.2.1.

Figure: 3.2.1

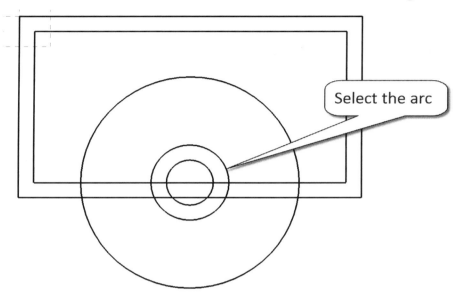

◆ [Specify the tangent point]: Select the **Quadrant** as shown in Figure: 3.2.2.

Figure: 3.2.2

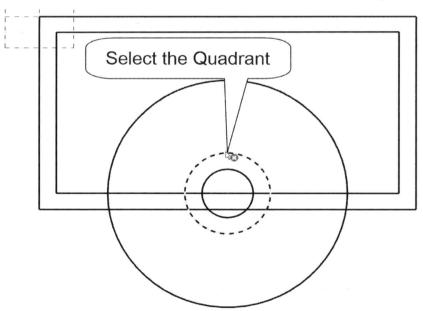

- [Select an arc]: Pick the arc as shown in <u>Figure: 3.2.3</u>.

Figure: 3.2.3

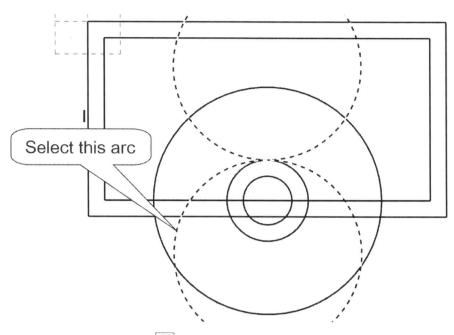

Select this arc

- Choose the **OK** button to exit the command.

- Select the **Fit** icon.
- The geometry should look as shown.

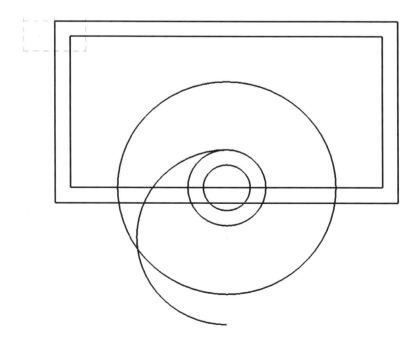

STEP 4: TRIM THE ARCS

Trim to Point trims an entity to a point or any defined position in the graphics window. If the point you enter does not lie on the selected entity, Mastercam calculates the closest position on the entity and trims the entity to that point.

Step Preview:

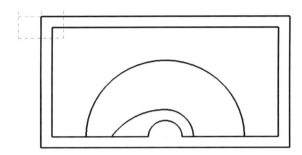

EDIT
* **Trim/Break.**

* **Trim/Break/Extend.**

4.1 Trim the entities using Trim to Point command

* Select the **Trim to Point** icon in the ribbon bar.
* [Select the entity to trim/extend]: Select the arc as shown in Figure: 4.1.1.
* [Indicate the trim/extend location]: Select the Endpoint as shown in Figure: 4.1.1.

Figure: 4.1.1

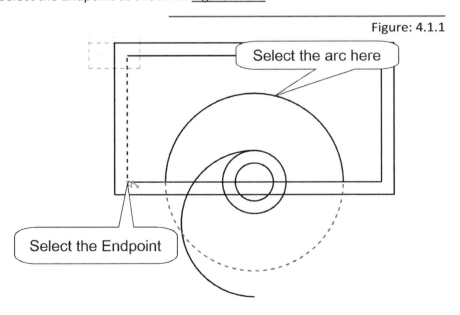

Select the arc here

Select the Endpoint

Mastercam. X²

- ◆ [Select the entity to trim/extend]: Select the arc as shown in <u>Figure: 4.1.2</u>.
- ◆ [Indicate the trim/extend location]: Select the Intersection as shown in <u>Figure: 4.1.2</u>.

Figure: 4.1.2

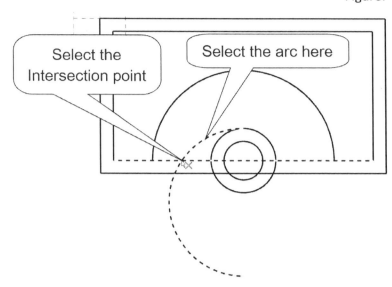

- ◆ [Select the entity to trim/extend]: Select the 0.375 radius circle as shown in <u>Figure: 4.1.3</u>.
- ◆ [Indicate the trim/extend location]: Select the Endpoint as shown in <u>Figure: 4.1.3</u>.

Figure: 4.1.3

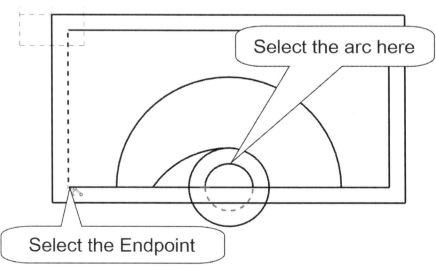

4.2 Trim the entities using Trim two entities

- Choose the icon **Trim 2 Entity** from the ribbon bar.
- [Select the entity to trim/extend]: Select Entity A as shown in <u>Figure: 4.2.1</u>.
- [Select the entity to trim/extend too]: Select Entity B as shown in <u>Figure: 4.2.1</u>.

Figure: 4.2.1

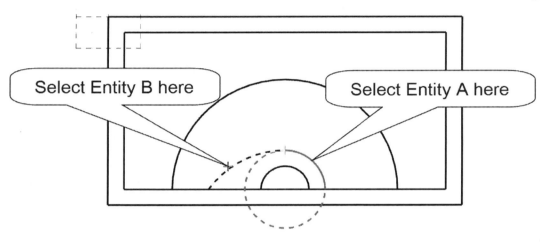

4.3 Trim Entities using Divide/Delete

- Select the command **Divide/Delete** from the ribbon bar.
- Pick the line in between the half circle endpoints as shown in <u>Figure: 4.3.1</u>.

Figure: 4.3.1

NOTE: **Divide/Delete** trims a line or arc to the intersection point between it.

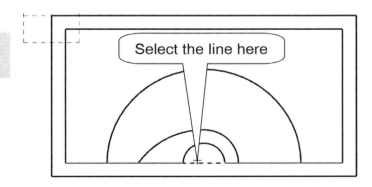

Mastercam. X

◆ Select the **OK** button to exit the **Trim/Break/Extend** command. ☑
◆ The part will appear as shown.

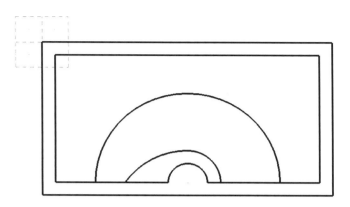

STEP 5: CREATE LINE PARALLEL

In this step you will learn how to create a line parallel knowing the distance and side to create the line on.

Step Preview:

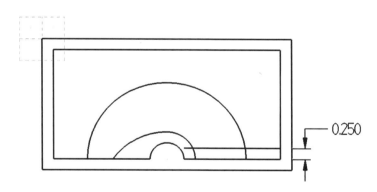

0.250

CREATE
◆ **Line.**

◆  **Parallel.**

◆ [Select a line]: Select the line as shown in <u>Figure: 5.0.1</u>.

Figure: 5.0.1

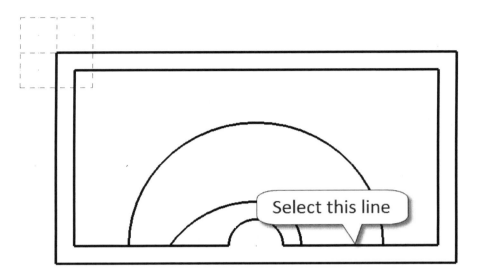

◆ [Select the point to place a parallel line through]: Pick a point above that line as shown in <u>Figure: 5.0.2</u>.

Figure: 5.0.2

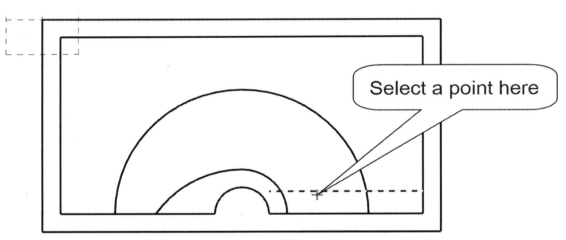

◆ In the **Ribbon bar** change the **Distance** to **0.25**.

◆ Choose the **OK** button to exit the command.

STEP 6: CREATE CHAMFERS

In this step you will learn how to create a chamfer on two corners of the part. You will create this chamfer knowing the width and angle.

Step Preview:

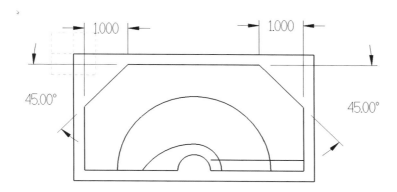

CREATE
* **Chamfer.**

*  **Entities.**
* In the **Ribbon bar** make sure the **Chamfer Style** is set to **1 Distance**, the **Width** is set to **1.0** and ensure **Trim** is enabled.

* Pick the vertical line and then the horizontal line as shown in Figure: 6.0.1.

Figure: 6.0.1

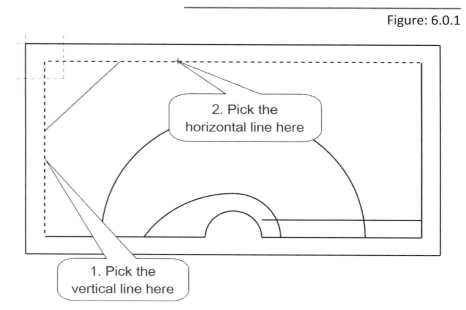

* Repeat the step for the opposite corner.

♦ Choose the **OK** button to exit the command.

STEP 7: CREATE POLAR LINES

In this step you will learn how to create a line knowing one endpoint and angle.

Step Preview:

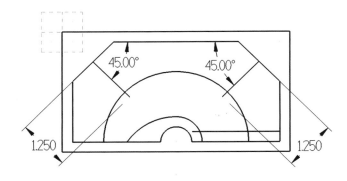

CREATE
♦ **Line.**

♦ **Endpoint.**

♦ [Specify the first endpoint]: Pick the **Midpoint** of the left chamfer.

♦ Ensure the **AutoCursor** icon has changed to represent the line midpoint.
♦ [Specify the second endpoint]: Sketch a line at any angle and any length as shown in Figure: 7.0.1.

Figure: 7.0.1

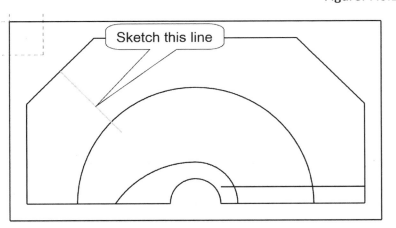

NOTE: At this point the line is still live and can be modified to any angle or length we desire.

◆ Enter a **Length** 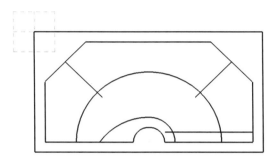 of **1.25** and an **Angle** of **-45.0** Degrees.
◆ Hit **Enter** on your keyboard to preview the line.

◆ Select the **Apply** button to continue.
◆ Pick the midpoint of the opposite chamfer and sketch a line.

◆ Enter a **Length** of **1.25** and an **Angle** of **270-45.0** degrees.

◆ Select the **OK** button to exit the create line endpoint command.
◆ The geometry should look as shown.

STEP 8: CREATE LINE PARALLEL

In this step you will learn how to create a line parallel knowing the distance and side to create the line on.

Step Preview:

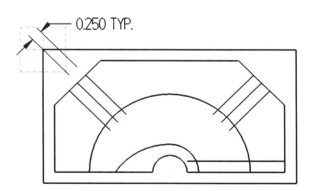

CREATE

♦ **Line.**

♦ 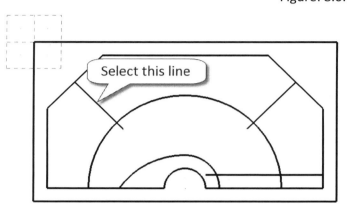 **Parallel.**

♦ Select the line as shown in <u>Figure: 8.0.1</u>.

Figure: 8.0.1

Select this line

♦ Pick a point on either side of this line.

♦ Input a **Distance** [⊢⊣] of **0.25**and hit **Enter** your keyboard.

♦ Select the **Flip** [⟷] button twice.

♦ This will position lines on either side of the originally selected entity as shown in <u>Figure: 8.0.2</u>.

Figure: 8.0.2

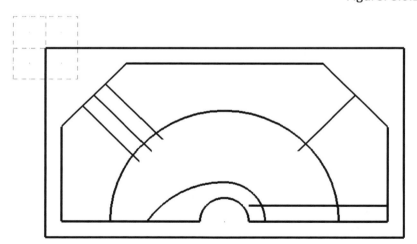

♦ Repeat the step for the opposite side of the part.

◆ The geometry should look as shown.

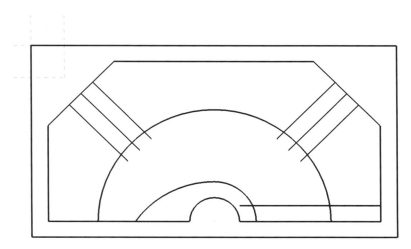

◆ Select the **OK** button to exit the create line parallel command.

STEP 9: DELETE ENTITIES

Step Preview:

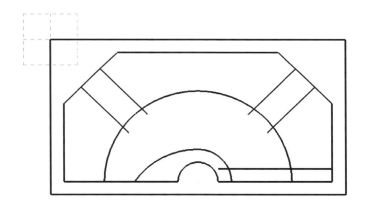

♦ Select the entities as shown in <u>Figure: 9.0.1</u>.

Figure: 9.0.1

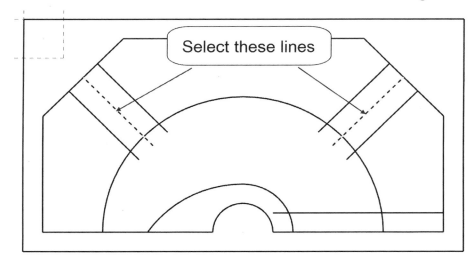

♦ Press the **Delete** key from the keyboard.

STEP 10: TRIM ENTITIES

To **Trim 1 Entity** select the entity you wish to trim, then select the entity you wish to trim to.

Step Preview:

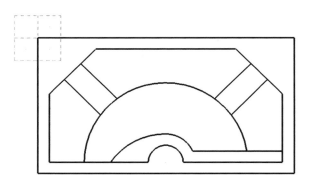

10.1 Trim entities using Trim 1 Entity command

EDIT
♦ **Trim/Break.**

♦ 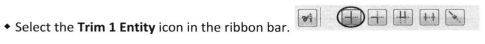 **Trim/Break/Extend.**

♦ Select the **Trim 1 Entity** icon in the ribbon bar.

- ◆ [Select the entity to trim]: Select the line as shown in <u>Figure: 10.1.1</u>.
- ◆ [Select the entity to trim to]: Pick the arc as shown in <u>Figure: 10.1.1</u>.

Figure: 10.1.1

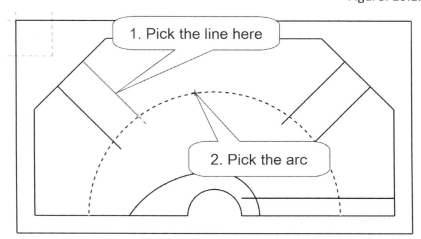

- ◆ Repeat the step for the other 4 lines.
- ◆ Your part should look as shown.

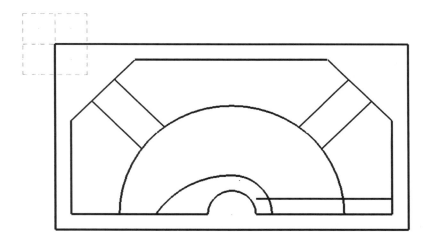

◆ Select the half circle and then pick the line as shown in <u>Figure: 10.1.2</u>.

Figure: 10.1.2

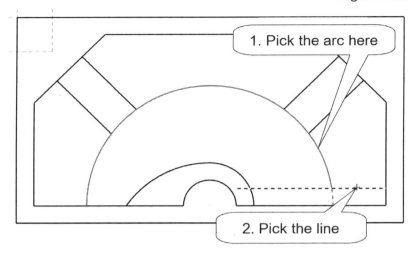

10.2 Trim entities using Trim 2 Entities

◆ Select the **Trim 2 Entities** icon in the ribbon bar.
◆ Select the line and arc as shown in <u>Figure: 10.2.1</u>.

Figure: 10.2.1

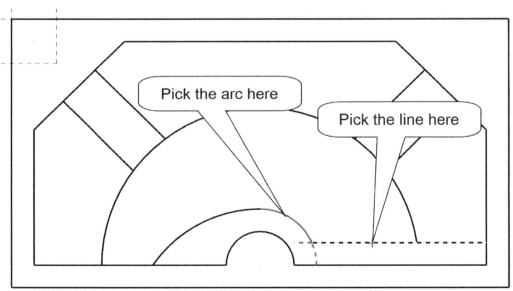

◆ Pick the **OK** button to exit the **Trim/Break/Extend** command.

◆ The part will appear as shown once complete.

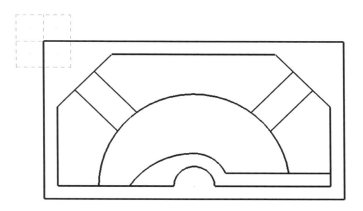

STEP 11: SAVE THE FILE

FILE

◆ 🖫 **Save As.**
◆ File name: "Your Name_6".

TOOLPATH CREATION

SUGGESTED FIXTURE:

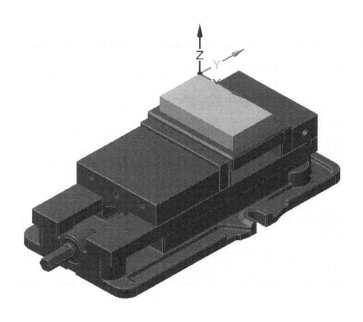

SETUP SHEET:

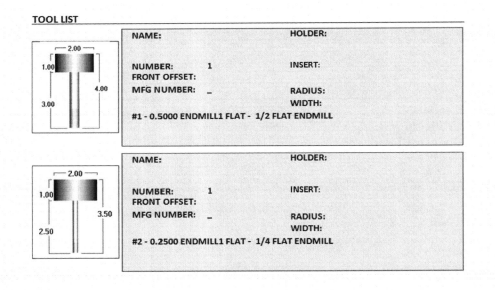

TOOL LIST

NAME:		HOLDER:
NUMBER:	1	INSERT:
FRONT OFFSET:		
MFG NUMBER:	_	RADIUS:
		WIDTH:

#1 - 0.5000 ENDMILL1 FLAT - 1/2 FLAT ENDMILL

NAME:		HOLDER:
NUMBER:	1	INSERT:
FRONT OFFSET:		
MFG NUMBER:	_	RADIUS:
		WIDTH:

#2 - 0.2500 ENDMILL1 FLAT - 1/4 FLAT ENDMILL

Mastercam. X⁸

STEP 12: SELECT THE MACHINE AND SET UP THE STOCK

In Mastercam, you select a **Machine Definition** before creating any toolpaths. The **Machine Definition** is a model of your machines capabilities and features. It acts like a template for setting up your machine. The machine definition ties together three main components. The schematic model of your machines components, the control definition that models your control capabilities, and the post processor that will generate the required machine code (G-code). For a Mill Level 1 exercise (2D toolpaths) we need just a basic machine definition.

> **NOTE:** For the purpose of this tutorial, we will be using the Default milling machine.

- To display the **Toolpaths Manager** press **Alt + O**.

- Use the **Fit** icon to fit the drawing to the screen.

MACHINE TYPE
- **Mill.**
- **Default.**

- Select the plus sign in front of **Properties** in the **Toolpaths Manager** to expand the **Toolpaths Group Properties.**

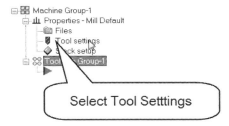

- Select **Tool Settings** to set the tool parameters.

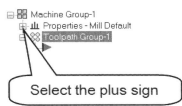

◆ Change the parameters to match the screen shot as shown in <u>Figure: 12.0.1</u>.

Figure: 12.0.1

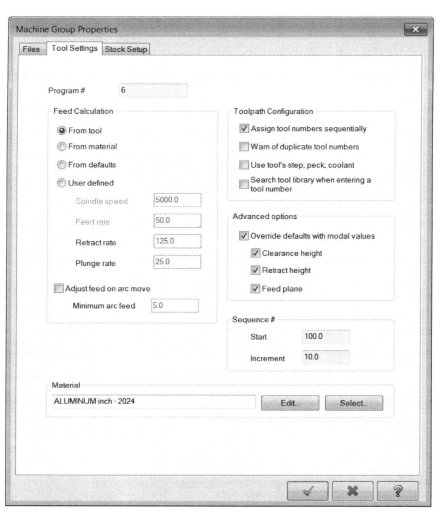

Program # is used to enter a number if your machine tool requires a number for a program name.

Assign tool numbers sequentially allows you to overwrite the tool number from the library with the next available tool number. (First operation tool number 1; Second operation tool number 2, etc.)

Warn of duplicate tool numbers allows you to get a warning if you enter two tools with the same number.

Override defaults with modal values enables the system to keep the values that you enter.

Feed Calculation set From tool uses feed rate, plunge rate, retract rate and spindle speed from the tool definition.

- Select the **Stock setup** tab to define the stock.
- Pick the **Rectangular** shape option.
- Pick the **All Entities** button and input a **Z** value of **1.0** as shown in Figure: 12.0.2.

Figure: 12.0.2

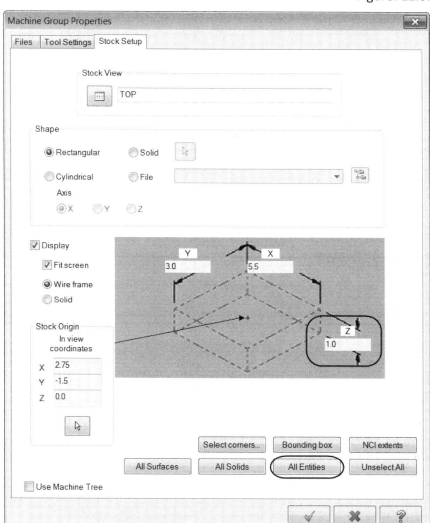

The **Stock Origin** values adjust the positioning of the stock, ensuring that you have equal amount of extra stock around the finished part.

Display options allow you to set the stock as Wireframe and to fit the stock to the screen. (Fit Screen)

NOTE: The **stock** model that you create can be displayed with the part geometry when viewing the file or the toolpaths, during backplot, or while verifying toolpaths. In the graphics, the plus shows you where the stock origin is. The default position is the middle of the stock.

- Select the **OK** button to exit **Machine Group Properties**.

- Select the **Isometric** view from the graphics view toolbar to see the stock.

- Use the **Fit** icon to fit the drawing to the screen.

◆ The stock model should appear as shown in <u>Figure: 12.0.3</u>.

Figure: 12.0.3

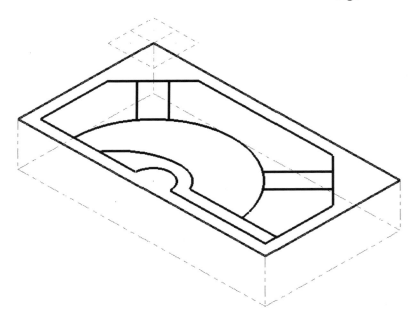

NOTE: You may not be able to see the stock clearly due to the fact that the stock is the same size as the part. The stock is not geometry and can not be selected.

There will not be a facing toolpath because the stock is already to size.

*Mastercam. X*⁸

STEP 13: 2D HIGH SPEED DYNAMIC MILL

2D High Speed Dynamic Mill utilizes the entire flute length of their cutting tools to produce the smoothest, most efficient tool motion for high speed pocketing and core milling. The **Dynamic Mill** toolpath machines pockets, material that other toolpaths left behind, and standing bosses or cores. The toolpath depends on the **Machining strategy** that you choose in the **Chain Options**. If the strategy choosed is **From outside**, the toolpaths starts at the outmost chain and moves freely outside of this area; the inner chain defines the limit of the toolpath. You can also machine pockets in which case the strategy selected is **Start inside** which keeps the tool inside the machining regions.

Toolpath Preview:

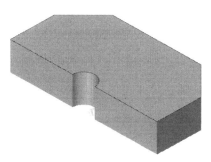

13.1 Break Lines prior to Chaining

> **NOTE:** We are breaking these pieces to be able to select the geometry chains required by the toolpath. This will ensure we cut the correct geometry.

EDIT
* **Trim/Break.**

* ✕ **Break Two Pieces.**

- [Select an entity to break]: Select the line as shown in <u>Figure: 13.1.1</u>.
- [Indicate the break position]: Pick the line Endpoint which is where we want to break the line as shown in <u>Figure: 13.1.1</u>.

Figure: 13.1.1

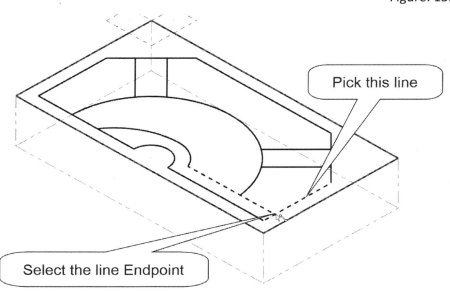

Pick this line

Select the line Endpoint

- [Select an entity to break]: Select the line as shown in <u>Figure: 13.1.2</u>.
- [Indicate the break position]: Select the endpoint of the arc as shown in <u>Figure: 13.1.2</u>.

Figure: 13.1.2

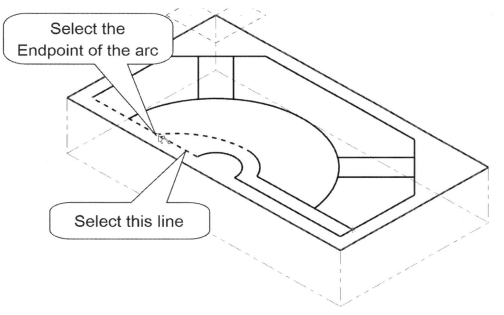

Select the Endpoint of the arc

Select this line

- Select the **OK** button to exit the command.

Mastercam. X⁸

13.2 Chain Selection

TOOLPATHS
* **2D High Speed.**

* 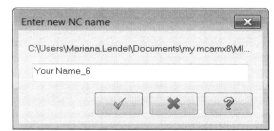 **Dynamic Mill.**

* When the new **NC name** dialog box appears select the **OK** button to accept the name.

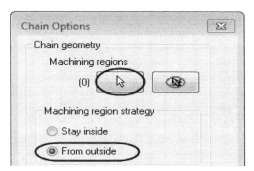

* In the **Chain Options**, **Machining region strategy**, enable **From outside** and click on the **Select** button as shown.

* When the **Chaining** dialog box appears leave the default settings.
* [Select 2D HST machining chain 1]: Select the rectangle as shown in <u>Figure: 13.2.1</u>.

Figure: 13.2.1

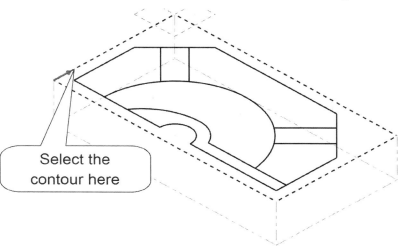

Select the contour here

- Select the **OK** button to exit **Chaining** dialog box.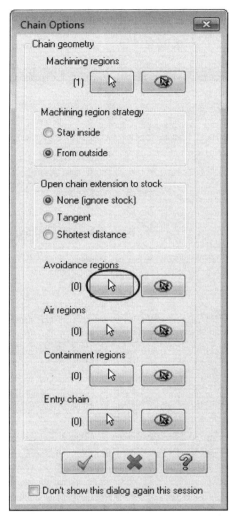
- In the **Chain Options, Avoidance regions**, click on the **Select** button as shown.

◆ [Select 2D HST avoidance chain 1]: Select the chain of the part as shown in <u>Figure: 13.2.2</u>.

Figure: 13.2.2

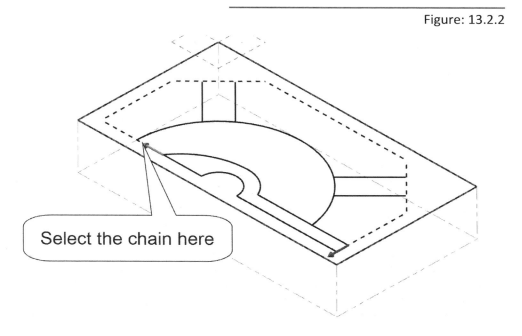

Select the chain here

> **NOTE:** The chain will stop at the branch point. A branch point in a chain is the point where the endpoints of three or more entities meet. Branch points indicate where there are different paths that the chain can take. When Mastercam encounters a branch point during chaining, it prompts you to choose the path for the chain to follow.

◆ [Branch point reached]: Pick the line past that point to continue the chain as shown in <u>Figure: 13.2.3</u>.

Figure: 13.2.3

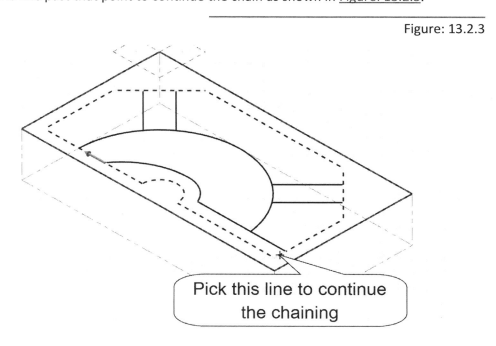

Pick this line to continue
the chaining

• Select the **OK** button to exit the **Chaining** dialog box.

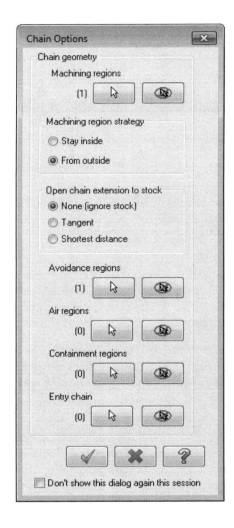

• Select the **OK** button to exit the **Chain Options** dialog box.
• In the toolpath type page **Dynamic Mill** with **From outside** option should be already selected.

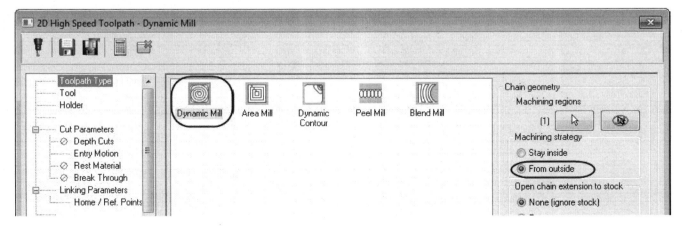

13.3 Select a 0.5" Flat Endmill from the Library and set the Tool Parameters

♦ Select **Tool** from the **Tree view list**.

♦ Click on the **Select library tool** button.
♦ Select the **Filter** button as shown.

♦ Select the **None** button and then under **Tool Types** choose the **Flat Endmill** icon.
♦ Under tool diameter pick **Equal** and input a value of **0.5** as shown in Figure: 13.3.1.

Figure: 13.3.1

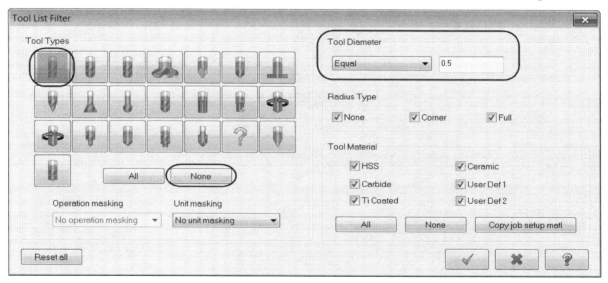

♦ Select the **OK** button to exit the **Tool List Filter**.
♦ In the **Tool Selection** dialog box you should only see a **1/2" Flat Endmill**.

#	Assembly Name	Tool Name	Holder Name	Dia.	Cor. rad.	Length	# Flutes	Typ
290	--	1/2 FLAT ENDMILL	--	0.5	0.0	1.0	4	En.

♦ Select the **1/2" Flat Endmill** in the **Tool Selection** page and then select the **OK** button to exit.

◆ Make all the necessary changes as shown in <u>Figure: 13.3.2</u>.

Figure: 13.3.2

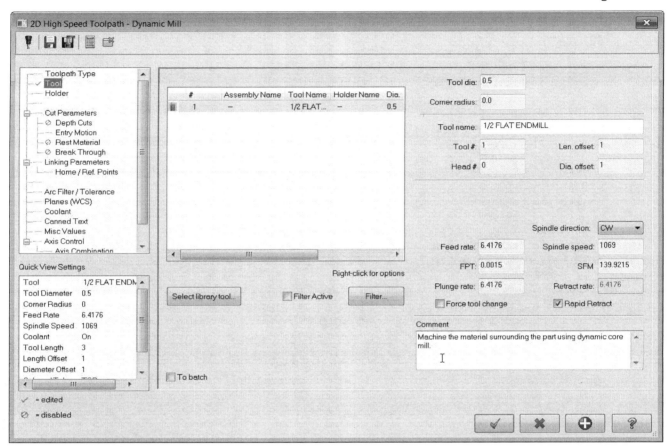

13.4 Set the Cut Parameters

♦ From the **Tree view list**, select **Cut Parameters** and ensure the parameters appear the same as shown in Figure: 13.4.1.

Figure: 13.4.1

Cutting method	Climb
Tip comp	Tip

Approach distance	0.5	Bottom left
First pass offset		0.1
First pass Feed reduction		0.0 %
Stepover	25.0 %	0.125
Min toolpath radius	10.0 %	0.05

Gap size
- ○ Distance — 0.5
- ◉ % of tool diameter — 100.0

Motion < Gap size, Micro lift
| Micro lift distance | 0.01 |
| Back feedrate | 100.0 |

Motion > Gap size, retract
Never

☑ Optimize cut order within pocket

Stock to leave on walls	0.0
Stock to leave on floors	0.0

13.5 Set the Depth Cuts Parameters

• From the **Tree view list**, select the **Depth Cuts Parameters** and disable **Depth Cuts** as shown in Figure: 13.5.1.

Figure: 13.5.1

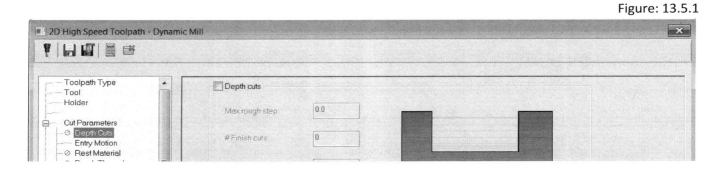

13.6 Set the Entry Motion

• Set the **Entry Method** to **Helix only**. Input a **Z clearance** value of **0.05** and a **Plunge angle** of **2.0** degrees as shown in Figure: 13.6.1.

Figure: 13.6.1

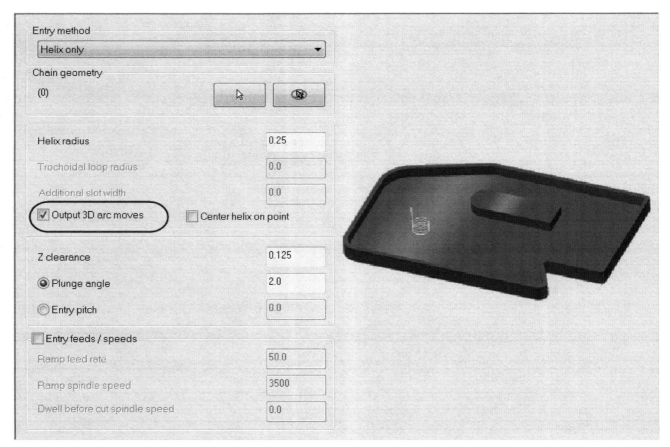

13.7 Set the Linking Parameters

◆ Select **Linking Parameters,** enable **Clearance**, input a value of **1.0** and input a **Depth** value of **-1.0** as shown in Figure: 13.7.1.

Figure: 13.7.1

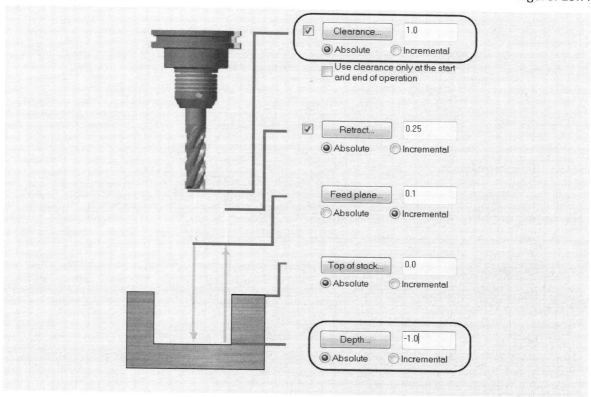

◆ Select the **OK** button to generate the toolpath.

STEP 14: BACKPLOT THE TOOLPATHS

Backplotting shows the path the tools take to cut the part. This display lets you spot errors in the program before you machine the part. As you backplot toolpaths, Mastercam displays additional information such as the X, Y, and Z coordinates, the path length , the minimum and maximum coordinates and the cycle time. It also shows any collisions between the workpiece and the tool.

* Make sure that the toolpaths are selected (signified by the green check mark on the folder icon). If the operation is not selected choose the **Select all operations** icon.

* Select the **Backplot selected operations** button.

NOTE: Mastercam launches a new window that allows you to check the part using **Backplot** or **Verify**. For more information on how to set and use **Backplot** and **Verify** please check Tutorial 2 page 152.

* Right mouse click in the graphics area and select **Fit**.
* Select the **Play** button in the **VCR** bar to run **Backplot**.

* The toolpath should look as shown.

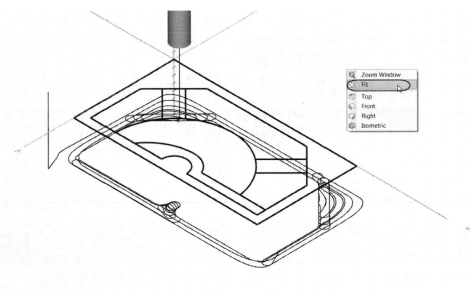

STEP 15: SIMULATE THE TOOLPATH IN VERIFY

Verify Mode shows the path the tools take to cut the part with material removal. This display lets you spot errors in the program before you machine the part. As you verify toolpaths, Mastercam displays additional information such as the X, Y, and Z coordinates, the path length , the minimum and maximum coordinates and the cycle time. It also shows any collisions between the workpiece and the tool.

♦ From **Mastercam Backplot Home** tab, switch to **Verify** and change the settings for the **Visibility** and **Focus** as shown in Figure: 15.0.1.

Figure: 15.0.1

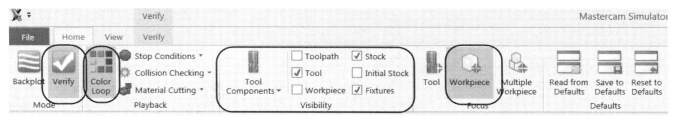

♦ Select the **Play** button in the **VCR** bar to run **Verify**.

♦ The part should appear as shown.

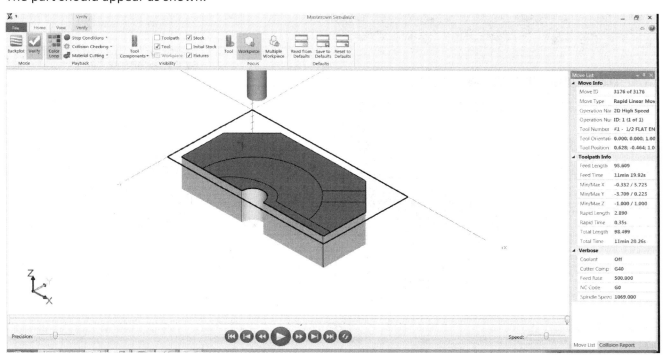

♦ To go back to Mastercam window, minimize Mastercam Simulator window as shown.

STEP 16: 2D HIGH SPEED AREA MILL

2D High Speed Area Mill toolpath machines pockets, material that other toolpaths left behind, and standing bosses or cores. Same as **Dynamic Mill,** based on the **Machining strategy** selected, it can generate the free flowing motion needed to machine features such as standing bosses and cores in a single operation. We need to chain the outer boundary of the part to define the machining region and then the inner boundary which will be defined as the avoidance region and will not be machined.

Toolpath Preview:

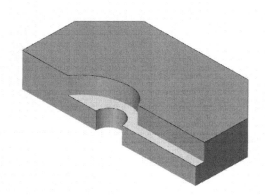

16.1 Chain the Entities

* Press **Alt** + **T** to remove the toolpath display.

TOOLPATHS
* **2D High speed.**

* 🔲 **Area.**

* In the **Chain Options**, **Machining regions**, enable **Core mill** and click on the **Select** button as shown.

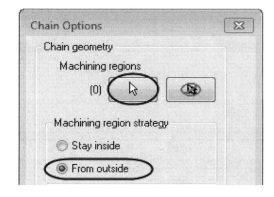

* When the **Chaining** dialog box appears leave the default settings.

• [Select 2D HST machining chain 1]: Select the rectangle as shown in <u>Figure: 16.1.1</u>.

Figure: 16.1.1

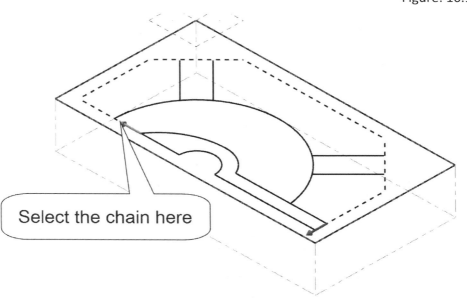

• [Branch point reached]: Pick the line past that point to continue the chain as shown in <u>Figure: 16.1.2</u>.

Figure: 16.1.2

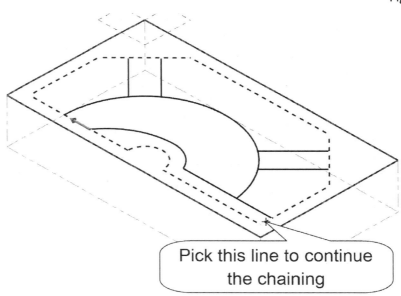

• Select the **OK** button to exit **Chaining** dialog box.

• In the **Chain Options, Avoidance regions**, click on the **Select** button as shown.

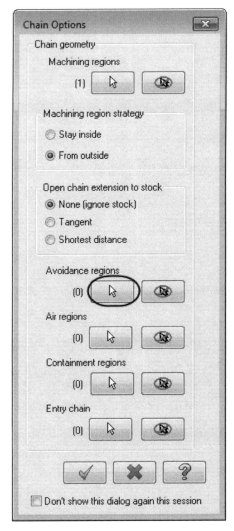

♦ [Select 2D HST avoidance chain 1]: Select the chain of the part as shown in Figure: 16.1.3.

Figure: 16.1.3

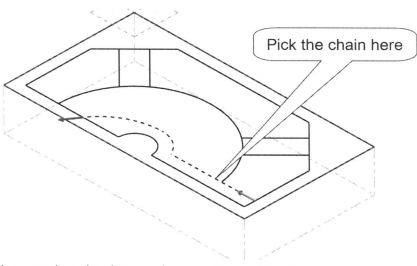

Pick the chain here

♦ [Branch point reach]: Select the branch to omplete the chain as shown in Figure: 16.1.4.

Figure: 16.1.4

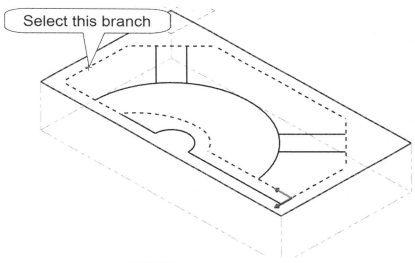

Select this branch

♦ Select the **OK** button to exit the **Chaining** dialog box.

• Select the **OK** button to exit the **Chain Options** dialog box.

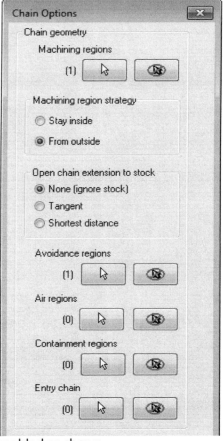

• On the **Toolpath type** page **Area Mill** will be selected and **From outside** enabled as shown.

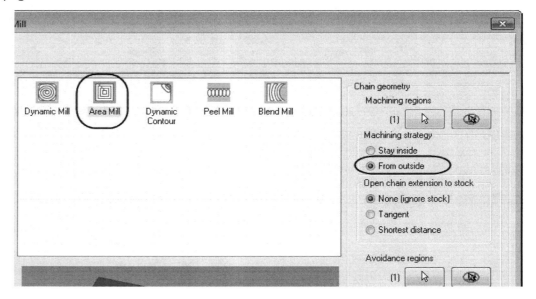

- Select the **Tool** page and make all the necessary changes as shown in <u>Figure: 16.1.5</u>.
- Select the **1/2" Flat Endmill** from the list.

Figure: 16.1.5

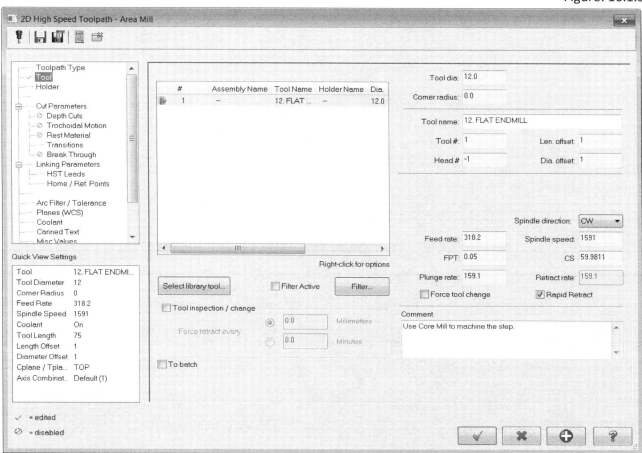

16.2 Set the Cut Parameters

♦ Choose **Cut Parameters** and enable **Smoothing** as shown in Figure: 16.2.1.

Figure: 16.2.1

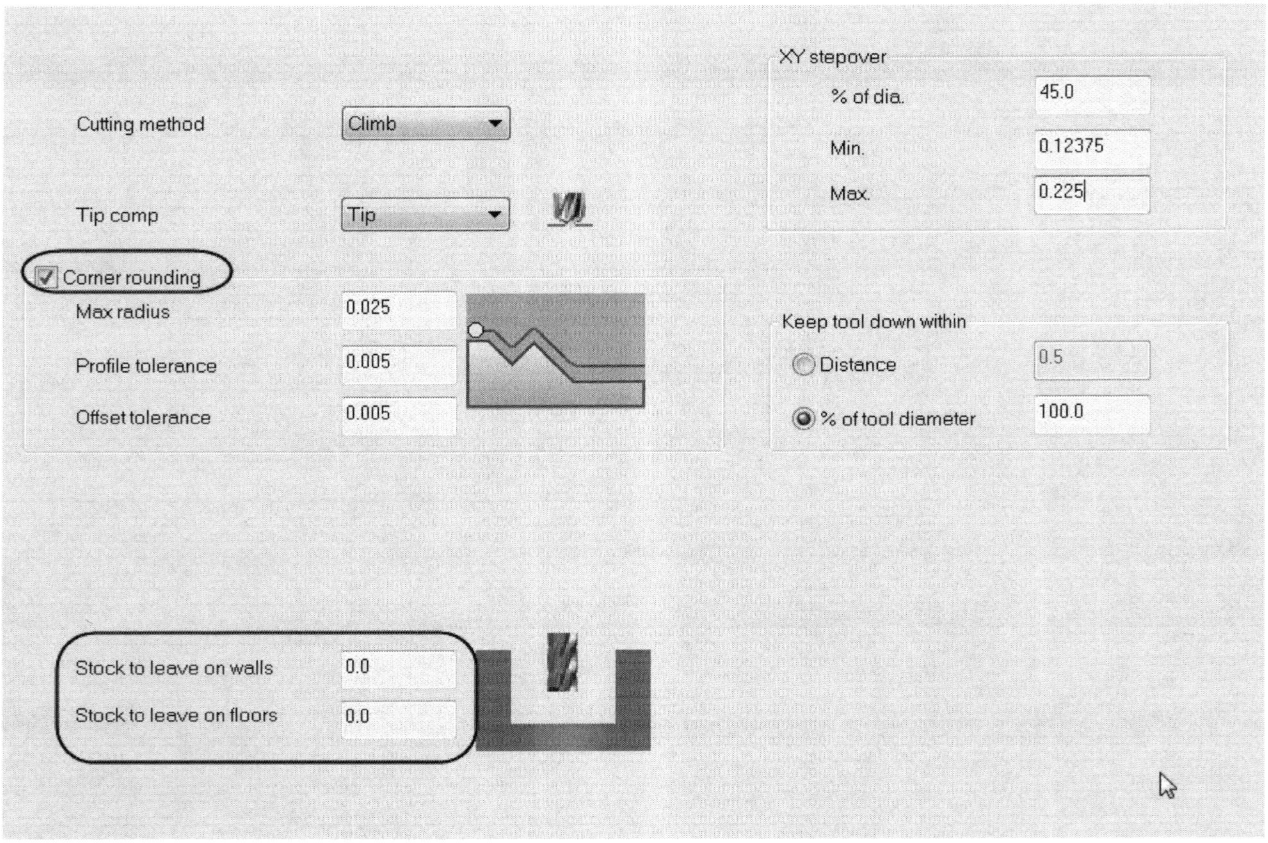

Cutting method   Climb

Tip comp   Tip

☑ Corner rounding

Max radius   0.025

Profile tolerance   0.005

Offset tolerance   0.005

XY stepover

% of dia.   45.0

Min.   0.12375

Max.   0.225

Keep tool down within

○ Distance   0.5

◉ % of tool diameter   100.0

Stock to leave on walls   0.0

Stock to leave on floors   0.0

16.3 Set the Depth Cuts Parameters

• From the **Tree view list**, select the **Depth Cuts Parameters** and enable **Depth Cuts** as shown in Figure: 16.3.1.

Figure: 16.3.1

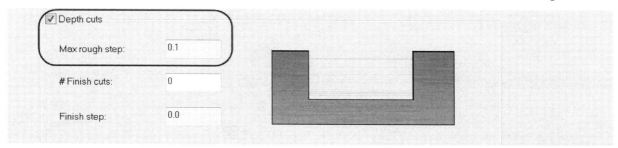

16.4 Set the Transitions

• Select transitions and enable **Entry helix** and enter a **Radius** of **0.475**. Enable **Output 3D arc moves** as shown in Figure: 16.4.1.

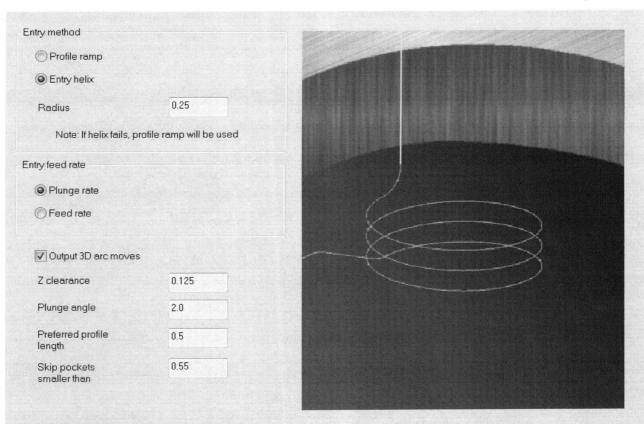

Mastercam. X⁸

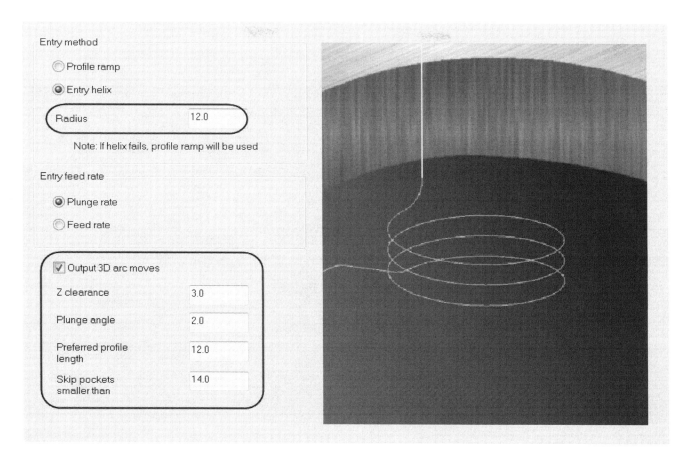

16.5 Set the Linking Parameters

◆ Select **Linking Parameters** and input a **Depth of -0.5** as shown in <u>Figure: 16.5.1</u>.

Figure: 16.5.1

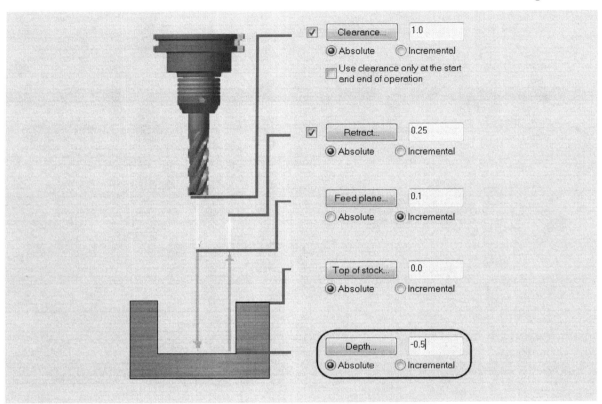

• Select the **OK** button to exit the **2D Area Mill** parameters.

16.6 Backplot the toolpath

♦ See page 584 to review **Backplot** procedure.

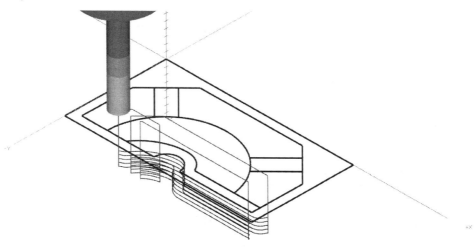

♦ To go back to Mastercam window, minimize **Mastercam Simulator** window as shown.

16.7 Verify both toolpaths

♦ See page 585 for more info.

♦ To verify all toolpaths, from the Toolpaths Manager, choose the **Select all operations** icon.

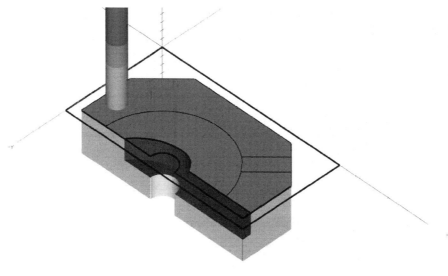

♦ To go back to Mastercam minimize Mastercam Simulator window.

STEP 17: 2D HIGH SPEED BLEND MILL

2D High Speed Blend Mill toolpath morphs smoothly between two open chains. You can create the toolpath along or across the selected chains. This machining strategy supports the full depth of cutting, utilizing more of the cutters flute length and resulting in less cycle time and tool wear.

Toolpath Preview:

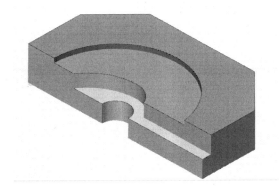

17.1 Chain the Entities

TOOLPATHS

♦ **2D High speed.**

♦ 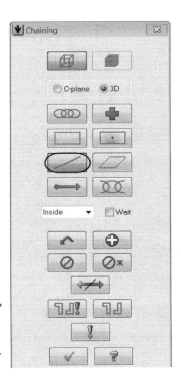 **Blend.**

♦ When the **Chaining** dialog box appears select the **Single** button.

The **Single** button allows you to select one entity (a single line, arc or spline) in a chain.

• Select the arc as shown in <u>Figure: 17.1.1</u>.

Figure: 17.1.1

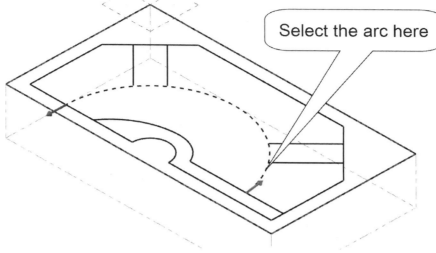

Select the arc here

• To chain the second arc choose the **Partial** chaining method as shown in <u>Figure: 17.1.2</u>.

Figure: 17.1.2

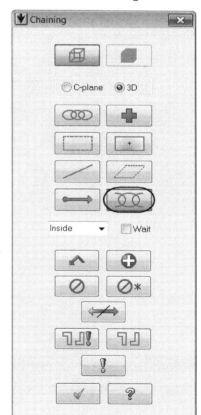

Partial creates an open chain with two mouse clicks. In the graphics window, click on the entity where you want to start the chain, then click where you want to end the chain.

* [Select the first entity]: Select the Entity A as shown in <u>Figure: 17.1.3</u>.

Figure: 17.1.3

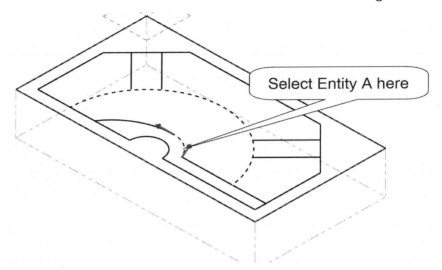

NOTE: Make sure the chain direction is as shown otherwise, in the **Chaining** dialog box click on the **Reverse** button.

* [Select the last entity]: Select Entity B as shown in <u>Figure: 17.1.4</u>.

Figure: 17.1.4

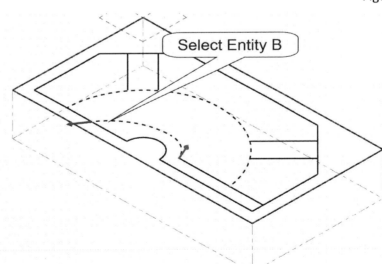

* Choose the **OK** button to exit the **Chaining** dialog box.

Mastercam. X²

• Select **Toolpath Type** from the **Tree view list** and pick **Blend Mill.**

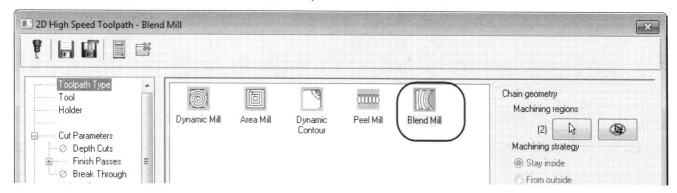

17.2 Select a 1/4" Flat Endmill from the Library and set the Tool Parameters

• Select **Tool** from the **Tree view list**.

• Click on the **Select library tool** button. [Select library tool...]
• Select the **Filter** button as shown.

• Select the **None** button and then under **Tool Types** choose the **Flat Endmill** Icon.
• Under tool diameter pick **Equal** and input a value **0.25** as shown in Figure: 17.2.1.

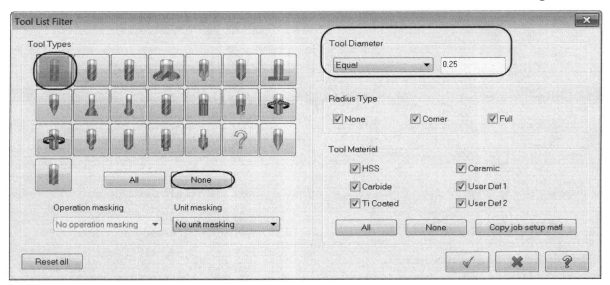

- Select the **OK** button to exit the **Tool List Filter.**
- In the **Tool Selection** dialog box you should only see a **1/4"** Flat Endmill.

#	Assembly Name	Tool Name	Holder Name	Dia.	Cor. rad.	Length	# Flutes	Ra..
285	--	1/4 FLAT ENDMILL	--	0....	0.0	0.5	4	No.

- Select the **1/4" Flat Endmill** in the **Tool Selection** page and then select the **OK** button to exit.
- Make the necessary changes as shown in Figure: 17.2.2.

Figure: 17.2.2

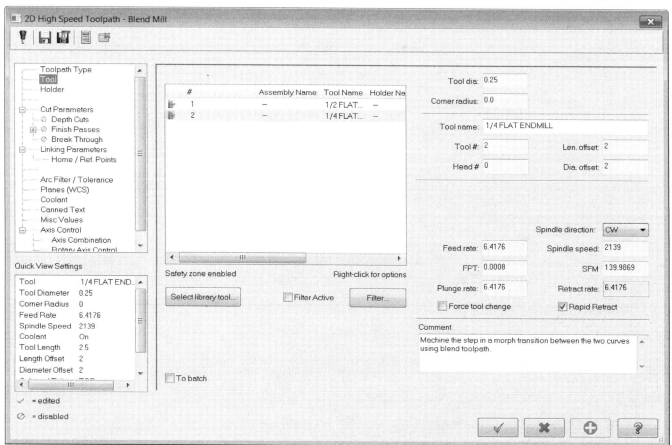

17.3 Set the Cut Parameters

• Set the **Cutting method** to **Zigzag** and **Along** as shown in <u>Figure: 17.3.1</u>. This will morph start the cut along the first chain and then morph it towards the second chain.

Figure: 17.3.1

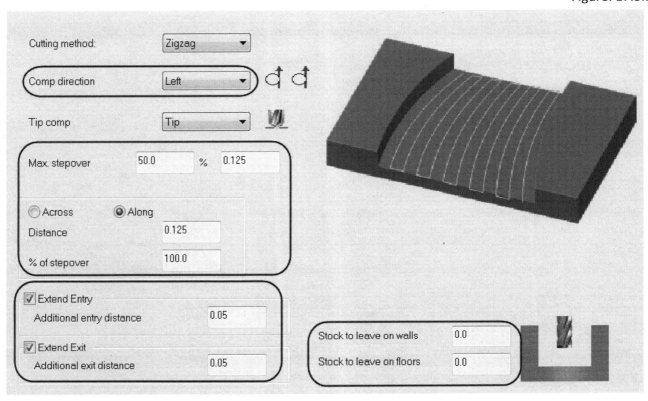

Compensation direction set to **Left** will allow the tool to travel to the left of the selected chains.

Along cuts in the along direction, stepping over in the across direction.

Max Stepover sets the distance between adjacent passes.

Distance/% of stepover sets the spacing between the temporary across moves. These moves are used to generate the final toolpath but are not included in the final toolpath.

17.4 Set Depth Cuts

◆ Ensure **Depth cuts** is off.

17.5 Finish passes

◆ Enable **Finish Pass** and change the parameters as shown in <u>Figure: 17.5.1</u>

Figure: 17.5.1

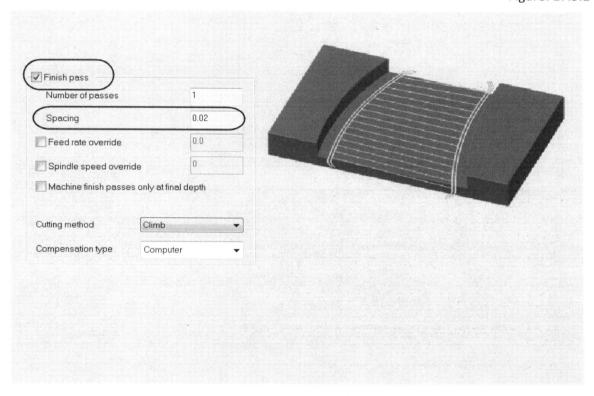

Finish pass page allows you to add finish passes along the selected chains of the toolpath.

Number of passes sets the number of finish passes.

Spacing sets the distance between the finish passes.

Machine finish passes only at final depth performs the finish passes only at the final cutting depth.

17.6 Set the Linking Parameters

• Enter a **Depth** of **-0.125** as shown in <u>Figure: 17.6.1</u>.

Figure: 17.6.1

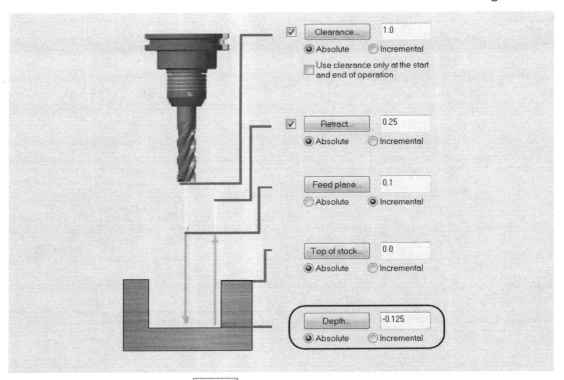

• Choose the **OK** button to generate the toolpath.

17.7 Backplot the toolpath

• **Backplot** the toolpath page 584 for more information.

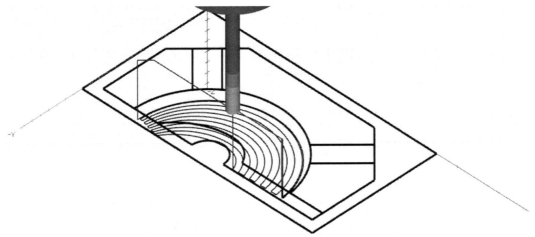

◆ To go back to Mastercam minimize Mastercam Simulator window.

17.8 Verify the toolpaths

◆ To **Verify** the toolpaths see page 585 for more information.

◆ To verify all toolpaths, from the Toolpaths Manager, choose the **Select all operations** icon.

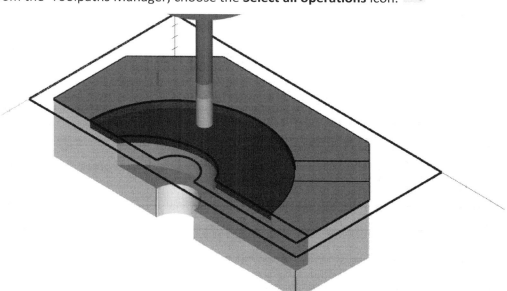

◆ To go back to Mastercam minimize Mastercam Simulator window.

STEP 18: 2D HIGH SPEED PEEL MILL

2D High Speed Peel Mill toolpath allows for efficient constant climb milling between two selected contours or along a single contour. It uses a trochodial style of motion to cut the slot. For single chains, you need to define the width of the cut. Otherwise the width is defined by the area between the two contours.

Toolpath Preview:

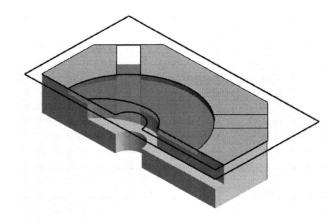

TOOLPATHS

◆ **2D High Speed.**

◆ **Peel.**

◆ Leave the default chaining method and select the lines as shown. Ensure both chains go in the same direction as shown in in Figure: 18.0.1.

Figure: 18.0.1

NOTE: To change the direction of chaining if needed, click on the **Reverse** button from the **Chaining** dialog box.

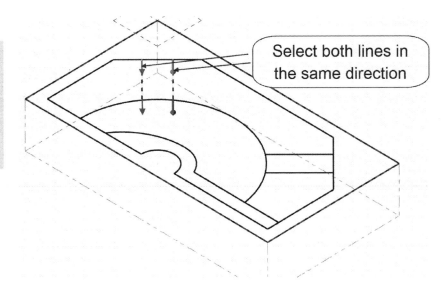

Select both lines in the same direction

- Choose the **OK** button to exit the **Chaining** dialog box.
- In the **Toolpath Type**, **Peel Mill** is already selected**.**

Dynamic Mill

Area Mill

Dynamic Contour

Peel Mill

Blend Mill

- Select the **Tool** page from the **Tree view list** and select the **1/4" Flat Endmill** from the list of tools.
- Make any necessary changes as shown in <u>Figure: 18.0.2</u>.

Figure: 18.0.2

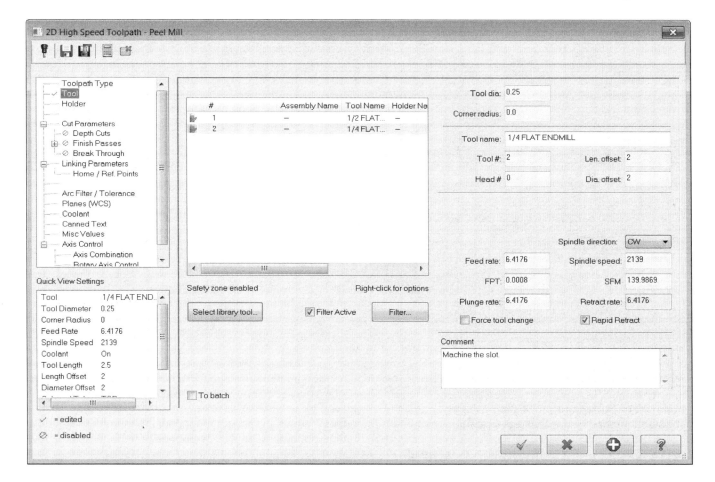

18.1 Set the Cut Parameters

♦ Select **Cut Parameters** and enter a **Min toolpath radius** of **2.5%** and a **Stepover** amount of **0.05** as shown in Figure: 18.1.1.
♦ Enable the **Extend entry** option and **Extend Exit**. Input a value to extend the entry by **0.5** and to extend the exit by **1.25** as shown in Figure: 18.1.1.

Figure: 18.1.1

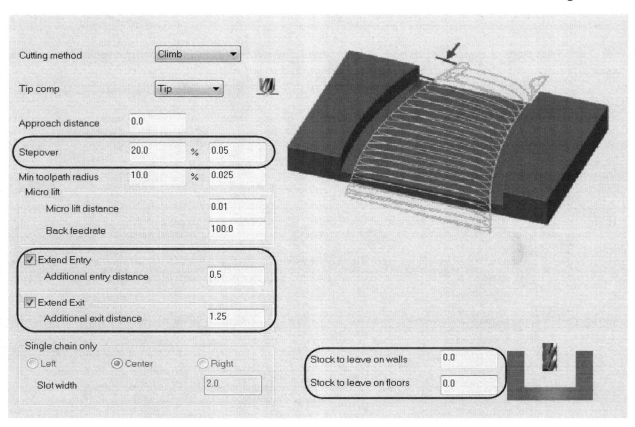

Stepover sets the distance between adjacent cuts of the toolpath.

Min toolpath radius defines the minimum radius of the arc that the tool follows along its semi-circular path.

Micro lift distance enter the distance the tool lifts off of the part on back moves. Micro lifts are slight lifts that help clear chips and minimize excessive tool heating.

Back feedrate controls the speed (inches per minute or millimeters per minute) of the backfeed movement of the tool. This allows 3D arcs between cuts to have a different feed rate than the rest of the toolpath, which can help reduce cycle time.

Extend Entry/Exit allows you to adjust the initial and final tool engagement with the material.

18.2 Set the Depth Cuts

• Ensure the **Depth Cuts** are disabled.

18.3 Set the Finish Pass Parameters

• Ensure **Finish passes** and **Machine Finish passes only at final depth** are enabled as shown in Figure: 18.3.1.

Figure: 18.3.1

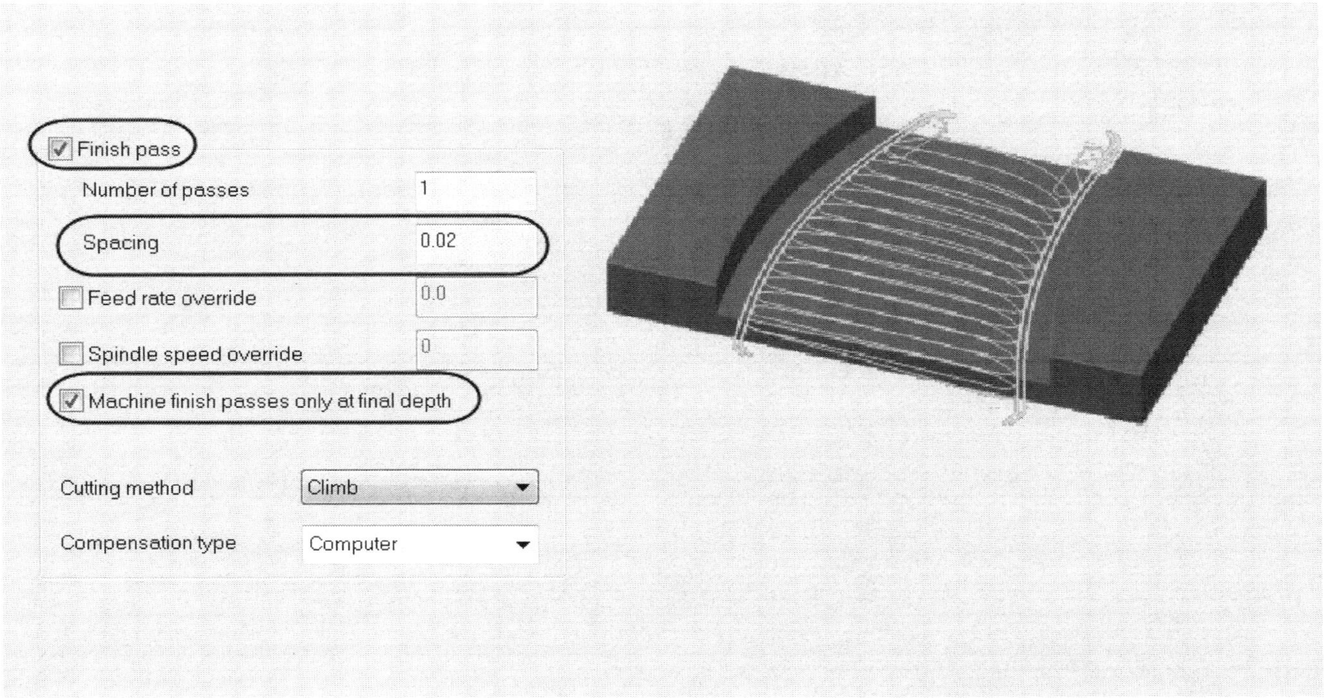

Finish Pass performs a high speed finish pass along the walls of the slot.

18.4 Set the Linking Parameters

* Set the **Depth** to **-0.5** as shown in Figure: 18.4.1.

Figure: 18.4.1

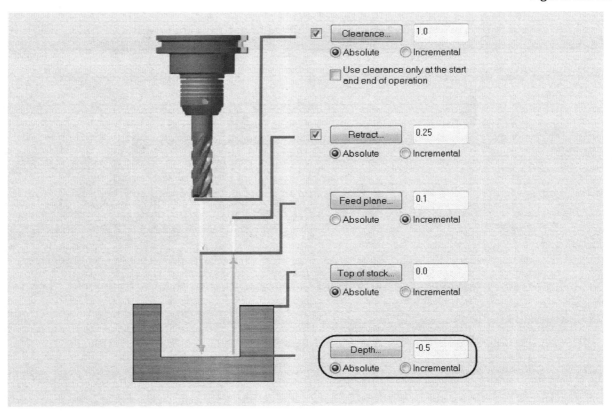

* Choose the **OK** button to generate the toolpath.

18.5 Backplot the toolpath

◆ See page 584 for more information.

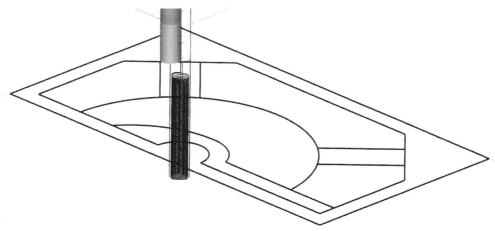

◆ To go back to Mastercam minimize Mastercam Simulator window.

18.6 Verify all toolpaths

◆ See page 585 for more information.

◆ To verify all toolpaths, from the Toolpaths Manager, choose the **Select all operations** icon.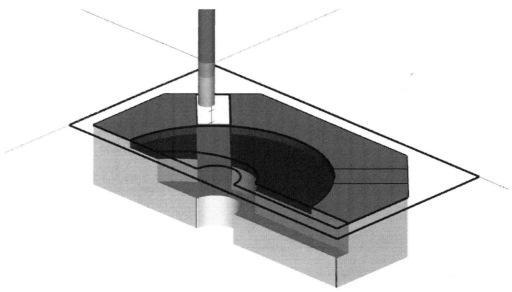

◆ To go back to Mastercam minimize Mastercam Simulator window.

STEP 19: 2D HIGH SPEED PEEL MILL

In this step you will learn how to copy an existing toolpath in the Toolpaths Manager. You will also learn how to rechain the geometry used in the toolpath.

Toolpath Preview:

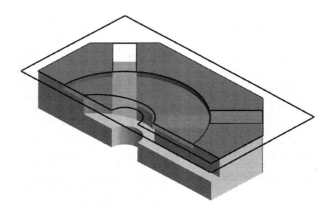

19.1 Copy the Previous Toolpath

♦ From the **Toolpaths Manager**, select only operation #4 (the peel mill toolpath).

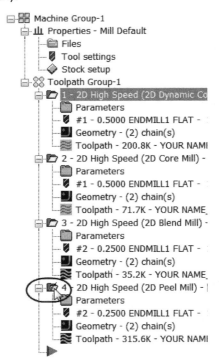

◆ Right click and hold the right mouse button down and drag the operation to a point below it as shown in Figure: 19.1.1.

Figure: 19.1.1

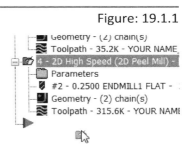

◆ Release the right mouse button and select the option **Copy After** as shown in Figure: 19.1.2.

Figure: 19.1.2

| Geometry - (2) chain(s) |
| Toolpath - 35.2K - YOUR NAME_ |
| 4 - 2D High Speed (2D Peel Mill) - |
| Parameters |
| #2 - 0.2500 ENDMILL1 FLAT - |
| Geometry - (2) chain(s) |
| Toolpath - 315.6K - YOUR NAME |

Move before
Move after
Copy before
Copy after
Cancel

• Make sure that the insert arrow is below the last toolpath as shown in <u>Figure: 19.1.3</u>; otherwise, pick the icon to move the insert arrow down.

Figure: 19.1.3

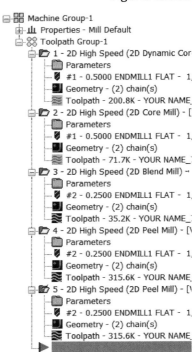

19.2 Re-Chain the Geometry

• In the operation #5, pick **Geometry**.

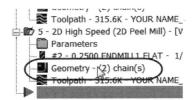

Mastercam X²

◆ Right mouse click in the **Chain Manager** and select **Rechain all** as shown.

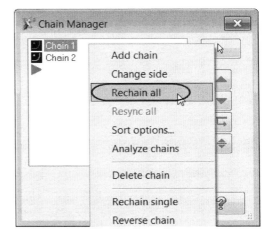

◆ When the chaining dialog box appears leave the default settings and choose the line as shown in <u>Figure: 19.2.1</u> (this time we will chain one entity only to create the toolpath).

Figure: 19.2.1

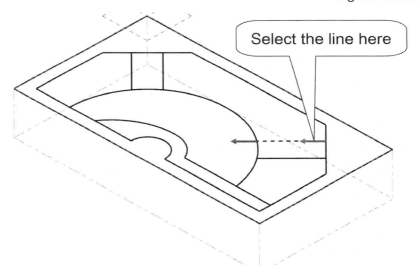

Select the line here

◆ Once the geometry has been selected choose the **OK** button to exit the **Chaining** dialog box.

◆ Choose the **OK** button again to exit the **Chain Manager**.

* Pick **Parameters** in **Operation #5.**

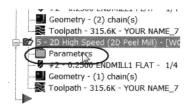

19.3 Set the Cut Parameters

* Select **Cut Parameters** and change **Single chain** only to **Left** and enter a **Slot width** of **0.5** as shown in Figure: 19.3.1.

Figure: 19.3.1

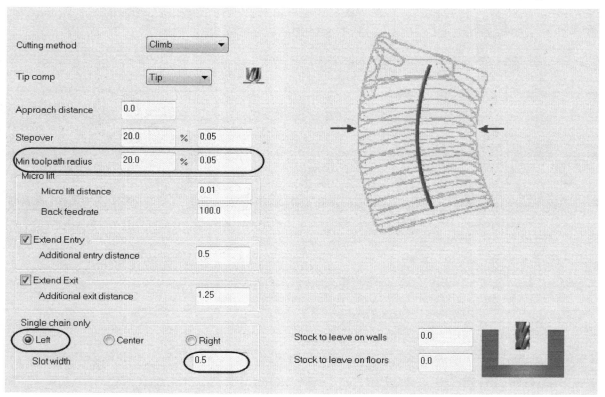

19.4 Set the Linking Parameters

♦ Select **Linking Parameters** and make sure that the **Depth** is set to **-0.5** as shown in <u>Figure: 19.4.1</u>.

Figure: 19.4.1

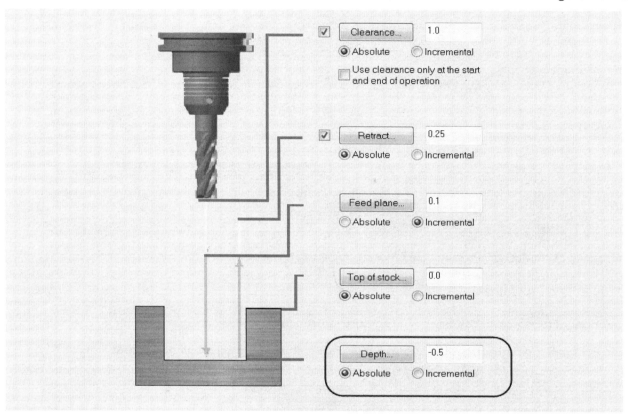

♦ Choose the **OK** button to exit the toolpath parameters.

♦ Pick the button to **Regenerate all dirty operations**. ⁱx

19.5 Backplot the toolpath

♦ To **Backplot** the toolpath see page 584 for more information.

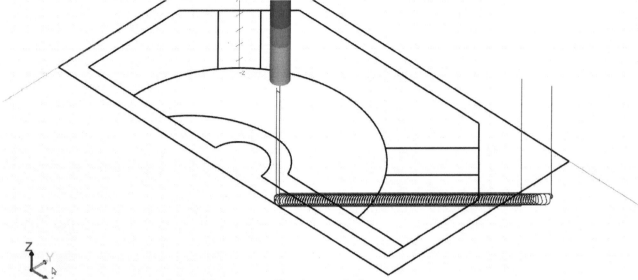

♦ To go back to Mastercam minimize Mastercam Simulator window.

19.6 Verify all toolpaths

♦ To Verify the toolpaths see page 585 for more information.

♦ To verify all toolpaths, from the Toolpaths Manager, choose the **Select all operations** icon.

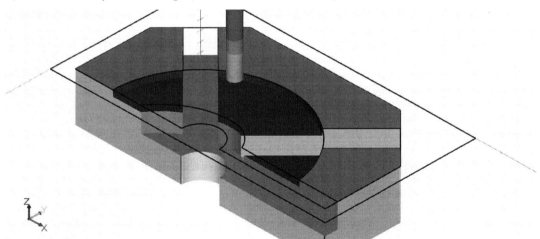

♦ To go back to Mastercam minimize Mastercam Simulator window.

STEP 20: POST THE FILE

- Ensure all operations are selected; if they are not, use the **Select all operations** button in the **Toolpaths Manager.**

- Select the **Post selected operations** button from the **Toolpaths Manager.** G1
- In the **Post processing** window make the necessary changes as shown in Figure: 20.0.1.

Figure: 20.0.1

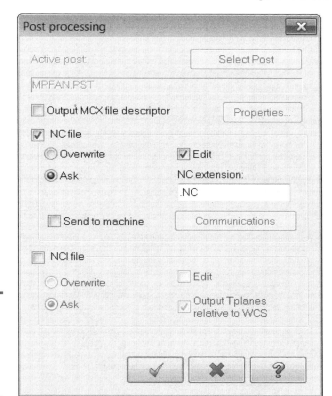

NC File enabled allows you to keep the NC file and to assign the same name as the MCX file.

Edit enabled allows you to automatically launch the default editor.

- Select the **OK** button to continue.
- Save your file and name it **YOUR NAME_6.NC**.

◆ A window with Mastercam Code Expert will be launcheded and the NC program will appear as shown.

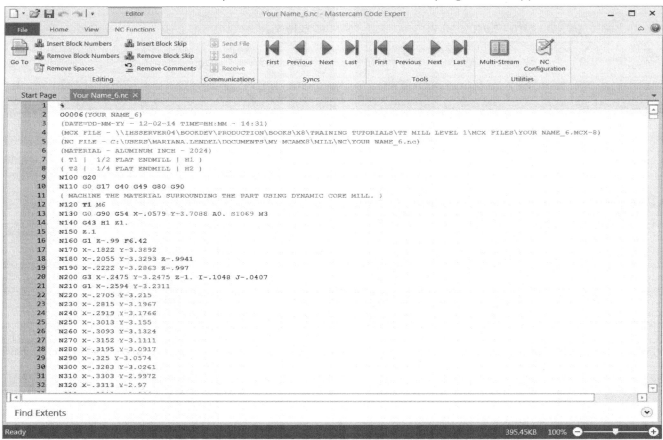

◆ Select the **"X"** box at the upper right corner to exit the editor.

STEP 21: SAVE THE UPDATED MCX FILE

Mastercam. X

REVIEW EXERCISE - STUDENT PRACTICE

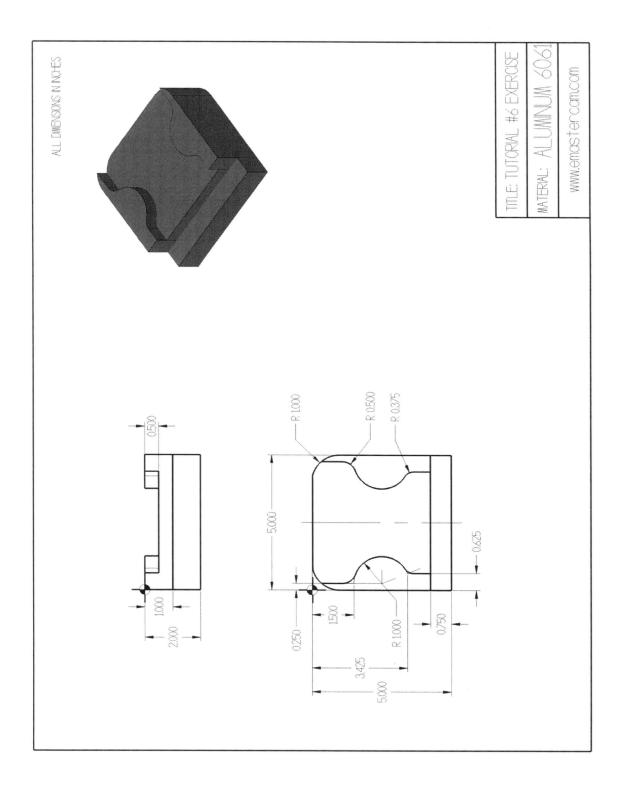

ALL DIMENSIONS IN INCHES

TITLE: TUTORIAL #6 EXERCISE

MATERIAL: ALUMINUM 6061

www.emastercam.com

0.500

R 1.000

R 0.500

R 0.375

5.000

0.625

1.000

2.000

0.250

1.500

R 1.000

0.750

3.425

5.000

CREATE THE GEOMETRY FOR TUTORIAL #6 EXERCISE

Use these commands to create the geometry:

- Create Rectangle.
- Create Line Endpoint.
- Create Arc Polar.
- Create Fillet Entities.

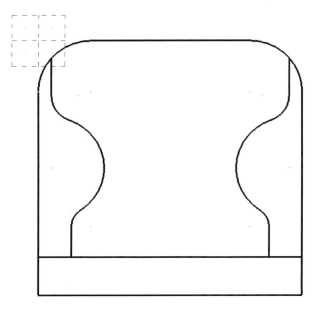

CREATE THE TOOLPATHS FOR TUTORIAL #6 EXERCISE

Create the Toolpaths for Tutorial #6 Exercise as per the instructions below.

Set the machine properties including the Stock Setup.
Remove the material on the step Contour (2D).
* Use a **7/8"Flat Endmill**.
* Based on your chaining direction ensure the **Compensation direction** is set correct.
* Enable **Depth Cuts**.
* **Lead In/Out**, ensure the arc radius is set to zero.
* No **Break Through, Multi Passes**.
* Set the depth according to the drawing.

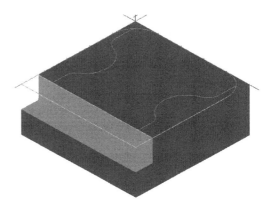

Remove the material around the fillets using Contour (2D).
* Use the **7/8" Flat Endmill**.
* Based on your chaining direction ensure the **Compensation direction** is set correct.
* Enable **Depth Cuts**.
* Set a **Lead In/Out** and **Break Through**.
* No **Multi Passes**.
* Set the depth according to the drawing.

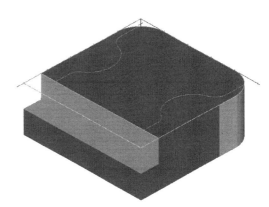

Create a 2D High Speed Blend Mill toolpath to remove the material in the center of the part.
* Select the two chains.
* Use a **1/2" Flat Endmill**.
* Select along for the tool cutting direction.
* Set the **Compensation** direction to **Inside**.
* **Extend Exit 0.5"**
* Disable **Depth Cuts** and **Break Through**.
* Set the depth according to the drawing.
* Your part will appear as shown.

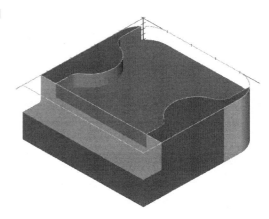

NOTES:

TUTORIAL #6 QUIZ

◆ What is the advantage of Dynamic Mill?

◆ What entities need to be chained to utilize Core Milling?

◆

◆ How does a Blend Mill toolpath work?

TUTORIAL #7

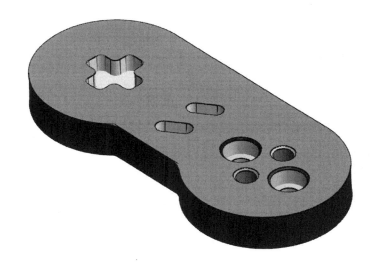

OVERVIEW OF STEPS TAKEN TO CREATE THE FINAL PART:

Import the CAD Model and prepare it to generate Toolpaths from:
- The student will open the Solidworks file in Mastercam.
- The student will use Translate 3D to rotate the part in the proper plane.
- The student will rotate the part in the Top plane.

Create the necessary Toolpaths to machine the part:
- The student will set up the stock size to be used and the clamping method used.
- The **2D HS Dynamic Mill** toolpath will be used to machine the pockets.
- The **Feature Based Drill** toolpath will be used to machine the four holes.
- The **2D HS Dynamic Mill** toolpath will be used to machine the outside profile.
- The **Contour** toolpath will be used to finish the outside profile.

Backplot and Verify the file:
- The Backplot will be used to simulate a step by step process of the tool's movements.
- The Verify will be used to watch a tool machine the part out of a solid model.

Post Process the file to generate the G-code:
- The Student will then post process the file to obtain an NC file containing the necessary code for the machine.

 This tutorial takes approximately one hour to complete.

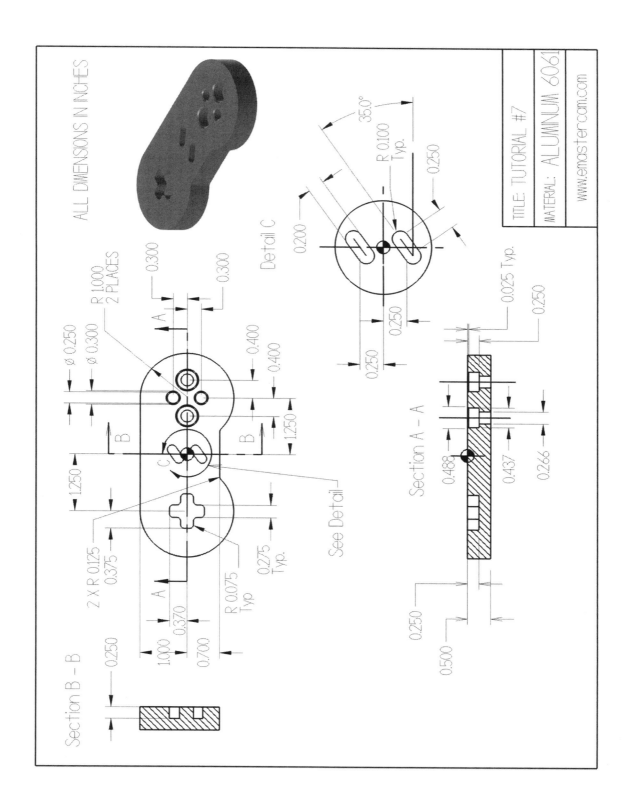

ALL DIMENSIONS IN INCHES

Detail C

R 0.100 Typ.
35.0°
0.250
0.200
0.250
0.250

TITLE: TUTORIAL #7
MATERIAL: ALUMINUM 6061
www.emastercam.com

Section A – A
0.025 Typ.
0.250
0.488
0.437
0.266
0.250
0.500

Section B – B
0.250
Ø 0.250
Ø 0.300
R 1.000 2 PLACES
A
B
C
B
A
1.250
1.250
2 X R 0.125
0.375
1.000
0.370
0.700
R 0.075 Typ
0.275 Typ.
See Detail
0.300
0.300
0.400
0.400
1.250

GEOMETRY CREATION

STEP 1: SETTING UP THE GRAPHIC USER INTERFACE

Please refer to the **Getting Started** section to set up the graphics user interface.

STEP 2: IMPORTING THE SOLIDWORKS FILE GEOMETRY

Mastercam lets you read (import) a variety of CAD file types into the Mastercam database. You can also write (export) Mastercam files to a variety of different file formats.
To import a SolidWorks file in Mastercam you have to use the Open function and then select from the File of type list the SolidWorks files.

Step Preview:

DOWNLOAD THE FILES FROM WWW.EMASTERCAM.COM/FILES.

♦ Save the file at a preferred location.

FILE

♦  **Open.**

♦ In the file name extension click on the drop down arrow as shown.

◆ From the **File of type list**, select **SolidWorks Files (*.sldprt;*sldasm)** as shown.

◆ Find and select **TUTORIAL #7.sldprt.**
◆ Click on the **Options** button.

◆ Leave the **Solids** enabled to import the file as a solid and enable **Edge** curves for Mastercam to automatically create curves at the edges of the solid. To better see the curves, enable also **Use System Color for imported Solids** as shown.

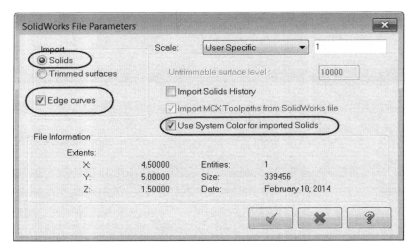

◆ Select the **OK** button to exit the **SolidWorks File Parameters** dialog box.

◆ Open the file.

◆ Select the **Isometric** graphic view.

◆ Select the **Fit** icon to fit the geometry to the screen.

◆ The geometry should look as shown.

> **NOTE:** In preparation to toolpath the part, the geometry has to be oriented same as the part sits on the machine table. In the next step you will rotate the part using the Translate 3D command.

STEP 3: ORIENTATE THE PART USING TRANSLATE 3D

Translate 3D allows you to move the geometry between views (from one plane to another). In your case will move the Back plane to Top.

Step Preview:

XFORM

-  **Translate 3D.**
- [Translate: select entities to translate]: Make a window around the solid as shown.

Select this corner

Select the opposite corner

- The entire geometry should be selected as shown.

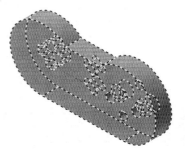

- Press **Enter** to finish the selections.

• In the **Translate 3D** enable **Move** and change the **Source View** to **Back** and leave the **Destination View** to **Top** as shown in Figure: 3.0.1.

Figure: 3.0.1

• The geometry preview should look as shown.

• Select the **OK** button to exit **Translate 3D**.

STEP 4: ROTATE THE PART

In this step you will learn how to rotate the part about the origin 180 degrees in the Top plane.

Step Preview:

XFORM

- ⌐ **Rotate.**
- [Rotate: select entities to rotate]: Make a window again all entities as shown.

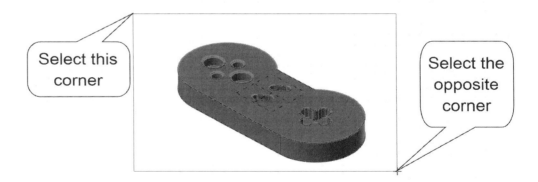

Select this corner

Select the opposite corner

- Press **Enter** to finish the selection.

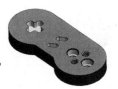

• In the **Rotate** dialog box enable **Move** and change the angle to **180** as shown in <u>Figure: 4.0.1</u>.

Figure: 4.0.1

• The preview should look as shown.

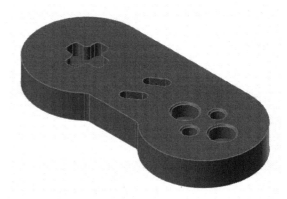

• Select the **OK** button to exit **Rotate**.

Mastercam X

• Choose the **Clear Colors** icon from the toolbars area to reset the colours back to the original.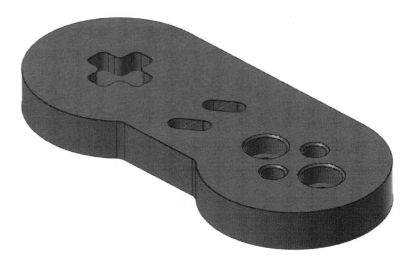

STEP 5: SAVE THE FILE

•   **Save As.**
• File name: "Your Name_7."

TOOLPATH CREATION

SUGGESTED FIXTURE:

Mastercam. X[8]

STEP 6: SELECT THE MACHINE AND SET UP THE STOCK

In Mastercam, you select a **Machine Definition** before creating any toolpaths. The **Machine Definition** is a model of your machines capabilities and features. It acts like a template for setting up your machine. The machine definition ties together three main components. The schematic model of your machines components. The control definition that models your control capabilities and the post processor that will generate the required machine code (G-code). For a Mill Level 1 exercise (2D toolpaths) we need just a basic machine definition.

> **NOTE:** For the purpose of this tutorial, we will be using the Default milling machine.

♦ To display the **Toolpaths Manager** press **Alt + O**.

♦ Use the **Fit** icon to fit the drawing to the screen.

MACHINE TYPE
♦ **Mill.**
♦ **Default.**

♦ Select the plus sign in front of **Properties** in the **Toolpaths Manager** to expand the **Toolpaths Group Properties.**

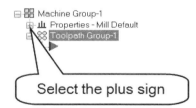

♦ Select **Tool Settings** to set the tool parameters.

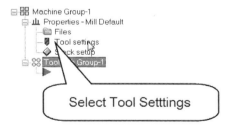

◆ Change the parameters to match the screen shot as shown in <u>Figure: 6.0.1</u>.

Figure: 6.0.1

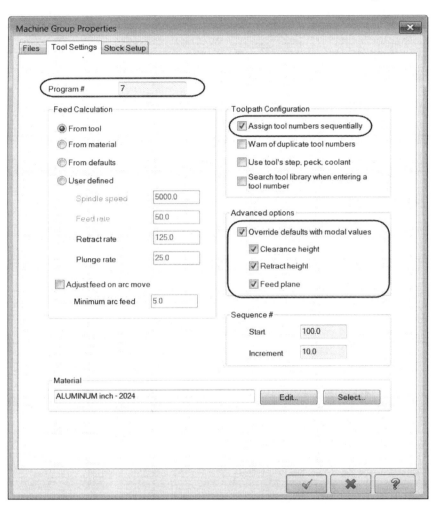

Program # is used to enter a number if your machine tool requires a number for a program name.

Assign tool numbers sequentially allows you to overwrite the tool number from the library with the next available tool number. (First operation tool number 1; Second operation tool number 2, etc.)

Warn of duplicate tool numbers allows you to get a warning if you enter two tools with the same number.

Override defaults with modal values enables the system to keep the values that you enter.

Feed Calculation set **From tool** uses feed rate, plunge rate, retract rate and spindle speed from the tool definition.

Mill Level 1 Training Tutorial

*Mastercam. X*⁸

- Select the **Stock setup** tab to define the stock.
- Pick the **Rectangular** shape option.
- Choose the **All Solids** button and the stock size will be input as shown in Figure: 6.0.2.

Figure: 6.0.2

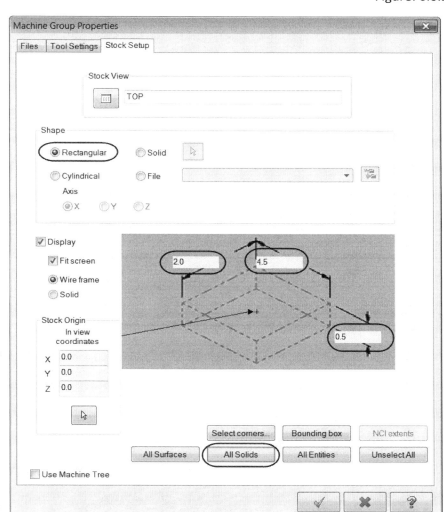

The **Stock Origin** values adjust the positioning of the stock, ensuring that you have equal amount of extra stock around the finished part.

Display options allow you to set the stock as **Wireframe** and to fit the stock to the screen. (Fit Screen)

NOTE: The **stock** model that you create can be displayed with the part geometry when viewing the file or the toolpaths, during backplot, or while verifying toolpaths. In the graphics, the plus shows you where the stock origin is. The default position is the middle of the stock.

- Select the **OK** button to exit **Machine Group Properties**.

- Select the **Isometric** view from the graphics view toolbar to see the stock.

- Use the **Fit** icon to fit the drawing to the screen. ⊞

◆ The stock model should appear as shown.

> **NOTE:** You may not be able to see the stock very clearly due to the fact that the stock is the same size as the part. The stock is not geometry and can not be selected.

STEP 7: 2D HIGH SPEED DYNAMIC MILL

2D High Speed Dynamic Mill utilizes the entire flute length of their cutting tools to produce the smoothest, most efficient tool motion for high speed pocketing. The toolpath supports a custom entry method and many others. Micro lifts further refine the dynamic milling motion and avoid excessive heat build up. Custom feeds and speeds optimize and generate safe tool motion. **Dynamic Mill** machines pockets, material that other toolpaths left behind, and standing bosses or cores. The toolpath depends on the **Machining strategy** that you choose in the **Chain Options**. The outside chain contains the toolpah; all inside chains are considered islands.

Toolpath Preview:

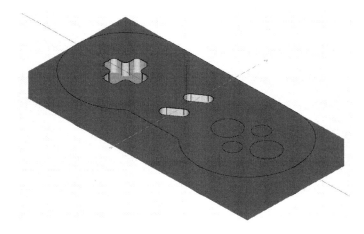

TOOLPATHS

♦ **2D High Speed.**

♦ **Dynamic Mill.**

♦ When the new NC name dialog box appears select the **OK** button to accept the name.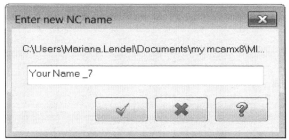

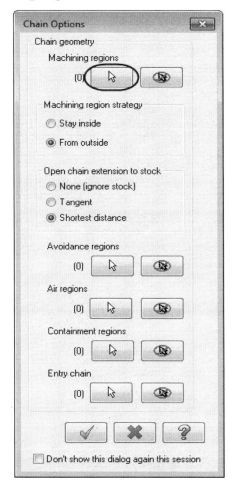

♦ From the **Chain Option** dialog box, click on the **Select** button in the **Machining Regions** as shown.

• In the **Chaining** dialog box enable **C-plane** as shown.

• Press **Alt + S** if needed to display the solid in unshaded mode.
• Select the bottom of the pockets as shown.

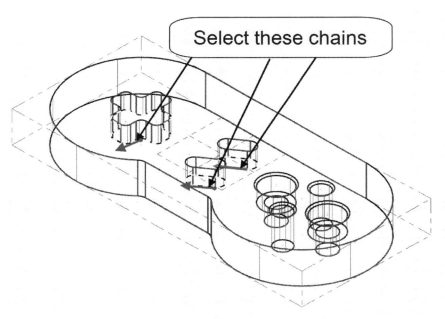

Select these chains

• Select the **OK** button to exit the **Chaining** dialog box.

Mastercam. X[8]

◆ In the **Chain Options** dialog box, **Machining regions** will have 3 chains and make sure that Stay inside is enabled as shown.

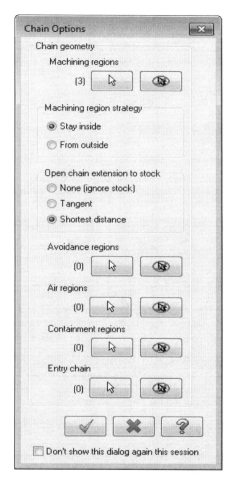

◆ Select the **OK** button to exit the **Chain Options** dialog box.
◆ In the **Toolpath Type** page, **Dynamic Mill** will be already selected as shown in <u>Figure: 7.0.1</u>.

Figure: 7.0.1

7.1 Select a 5/32" Flat endmill from the library and set the Tool Parameters

◆ Select **Tool** from the Tree view list.

◆ Click on **Select library tool** button. `Select library tool...`
◆ Select the **Filter** button.

◆ Select the **None** button and then under **Tool Types** choose the **Flat Endmill** icon.
◆ Under tool diameter pick **Equal** and input a value **5/32**as shown in <u>Figure: 7.1.1</u>.

Figure: 7.1.1

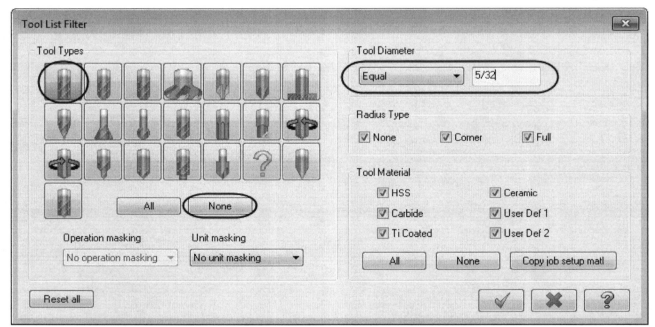

◆ Select the **OK** button to exit the **Tool List Filter.**
◆ In the **Tool Selection** dialog box you should only see a **5/32" Flat Endmill**.

#	Assembly Name	Tool Name	Holder Name	Dia.	Cor. rad.	Length	# Flutes	Ra...	Type
283	--	5/32 FLAT END...	--	0.15625	0.0	0.375	4	No...	En...

◆ Select the **5/32" Flat Endmill** in the **Tool Selection** page and then select the **OK** button to exit.

◆ Make all the necessary changes as shown in <u>Figure: 7.1.2</u>.

Figure: 7.1.2

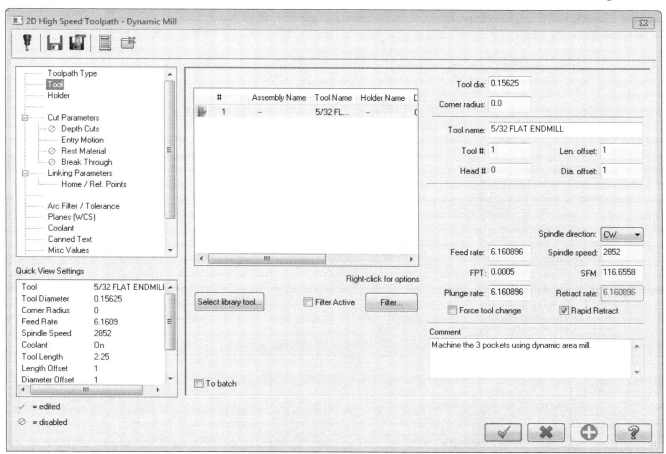

7.2 Set the Cut Parameters

* From the **Tree view list**, select **Cut Parameters**. The previously used settings will still be there.
* Change the settings for this second toolpath as shown in <u>Figure: 7.2.1</u>.

Figure: 7.2.1

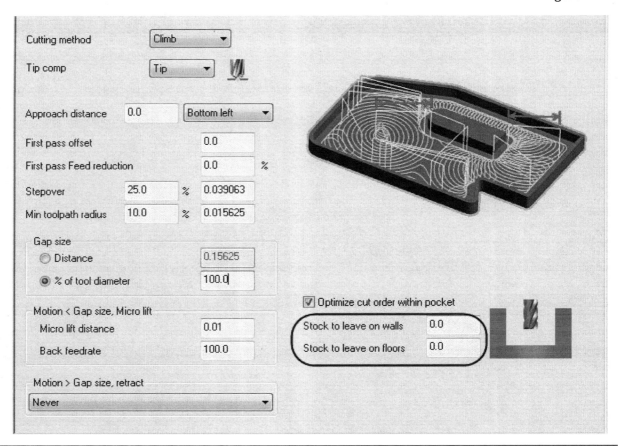

Stepover sets the distance between cutting passes in the X and Y axis.

Toolpath radius reduces sharp corner motion between cut passes.

Micro lift distance enters the distance the tool lifts off the part on the back moves. Microlifts are slight lifts that help clear chips and minimize excessive tool heating.

Back feedrate controls the speed of the backfeed movement of the tool.

Motion > Gap Size, retract controls retracts in the toolpath when making a non-cutting move within an area where the tool can be kept down or microlifted.

Optimize cut order defines the cut order Mastercam applies to different cutting passes in the dynamic mill toolpath.

7.3 Set the Entry Motion

◆ Entry motion configures an entry method for the dynamic mill toolpath which determines not only how and where the tool enters the part, but the cutting method/machining strategy used by the toolpath.The previous settings will be saved.

◆ All we want to do is change the **Entry method** to **Profile** as shown in Figure: 7.3.1.

Figure: 7.3.1

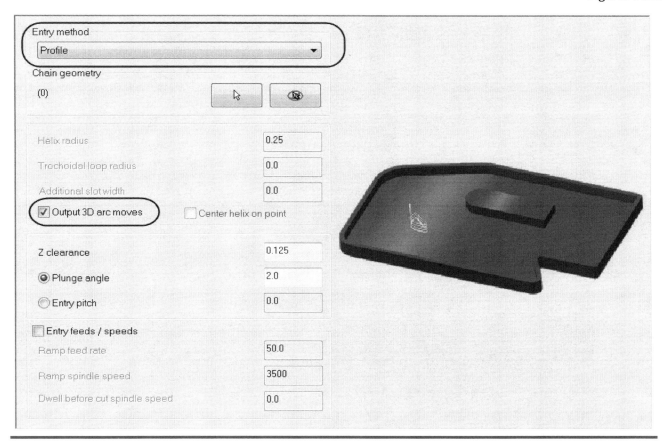

Entry method set to **Profile** creates a boundary based on the shape of the selected chain and uses the tool to ramp into the part. The slot is cleared by taking lighter cuts in the Z axis until the tool reaches the full depth.

Z clearance adds an extra height used in the ramping motion down from a top profile. It ensures that the tool has fully slowed down from rapid speeds before touching the material.

Plunge angle sets the angle of descent for the entry move, and determines the pitch.

7.4 Set the Linking Parameters

♦ Select **Linking Parameters** and change the **Top of Stock** value to **Absolute 0.0** and the **Depth** to **Incremental 0.0** as shown in <u>Figure: 7.4.1</u>.

Figure: 7.4.1

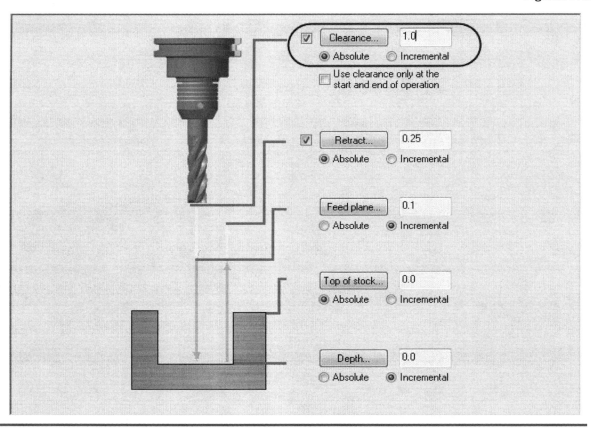

Incremental value for the **Depth** is measured at the chained geometry. In this tutorial the pocket chains were selected at the bottom which is their final depth.

♦ Select the **OK** button to generate the toolpath. ✓

STEP 8: BACKPLOT THE TOOLPATHS

Backplotting shows the path the tools take to cut the part. This display lets you spot errors in the program before you machine the part. As you backplot toolpaths, Mastercam displays additional information such as the X, Y, and Z coordinates, the path length , the minimum and maximum coordinates and the cycle time. It also shows any collisions between the workpiece and the tool.

* Select the **Backplot selected operations** button.

> **NOTE:** Mastercam launches a new window that allows you to check the part using **Backplot** or **Verify**. For more information on how to set and use **Backplot** and **Verify** please check Tutorial 2 page 152.

* Right mouse click in the graphics area and select **Fit**.
* Enable **Workpiece** in the **Visibility** area.
* Select the **Play** button in the **VCR** bar to run **Backplot**.

* The toolpath should look as shown.

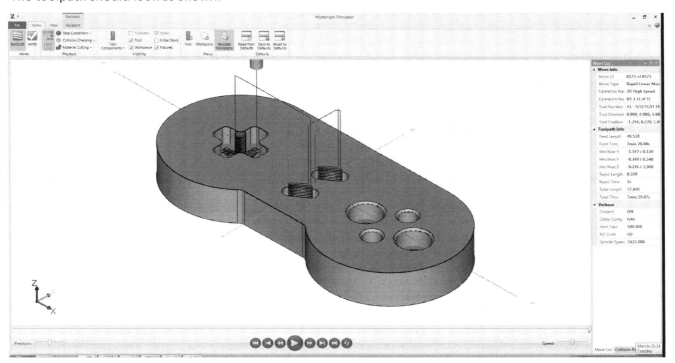

STEP 9: SIMULATE THE TOOLPATH IN VERIFY

Verify Mode shows the path the tools take to cut the part with material removal. This display lets you spot errors in the program before you machine the part. As you verify toolpaths, Mastercam displays additional information such as the X, Y, and Z coordinates, the path length , the minimum and maximum coordinates and the cycle time. It also shows any collisions between the workpiece and the tool.

• From **Mastercam Backplot Home** tab, switch to **Verify** and change the settings for the **Visibility** and **Focus** as shown in Figure: 9.0.1.

Figure: 9.0.1

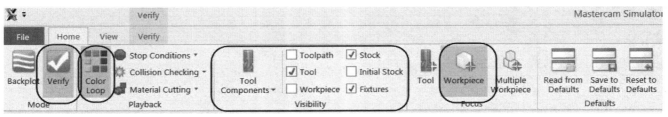

• Select the **Play** button in the **VCR** bar to run **Verify**.

• The part should appear as shown.

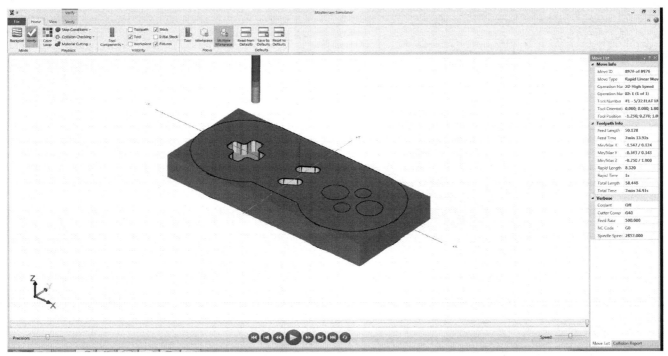

• To go back to Mastercam window, minimize Mastercam Simulator window as shown.

STEP 10: DRILL THE HOLES USING FBM DRILL

FBM Drill automatically detects holes in a solid based on your specific criteria and to generate a complete series of drilling and chamfering. FBM drill also generates circle mill or helix bore operations for large-hole features when you activate these settings.

Toolpath Preview:

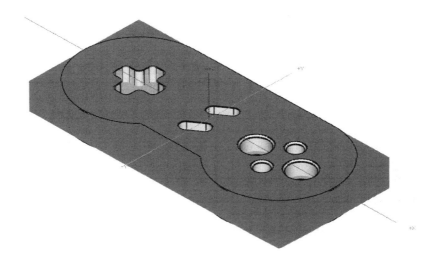

TOOLPATHS

◆ 🔲 **FBM Drill.**

♦ When the **FBM Toolpaths - Setup page** appears, enable **Automatic initial hole detection.**
♦ Change the **Grouping** to **Plane** to group the operations by the plane in which the holes lie as shown in
Figure: 10.0.1.

Figure: 10.0.1

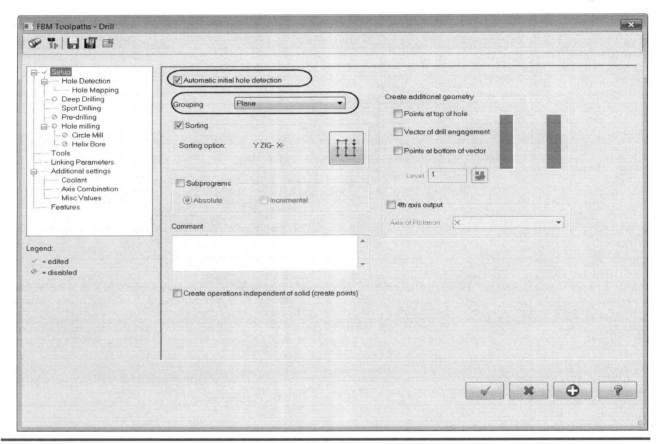

Automatic initial hole/feature detection when selected, Mastercam automatically detects features when you choose
the FBM operation. If you save the settings to your toolpath .DEFAULTS file and use that final in the active machine
group, Mastercam automatically detects features everytime you choose the FBM operation.

Grouping controls how the drill cycles that FBM Drill creates are organized in the Toolpath Manager. Mastercam orders
operations within groups into subgroups by operation type.

Plane groups all operations based on the plane of the hole.

Create additional geometry select one or more options to create geometry for detected hole features without
generating toolpaths. The geometry is saved to a level you choose in this section and is non associative.

10.1 Hole Detection

♦ Choose **Hole Detection** to control the types of holes **FBM Drill** detects. Enable/disable the options as shown in <u>Figure: 10.1.1</u>.

Figure: 10.1.1

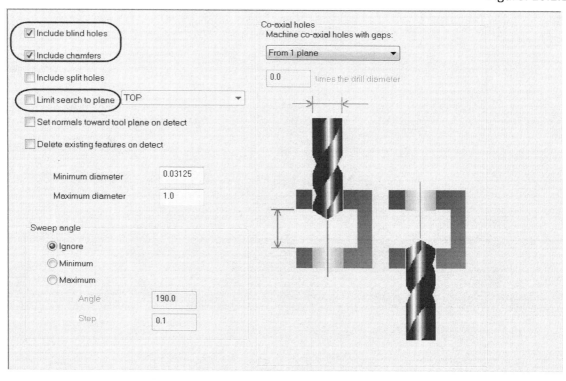

Include blind holes will search your part for blind holes (holes that do not go through the entire solid).

Include chamfers searches for holes with chamfers.

Include split holes searches the part for holes that are incomplete.

Limit search to plane detects features that can only be machined in the selected plane.

Minimum diameter finds holes which are equal to or greater than this value.

Maximum diameter finds holes which are equal to or less than this value.

Sweep angle lets you set a tolerance for how complete holes needs to be in terms of its included angle to be detected by and included in the FBM Drill operation.

Machine co-axial holes with gaps determines whether Mastercam treats multiple holes that share a common axis as a single hole, or as multiple holes from different planes.

10.2 Spot Drilling

♦ Select **Spot Drilling** to activate and define the spot drilling toolpaths for the **FBM Drill** operation.
♦ Enable the option **Use this tool for all spot drill** operations as shown in <u>Figure: 10.2.1</u>.

> **NOTE:** It takes couple of minutes to enable the **Use this tool for all spot drill**.

Figure: 10.2.1

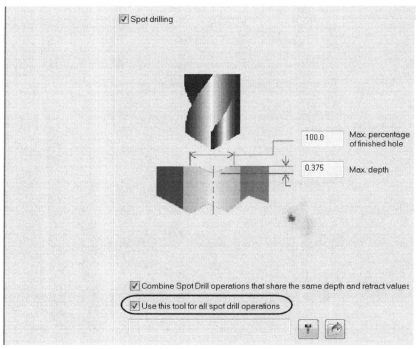

Use this tool for all spot drill operations allows you to choose a specific spot drill cycle generated by the FBM Drill operation.

♦ Pick the button **Select tool from library.**
♦ This will let you choose a tool from the current tool library.
♦ Find and select the **1/2" Spotdrill** from the list.

#	Assembly Name	Tool Name	Holder Name	Dia.	Cor. rad.	Length	Type	# Flutes	Ra...
19	--	9 CENTER DRILL	--	0.875	0.0	0.80...	Ce...	2	No...
20	--	10 CENTER DRILL	--	1.0	0.0	0.91...	Ce...	2	No...
21	--	1/8 SPOTDRILL	--	0.125	0.0	2.0	Sp...	2	No...
22	--	1/4 SPOTDRILL	--	0.25	0.0	2.0	Sp...	2	No...
23	--	3/8 SPOTDRILL	--	0.375	0.0	2.0	Sp...	4	No...
24	--	1/2 SPOTDRILL	--	0.5	0.0	2.0	Sp...	2	No...
25	--	3/4 SPOTDRILL	--	0.75	0.0	2.0	Sp...	4	No...
26	--	1. SPOTDRILL	--	1.0	0.0	2.0	Sp...	4	No...

♦ Select the **OK** button and the **Spot drill** will appear in the box to the left of the buttons.

10.3 Pre-Drilling

• This page defines pre-drilling cycles that rough out the drilled holes before the finish drill cycle.
• Leave **Pre-drilling** settings as shown in Figure: 10.3.1.

Figure: 10.3.1

Pre-drilling Mastercam creates pre-drilling operations that rough out the detected holes before creating any finished drill and chamfer operations.

Pre-drill pilot holes only Select to deactivate all pre-drill roughing cycles except for assigned pilot holes cycles. This also deactivates the parameters for minimum diameter, increment and stock to leave on the page because they are not applicable. FBM Drill generates only pilot holes pre-drill cycles followed by finish hole cycles.

10.4 Tools

♦ This page controls the tools Mastercam selects for the drill cycles that the **FBM Drill** operation creates.
♦ Enable/disable the parameters as shown in Figure: 10.4.1.

Figure: 10.4.1

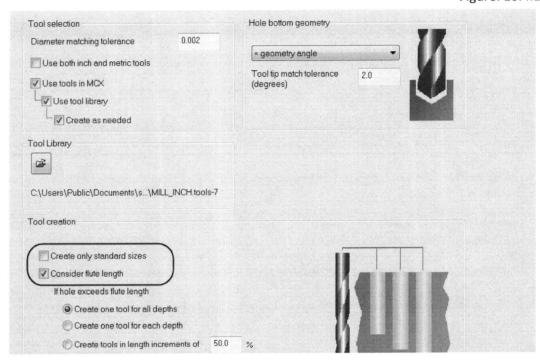

Diameter matching tolerance Mastercam uses this value to determine how closely the diameter of the tool and the hole must match before selecting an appropriate tool.

Tool Selection lets you pick one or more of the following options to tell Mastercam where to locate tools for the FBM-generated toolpaths.

Use tools in MCX looks in the current Mastercam file for an appropriate tool. The tools do not have to be used in previous operations to be available to the FBM operations.

Use tool library searches the selected tool library for the necessary tools.

Create as needed creates the necessary tools using the tool creation parameters you define.

Hole Bottom Geometry defines the realationship of the bottom hole geometry to the tool tip geometry.

= geometry angle the tool tip angle must match the hole bottom geometry within the specified tool tip match tolerance.

> geometry angle the tool tip must be greater than the floor angle geometry.

< geometry angle the tool tip angle must be smaller than the floor angle.

10.5 Linking Parameters

This page defines how **FBM Drill** calculates clearance height and retract height for the drilling cycles.

◆ Set the parameters as shown in <u>Figure: 10.5.1</u>.

Figure: 10.5.1

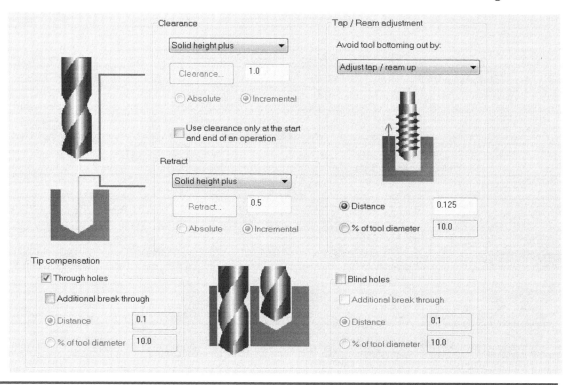

Clearance is the height at which the tool moves to and from the part. There are several options available from where the height is measured:

>   **Solid height plus** adds a fixed height above the highest point of the solid model.
>
>   **Stock model plus** adds a specified height above the stock model.
>
>   **Top of hole plus** adds clearance distance above the top of each hole.
>
>   **Top of Coaxial holes plus** for holes that share the same axis, it sets the clearance above the highest hole on the shared axis.
>
>   **Manual** allows you to set the clearance using all options in any combination.

Retract is the height at which the tool moves before the next tool pass. The same options are available as for Clearance height.

Tap/Ream adjustment determines whether tapped and reamed holes are fully finished.

Tip compensation compensates for the tool tip.

10.6 Features

This page allows you to manage the list of hole features that FBM Drill detects in the solid model.

- Choose the button to **Detect the Features** for Mastercam to detect the holes as shown in Figure: 10.6.1.
- Click on **State** to organize the features better, and scroll down until you reach the unassigned areas as shown in Figure: 10.6.1.

Figure: 10.6.1

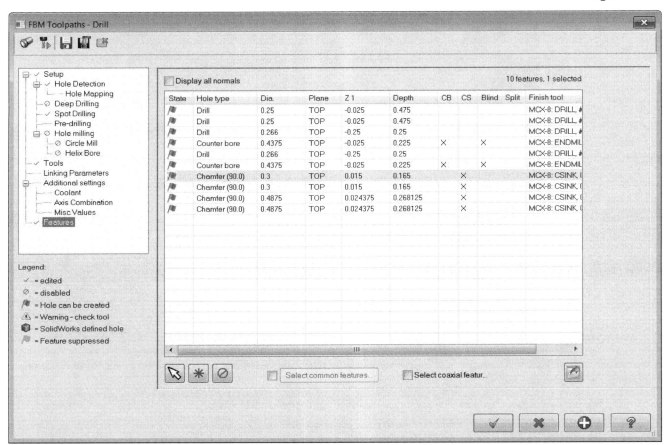

- Choose the **OK** button to generate the **FBM Drill Toolpath**.

10.7 Backplot the toolpaths

- ◆ Click on the **Select all operations** icon in the **Operatoins Manager.**
- ◆ To **Backplot** the toolpaths see page 653 to review the procedure.
- ◆ The toolpaths should look as shown.

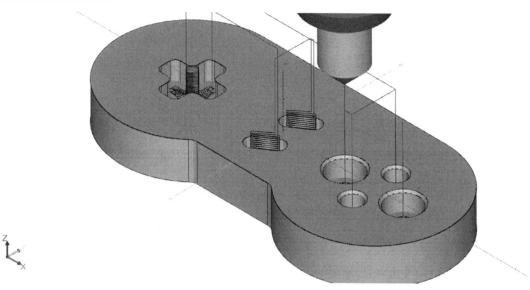

10.8 Verify the toolpaths

- ◆ To **Verify** the toolpaths see page 654 to review te procedure.
- ◆ The part should look as shown.

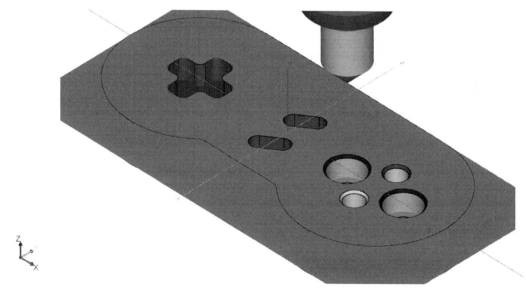

STEP 11: MACHINE THE OUTSIDE OF THE PART USING DYNAMIC MILLING

2D High Speed Dynamic Mill utilizes the entire flute length of their cutting tools to produce the smoothest, most efficient tool motion for high speed pocketing and core milling.

The **Dynamic Mill** toolpath machines pockets, material that other toolpaths left behind, and standing bosses or cores. The toolpath depends on the **Machining strategy** that you choose in the **Chain Options.** If the strategy choosed is **From outside**, the toolpaths starts at the outmost chain and moves freely outside of this area; the inner chain defines the limit of the toolpath. You can also machine pockets in which case the strategy selected is **Start inside** which keeps the tool inside the machining regions.

Toolpath preview:

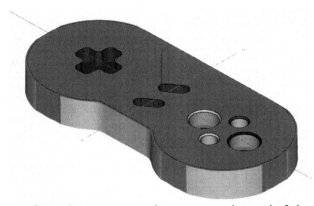

* Click on the **Move insert arrow down icon** to move the arrow at the end of the toolpaths as shown in

    <u>Figure: 11.0.1</u>. 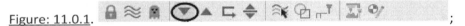 ;

Figure: 11.0.1

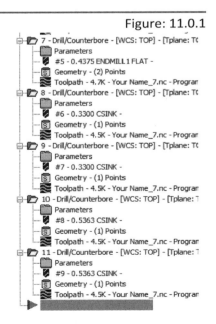

* In the **Toolpaths Manager,**click the **Select all operations.**
* Press **Alt + T** to remove the toolpath display.

TOOLPATHS

- **2D High Speed.**

- 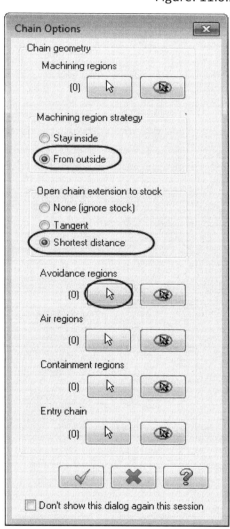 **Dynamic Mill.**

- In the **Chain Options**, **Machining regions** enable **From outside** and in the **Open chain extension to stock** enable **Shortest distance** as shown Figure: 11.0.2.

- Click on the **Select** button in the **Avoidance regions** as shown Figure: 11.0.2.

Figure: 11.0.2

- Enable **C-plane** in the **Chaining** dialog box as shown.

- [Select 2D HST avoidance chain]: Select the chain as shown.

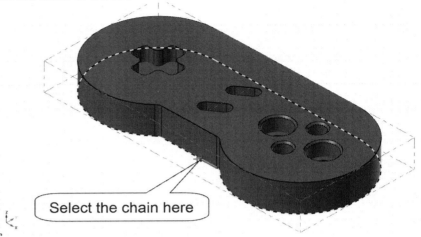

Select the chain here

- Select the **OK** button to exit the **Chaining** dialog box.
- The **Chain Options** dialog box should look as shown.

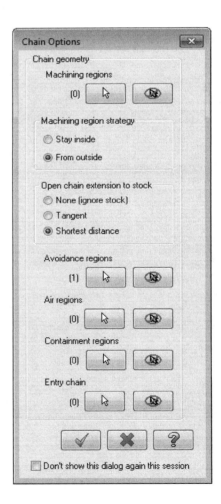

Core mill enabled ensures that the tool will approached the part from the outside.

Open chain extension to stock set to **Shortest distance** sets how the system calculates the amount of the material that has to be removed based on the defined stock.

Avoidance regions allows you to select the profile that describes the shape up to where the material will be removed.

- Select the **OK** button to exit the **Chain Options** dialog box.

- In the toolpath type page **Dynamic Mill** with **From outside** option should be already selected.

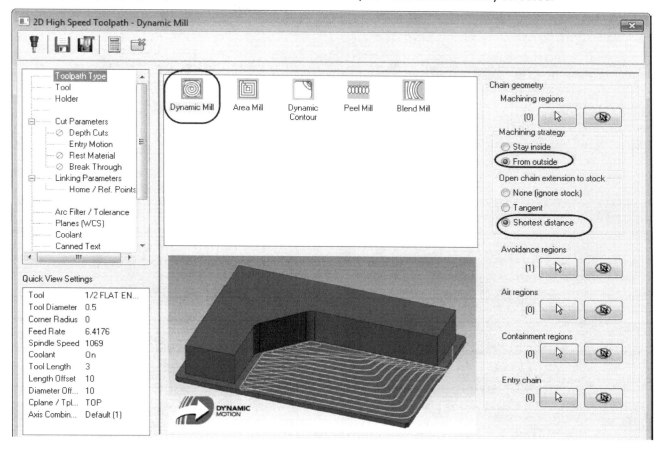

11.1 Select a 0.5" Flat Endmill from the Library and set the Tool Parameters

- Select **Tool** from the **Tree view list**.

- Click on the **Select library tool** button. `Select library tool...`
- Select the **Filter** button as shown.

• Select the **None** button and then under **Tool Types** choose the **Flat Endmill** icon.
• Under tool diameter pick **Equal** and input a value of **0.5** as shown in <u>Figure: 11.1.1</u>.

Figure: 11.1.1

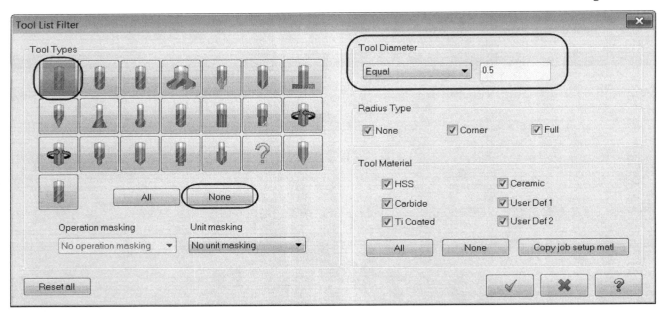

• Select the **OK** button to exit the **Tool List Filter.**
• In the **Tool Selection** dialog box you should only see a **1/2" Flat Endmill**.

#	Assembly Name	Tool Name	Holder Name	Dia.	Cor. rad.	Length	# Flutes	Type	Ra...
290	--	1/2 FLAT ENDMI...	--	0.5	0.0	1.0	4	En...	No...

• Select the **1/2" Flat Endmill** in the **Tool Selection** page and then select the **OK** button to exit.

◆ Make all the necessary changes as shown in <u>Figure: 11.1.2</u>.

Figure: 11.1.2

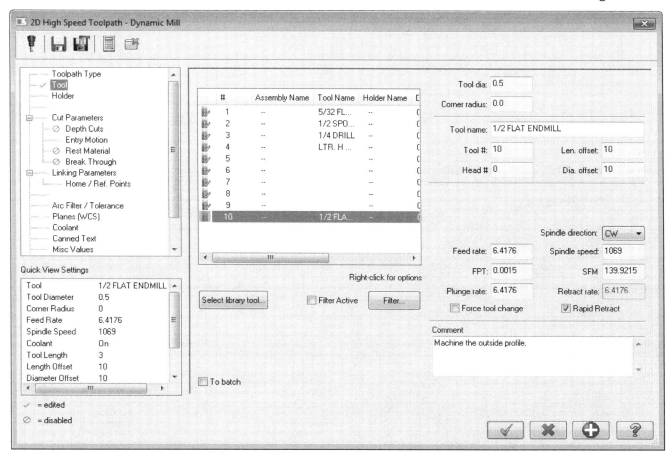

11.2 Set the Cut Parameters

♦ From the **Tree view list**, select **Cut Parameters** and ensure the parameters appear the same as shown in
<u>Figure: 11.2.1</u>.

Figure: 11.2.1

| Cutting method | Climb |
| Tip comp | Tip |

Approach distance	0.0	Bottom left
First pass offset	0.1
First pass Feed reduction	0.0 %
Stepover	25.0 %	0.125
Min toolpath radius	10.0 %	0.05

Gap size
- ○ Distance — 0.5
- ◉ % of tool diameter — 100.0

Motion < Gap size, Micro lift
| Micro lift distance | 0.01 |
| Back feedrate | 100.0 |

Motion > Gap size, retract
Never

☑ Optimize cut order within pocket

| Stock to leave on walls | 0.03 |
| Stock to leave on floors | 0.0 |

11.3 Set the Depth Cuts Parameters

* From the **Tree view list**, select the **Depth Cuts Parameters** and disable **Depth Cuts** as shown in Figure: 11.3.1.

Figure: 11.3.1

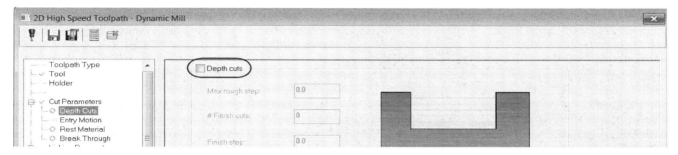

11.4 Set the Entry Motion

* Set the **Entry Method** to **Helix only**. Input a **Z clearance** value of **0.125** and a **Plunge angle** of **2.0** degrees as shown in Figure: 11.4.1.

Figure: 11.4.1

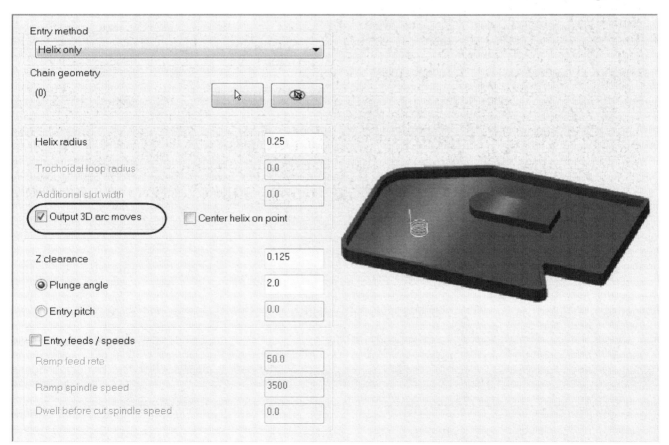

11.5 Set the Linking Parameters

♦ Select **Linking Parameters,** enable **Clearance**, input a value of **1.0** and input a **Depth** value of **-0.5** as shown in Figure: 11.5.1.

Figure: 11.5.1

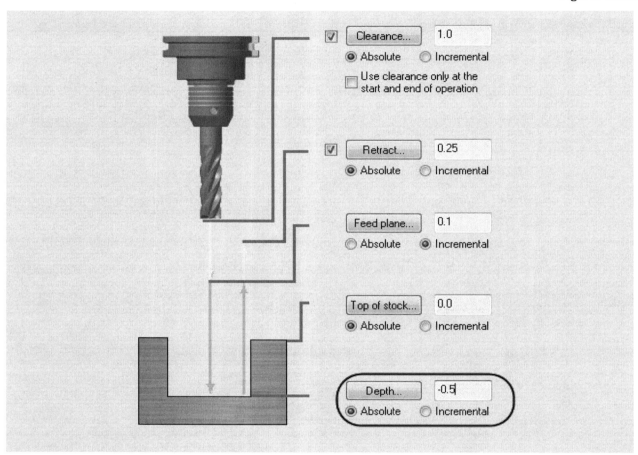

♦ Select the **OK** button to generate the toolpath.

11.6 Backplot the toolpath

♦ **Backplot** the toolpath page 152 for more information.

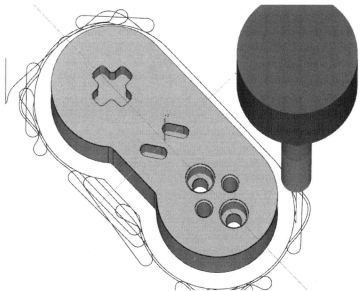

♦ To go back to Mastercam minimize Mastercam Simulator window.

11.7 Verify the toolpaths

♦ To **Verify** the toolpaths see page 155 for more information.

♦ To verify all toolpaths, from the Toolpaths Manager, choose the **Select all operations** icon.

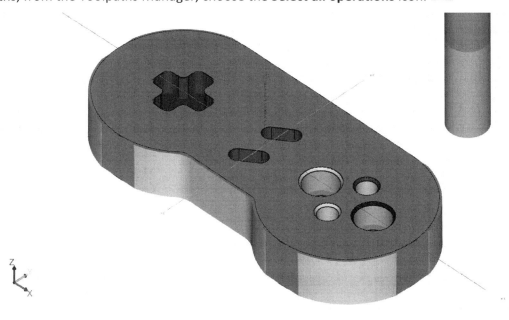

To go back to Mastercam minimize Mastercam Simulator window.

STEP 12: CONTOUR TOOLPATH

A **Contour** toolpath removes material along a path defined by a chain of curves. A Contour toolpath only follows a chain, it does not clean out an enclosed area. You will use this toolpath to finsh the outside profile.

Toolpath Preview:
◆ Press **Alt** + **T** to remove the toolpath display if needed.

TOOLPATHS

◆  **Contour.**

◆ Enable **C-plane** in the **Chaining dialog** box as shown.

◆ Select the chain and ensure the chaining direction is the same as shown in <u>Figure: 12.0.1</u>.

Figure: 12.0.1

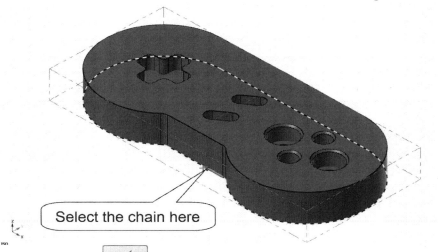

Select the chain here

◆ Select the **OK** button to exit the **Chaining** dialog box.

◆ In the **Toolpath Type** page, the **Contour** toolpath will be selected.

Contour Pocket Facing Slot Mill

12.1 Select the 1/4" Flat endmill from the library and set the Tool Parameters

◆ Using the **Filter** option select the **1/4 " 6. Flat Endmill** from the library as shown in the previous steps.
◆ Make all the necessary changes as shown in Figure: 12.1.1.

Figure: 12.1.1

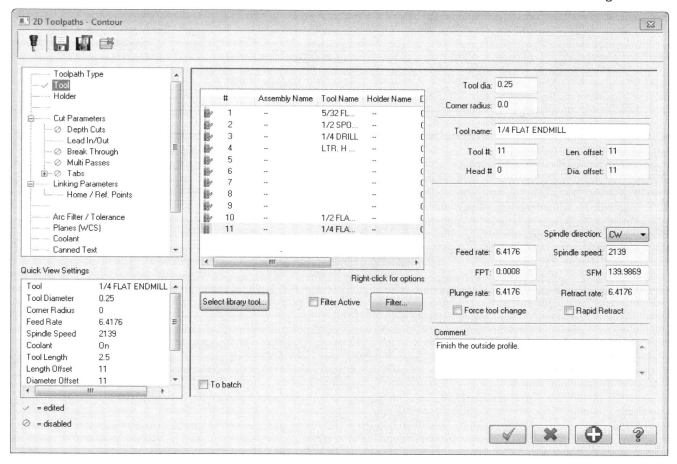

12.2 Cut Parameters

◆ Select the **Cut Parameters** and make the necessary changes as shown in Figure: 12.2.1.

Figure: 12.2.1

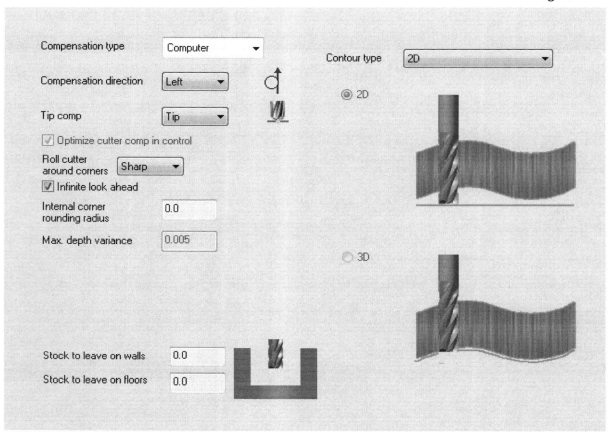

Roll cutter around corners inserts arc moves around corners in the toolpath.

None guarantees all sharp corners.

Sharp rolls the tool around sharp corners (135 degrees or less).

All rolls the tool around all corners and creates smooth tool movement.

12.3 Depth Cuts

◆ Select **Depth cuts** and make sure is disabled as shown.

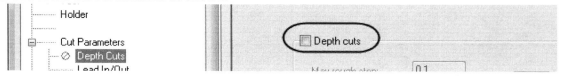

12.4 Lead In/Out

♦ Choose the option **Lead In/Out** and input an **Overlap** value. Make any other necessary changes as shown in Figure: 12.4.1.

Figure: 12.4.1

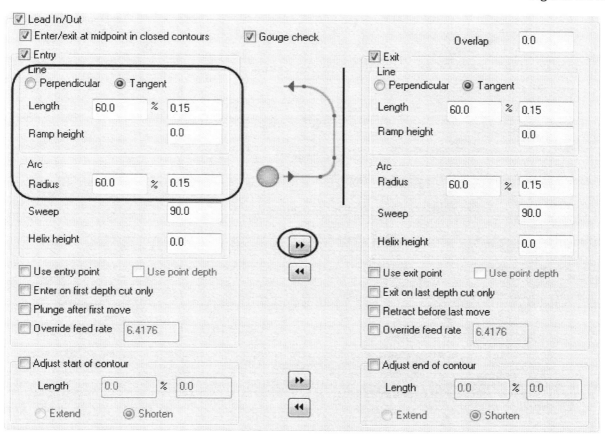

Lead In/Out allows you to select a combination of a Line and an Arc at the beginning and/or end of the contour toolpath for a smooth entry/exit while cutting the part.

Length set to 60% of the tool diameter to ensure that the linear movement is bigger than the tool radius in case **Cutter Compensation** in **Control** was used.

Radius set to 60% of the tool diameter ensures that the arc movement is bigger than the tool radius to generate an arc output.

Overlap sets how far the tool goes past the end of the toolpath before exiting for a cleaner finish.

12.5 Linking Parameters

◆ Select **Linking Parameters** from the **Tree view list**. Set the **Top of stock** to **zero** and the **Depth** to **Incremental** and **0.0** as shown in <u>Figure: 12.5.1</u>.

Figure: 12.5.1

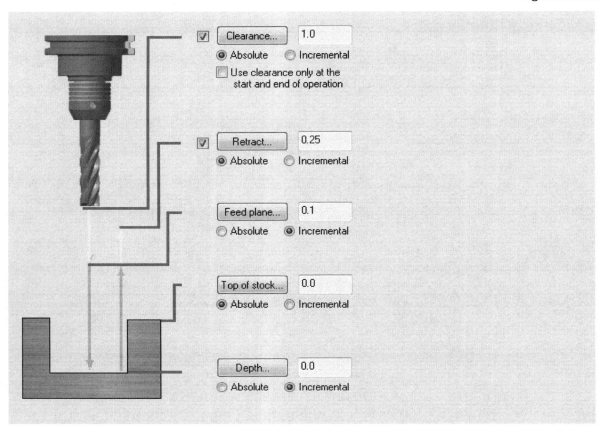

◆ Select the **OK** button to exit the **2D Toolpaths - Contour**.

12.6 Verify the toolpaths

♦ Select all operations.

♦ Click on the **Verify selected operation** icon.

♦ For information on how to set the verify parameters and to simulate the toolpath, please check page 155.

♦ The finish part will appear as shown in Figure: 12.6.1.

Figure: 12.6.1

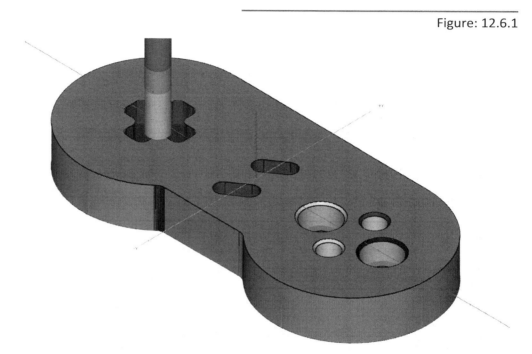

♦ To go back to Mastercam window, minimize Mastercam Simulator window as shown.

STEP 13: POST THE FILE

* Ensure all operations are slected, if they are not use the button **Select all operations** in the **Operatoins Manager.**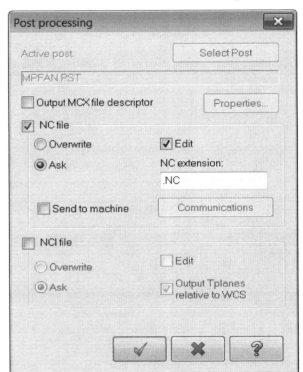

* Select the **Post selected operations** button from the **Toolpaths Manager.** G1
* In the **Post processing** window make the necessary changes as shown in Figure: 13.0.1.

Figure: 13.0.1

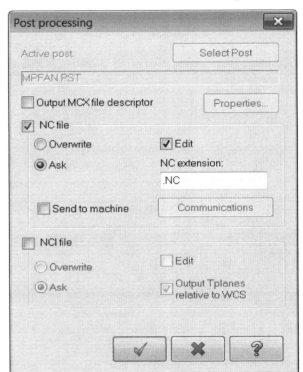

NC File enabled allows you to keep the NC file and to assign the same name as the MCX file.

Edit enabled allows you to automatically launch the default editor.

* Select the **OK** button to continue.
* Save "Your Name_7.NC" file.

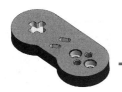

◆ A window with Mastercam Code Expert will be launcheded and the NC programs will appear as shown in Figure: 13.0.2.

Figure: 13.0.2

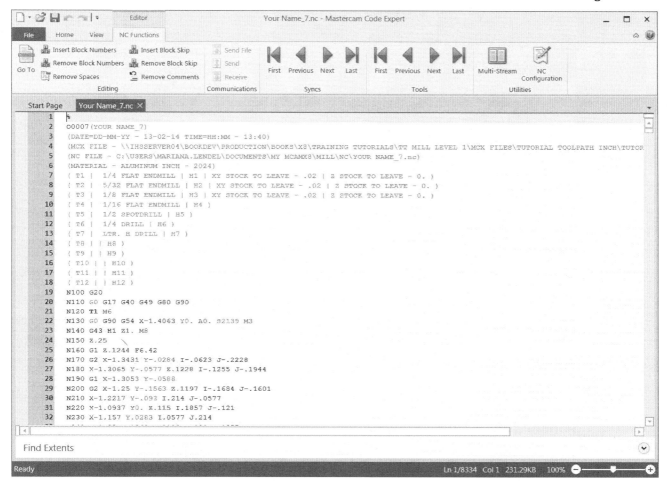

◆ Select the **"X"** box at the upper right corner to exit the editor.

STEP 14: SAVE THE UPDATED MCX FILE

REVIEW EXERCISE -STUDENT PRACTICE

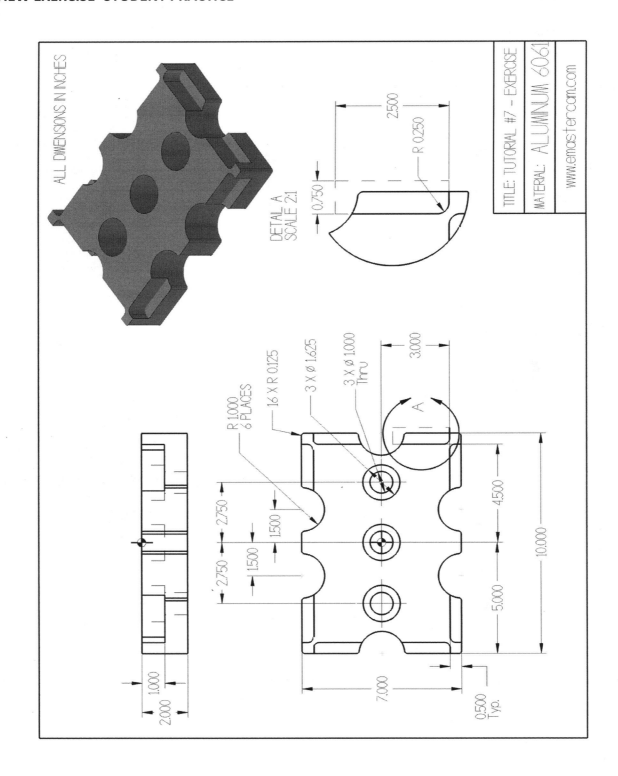

ALL DIMENSIONS IN INCHES

DETAIL A
SCALE 2:1

2.500
R 0.250
0.750

TITLE: TUTORIAL #7 – EXERCISE
MATERIAL: ALUMINUM 6061
www.emastercam.com

R 1.000
6 PLACES
16 X R 0.125
3 X Ø 1.625
3 X Ø 1.000
Thru

3.000
4.500
10.000
5.000

2.750
2.750
1.500
1.500

A

7.000
0.500
Typ.

1.000
2.000

Mastercam. X

IMPORT THE GEOMETRY FOR TUTORIAL #7 EXERCISE

Import CAD Model and prepare it for machining.

* Open the file from SolidWorks.

Rotate between views.

* Use **Xform Translate 3D** to rotate the part between views.
* Set the **Source plane** to **Back** and the **Destination plane** to **Top**.

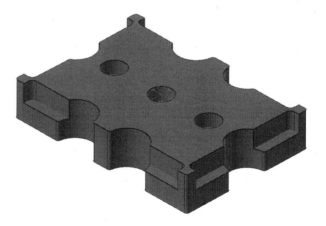

CREATE THE TOOLPATHS FOR TUTORIAL #7 EXERCISE

Create the Toolpaths for Tutorial #7 Exercise as per the instructions below.

Set the machine properties including the Stock.

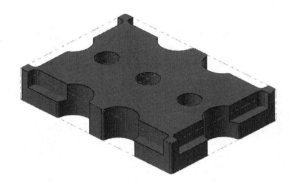

FBM Drill.
* Enable **Automatic initial hole detection**.
* **Grouping** set to **Plane**.
* **Include blind holes**.
* **Include chamfers**.
* **Maximum diameter** set to **1.5**.
* **Spot drilling** and **Combine Spot Drill operations that share the same depth** enabled.
* **Max percentage of finished hole** set to **100%** and **Max depth** set to **0.375**.
* **Pre-drilling** and **Pre-drill pilot holes only** enabled.
* In **Tool selection** have **Use tools in MCX**, **Use tool library** and **Create as needed** enabled.
* In **Tool creation** disable **Create only standard tools**, enable **Consider flute length** and **Create one tool for all depths**.
* In the **Linking Parameters** have **Clearance** set to **Solid height plus** and **1.0** and **Retract** set to **Solid height plus** and **0.5**.
* Enable **Through holes**.
* Click on **Detect** the **features**.

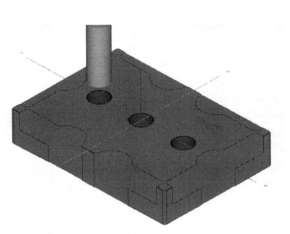

Machine the outside profile using 2D HS Dynamic Mill.

◆ In the **Chain Options** enable **From outside, Shortest distance for extension** to **stock**.

◆ Click on the **Select** button in the **Avoidance regions** and with **C-plane** enabled select the bottom contour.

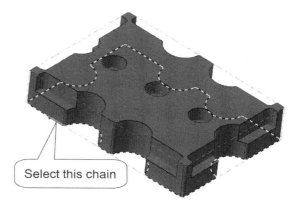

Select this chain

◆ Select the **1/2" Flat Endmill**.
◆ **First pass offset =0.1**.
◆ **Stepover = 25%**.
◆ **Min toolpath radius = 10%**.
◆ **Micro lift distance = 0.01**.
◆ Enable **Optimize cut order within pocket.**
◆ **Stock to leave on walls** = 0.03.
◆ **Stock to leave on floors** = 0.0.
◆ **Entry motion Helix only; Radius 0.25**.
◆ **Clearance = 1.0** (Absolute).
◆ **Retract = 0.25**(Absolute).
◆ **Feed Plane = 0.1** (Incremental).
◆ **Depth = -2.0**(Absolute).

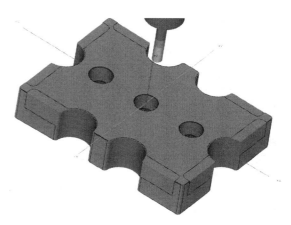

Machine the steps using 2D HS Dynamic Mill.

♦ In the **Chain Options** enable **From outside**, **None for extension.**

♦ Click on the **Select** button in the **Machining regions** and with **C-plane** enabled select the bottom contour.

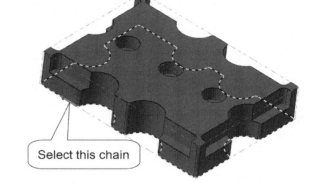

Select this chain

♦ Click on the **Select** button in the **Avoidance regions** and with **C-plane** enabled select the top contour as shown in previous operation.

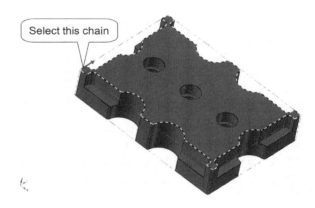

Select this chain

♦ Select the same **1/2" Flat Endmill.**
♦ **First pass offset =0.1.**
♦ **Stepover = 25%.**
♦ **Min toolpath radius = 10%.**
♦ **Micro lift distance = 0.01.**
♦ Enable **Optimize cut order within pocket.**
♦ **Stock to leave on walls = 0.03.**
♦ **Stock to leave on floors = 0.0.**
♦ **Entry motion Helix only; Radius 0.25.**
♦ **Clearance = 1.0** (Absolute).
♦ **Retract = 0.25** (Absolute).
♦ **Feed Plane = 0.1** (Incremental).
♦ **Top of stock = 0.0** (Absolute).
♦ **Depth = -1.0**(Absolute).

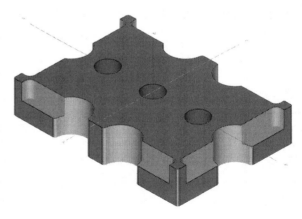

Finish the bottom profile using Contour toolpath.
- Enable C-plane and select the bottom profile as shown before in the Clock Wise direction.
- Select a **3/8" Flat Endmill**.
- **Contour type 2D**.
- **Compensation type** in **Computer**.
- **Compensation direction** set to **Left**.
- **Stock to leave on** either **walls** or **floors** = **0.0**.
- Lead in out set to defaults.
- **Clearance = 1.0** (Absolute).
- **Retract = 0.25** (Absolute).
- **Feed Plane =0.1 (Incremental).**
- **Top of stock = 0.0** (Absolute).
- **Depth = 0.0** (Incremental).

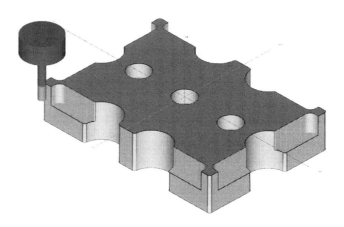

Finish the step profile using Contour toolpath.
- Enable C-plane and select the top profile as shown before in the Clock Wise direction.
- Use the same **3/8" Flat Endmill**.
- **Contour type 2D**.
- **Compensation type** in **Computer**.
- **Compensation direction** set to **Left**.
- **Stock to leave on** either **walls** or **floors** = **0.0**.
- Lead in out set to defaults.
- **Clearance = 1.0** (Absolute).
- **Retract = 0.25** (Absolute).
- **Feed Plane = 0.1** (Incremental).
- **Top of stock = -0.0** (Absolute).
- **Depth = -1.0** (Absolute).

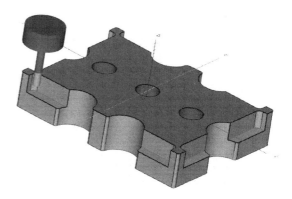

NOTES:

Mastercam. X⁸

TUTORIAL #7 QUIZ

• What does FBM Drill allow you to do?

• What does Open chain extension to stock set to Shortest distance do?

• What does Avoidance regions selection do?

CREATING/EDITING TOOLS

Objectives:

✓ The Student will learn how to create and modify tools.

CREATING AND EDITING A MILL TOOL LIBRARY

NOTE: The purpose of tool libraries is to hold the tool data. The libraries can be edited or added to by following the directions below. Each time the **Tool Type** or **Cutter diameter** is changed in the **Toolpath parameters**, the tool library recalculates the feed rate and spindle speed. The following menu selections will allow you to create a new tool.

CREATING A NEW TOOL

MACHINE TYPE
* **Mill.**
* **Default .**

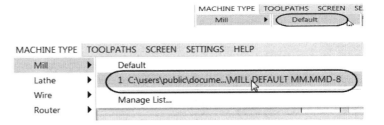

Option 1: Create a new tool using the Tool Manager

TOOLPATHS

* ⊤ **Tool Manager.**
* **Right click** in the tool display area.

◆ Select **Create new tool** as shown.

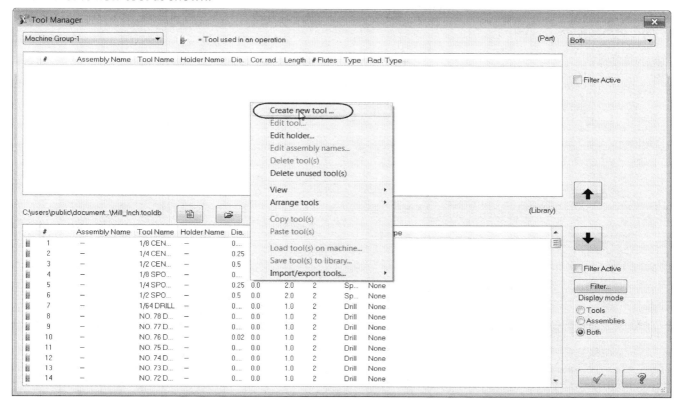

Option 2: Create a new tool inside of the Toolpath Parameters

Create a rectangle.

TOOLPATHS

- 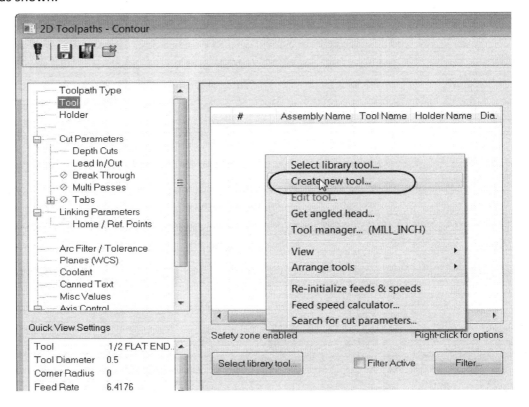 **Contour.**
- Chain the contour.
- From the **Tree view list,** select **Tool**.
- **Right-click in** the tool display area.
- Select **Create new tool** as shown.

Mill Level 1 Training Tutorial *Mastercam. X*

1. *What type of tool would you like to create?*

The **Create New Tool** dialog box displays all the default tool type options in Mastercam.

◆ The following screen will appear as shown.

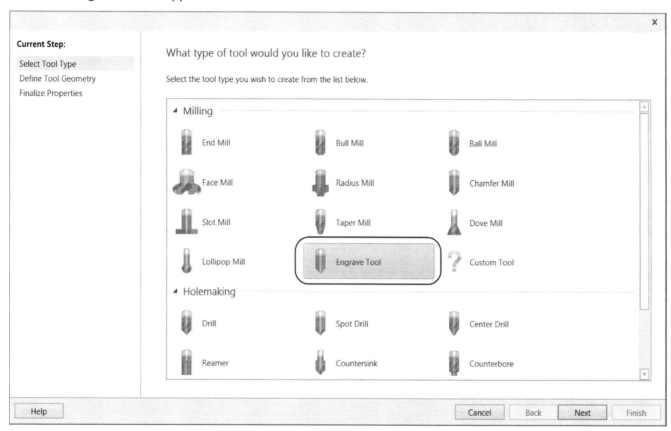

◆ Choose the tool type you wish to modify and then select **Next** button.

2. Define geometric tool parameters.

Define geometric tool parameters lets you enter new parameters or edit current parameters of Mill tools. A description of each parameter in the **Define geometric tool parameters** is listed below.

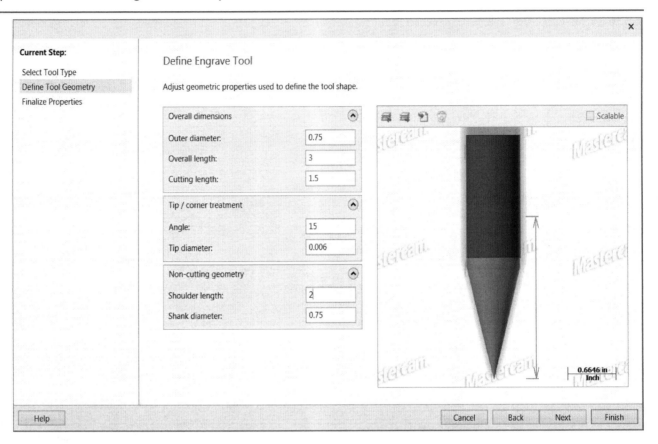

NOTE: The fields on the tabs change depending on the type of tool you are creating.

Overall Dimensions

Outer Diameter - sets the diameter of the tool.

Overall Length - sets the length of the tool.

Cutting Length - sets the length from the top of the flutes to the tip of the tool.

Tip/CornerTreatment

Corner Type- allows you to choose between None, Chamfer, Corner radius and Full radius.

Angle - measures the angle from the center line of the tool to the outer angle of the tool.

Tip diameter - sets the tool tool tip diameter.

Non-Cutting Geometry

Shoulder Length - sets the distance from the top of the shoulder to the tip of the tool.

Shank Diameter - sets the diameter of the tool shank.

◆ Set the dimension values and then select **Next** button.

3. *Finalize miscellaneous properties*

This area allows you to type information such as Name, Manufacturer Name and Manufacture's tool code. It also allows you to enter the tool offset numbers, the feeds and speeds, the material, coolant settingsand other settings.

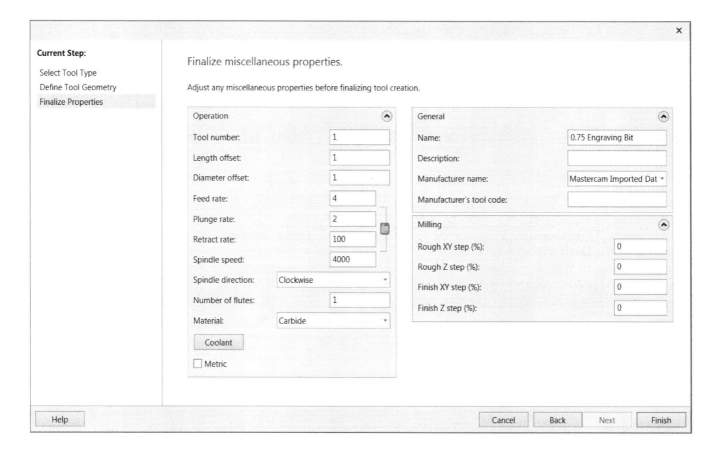

Operation

Tool Number - sets the default tool assembly number.

Length Offset - sets the number that corresponds to a register in the machine that compensates for the tool length.

Diameter Offset - sets the number that corresponds to a register in the machine that offset the diameter.

Feed Rate - sets the default feed rate.

Plunge Rate - sets the default plunge rate.

Retract Rate - sets the default retract rate.

Spindle Speed - sets the spindle speed in RPM.

Spindle Direction - allows you to choose the spindle direction between Clockwise, Counterclockwise and Static.

Number of flutes - specifies the number of flutes on the tool which is used to calculate the feed rate.

Material - displays the tool material.

Coolant - allows you to set the canned text coolant options.

Metric - allows you to enable metric tools.

General

Name - allows you to type the name of the tool.

Description - displays additional info.

Manufacturer name - allows you to type the name of the Manufacturer.

Manufacturer's tool code - allows you to type the tool code.

Milling

Rough XY step (%)- allows you to set the size of a roughing step in the X and Y axes for the tool. The system measures this distance as a percentage of the tool diameter.

Rough Z step (%) - allows you to set the size of a roughing step in the Z axis for the tool. The system measures this distance as a percentage of the tool diameter.

Finish XY step (%) - allows you to set the size of a finish step in the X and Y axes for the tool. The system measures this distance as a percentage of the tool diameter.

Finish Z step (%) - allows you to set the size of a f step in the Z axis forinish the tool. The system measures this distance as a percentage of the tool diameter.

EDITING AN EXISTING TOOL

Option 1: Edit an existing tool using the Tool Manager

TOOLPATH

♦ **Tool Manager.**
♦ **Right click** on the existing tool.
♦ Select **Edit tool** as shown.

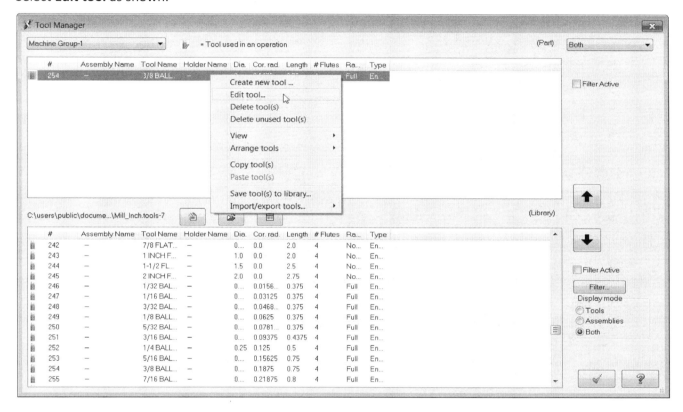

Option 2: Editing an existing tool inside of the toolpath parameters

◆ In Toolpath parameters dialog box, right click on the existing tool and then select **Edit tool** as shown.

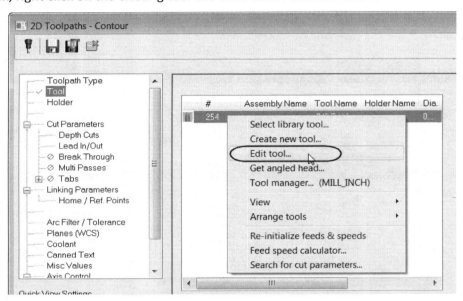

◆ Make the changes the tool.
◆ Once you select the Finish button the tool will be automatically saved with the new changes.

QUIZ ANSWERS

> ## Objectives:
>
> ✓ The answers to the 7 Tutorial quizzes.

MILL LEVEL 1 TUTORIAL QUIZ ANSWERS

Tutorial 1 Answers

- What is a Contour Toolpath used for?
  - Contour toolpaths remove the material along a path defined by a chain of curves. Contour toolpaths only follow a chain; they do not clean out an enclosed area.

- What is a Facing Toolpath used for?
  - **Facing toolpath** quickly removes material from the top of the part to create an even surface for future operations.

- What does a Pocket Toolpath allow you to do?
  - **Pocket toolpaths** remove the material from an enclosed boundary.

- What does Backplot do?
  - **Backplotting** shows the path the tools take to cut the part. This display lets you spot errors in the program before you machine the part. As you backplot toolpaths, Mastercam displays the current X, Y, and Z coordinates in the lower left corner of the screen.

- What does verify allow you to do?
  - **Verify** allows you to use a solid model to simulate the machining of a part. The model created by verification represents the surface finish, and shows collisions, if any exist.

Tutorial # 2 Answers

- What does Slot mill toolpath do?
  - **Slot Mill** toolpath allows Mastercam to efficiently machine obround slots. These are slots that consist of 2 straight lines and two 180-degree arcs at the ends.

- What does 2D HS Dynamic mill do?
  - **2D HS Dynamic** machines, utilizing the entire flute length of their cutting tools, to machine open pocket shapes, standing core shapes or pockets. To machine standing cores the toolpath uses the outmost chain as the stock boundary. The tool moves freely outside of this area; the inner chain defines the limit of the toolpath.

- What does 2D HS Dynamic Contour mill do?
  - **2D HS Dynamic Contour** toolpath utilizes the entire flute length of the cutting tools and is used to mill material off walls. It does support both closed or open chains.

- What is the process used to be able to post different operations as different programs?
  - Create a new toolpath group and then rename it.

Tutorial # 3 Answers

◆ What does Area Mill do?

◆ **Area Mill** takes small cuts to machine open pocket shapes, standing core shapes or pockets based on the machining region strategies.

◆ What does smoothing do?

◆ **Smoothing** replaces sharp corners with arcs for faster and smoother transitions in tool direction.

◆ What does pocket remachining do?

◆ Calculates areas where the pocket roughing tool could not machine the stock and creates a remachining pocket toolpath to clear the remaining material.

Tutorial # 4 Answers

◆ What does a Circle Mill toolpath do?

◆ **Circle mill toolpath** is used to mill circular pockets based on a single point. Mastercam will pocket out a circular area of the diameter and to the depth that you specify.

◆ What does a **Dwell before cut spindle speed** do?

◆ Adds a dwell after the entry ramp into the cut. This pause allows the spindle to ramp up to the desired spindle speed before starting the cutting passes.

◆ What does a transform toolpath operation do?

◆ It allows you to run the same toolpath in different locations. You can transform a single toolpath or several at a time.

Tutorial # 5 Answers

◆ What settings do you need to use to remachine a pocket using High Speed Area Mill Toolpath?

◆ 2D High Speed Area Mill toolpath with the Rest Material enabled targets material left behind by previous toolpaths.

◆ What is the use of WCS in Mastercam?

◆ This tells Mastercam how your part is position or orientated in the machine.

◆ After creating a new toolpath group why do you rename the NC file?

◆ To create two separate programs.

Tutorial # 6 Answers

◆ What does the Translate 3D do?

Translate 3D allows you to move the geometry between views (from one plane to another).

◆ How does a Blend Mill toolpath work?

2D High Speed Blend Mill toolpath morph smoothly between two open chains.

◆ What does Peel Mill toolpath do?

◆ 2D High Speed Peel Mill toolpath allows for efficient constant climb milling between two selected contours or along a single contour. It uses a trochodial style of motion to cut the slot.

Tutorial # 7 Answers

◆ What does FBM Drill do?

◆ **FBM Drill** automatically detects holes in a solid based on your specific criteria and to generate a complete series of drilling and chamfering. FBM drill also generates circle mill or helix bore operations for large-hole features when you activate these settings.

What does Open chain extension to stock set to Shortest distance do?

Open chain extension to stock set to **Shortest distance** sets how the system calculates the amount of the material that has to be removed based on the defined stock.

◆ What does Avoidance regions selection do?

Avoidance regions allows you to select the profile that describes the shape up to where the material will be removed.

Mill Level 1 Training Tutorial

Mastercam. X⁸